WITHDRAW

JUL 0 1

DAVID O. McKAY LIBRARY
BYU-IDAHO

DEPOSITED BY
U. S. GOVT.

JUL 2 5 1973

RICKS COLLEGE

DATE DUE

APR 1 6 1984			
MAY 2 1 1986			
APR 1 3 1989			
AUG 2 5 1992			
GAYLORD			PRINTED IN U.S.A.

NASA SP–303

the Quiet Sun

Edward G. Gibson
MANNED SPACECRAFT CENTER
HOUSTON, TEXAS

Scientific and Technical Information Office   1973
NATIONAL AERONAUTICS AND SPACE ADMINISTRATION
Washington, D.C.

For sale by the Superintendent of Documents,
U.S. Government Printing Office, Washington, D.C. 20402
Price $6.20 domestic postpaid or $5.75 cents GPO Bookstore
Stock No. 3300–0454
Library of Congress Catalog Card No. 72–600092

Foreword

The discovery of the high temperature of the solar corona by Edlen in 1942 revitalized solar physics both by posing new and fundamental problems and by stimulating the development of the theoretical and observational techniques needed for their solution. The most important unsolved mystery surrounding the quiet sun is still the explanation of how the sun's temperature increases outward from 4500 K in the photosphere to 2 000 000 K in the corona without violating the first law of thermodynamics. If we are now close to solving this puzzle, as I suspect we are, it is largely because theorists have access to measurements made over more than 36 octaves of the solar spectrum, from gamma rays to long radio waves, measurements that are being made with solar instruments on the ground, in balloons and rockets, and in orbiting solar observatories.

This all-wavelength attack on the problems of the quiet sun will be climaxed in the spring and summer of 1973 when solar astronomers at observatories in many parts of the world will join with the experimenters on the NASA Skylab mission in a coordinated program of observations aimed at the solution of the coronal heating problem and many others as well.

One of the principal figures in this unprecedented adventure in international scientific cooperation is Edward G. Gibson, the author of this book, who has been selected to fly on the Skylab mission together with eight other astronauts. As part of the preparation for the mission, the astronauts underwent an intensive period of study and training in order to become familiar with the scientific goals of the mission, with the operation of the sophisticated onboard instrumentation, and with the complexities of the solar observing program. One obvious requirement of the training program was a modern, up-to-date textbook of solar physics, and since no such work was available, Dr. Gibson undertook to produce one himself. The book is written from the point of view of a physicist seeking to understand and interpret solar observations in the framework of theoretical physics. This orientation as well as the primary purpose of the book combine to make it a unique and valuable contribution to the literature of solar physics, and a superb textbook for college-level and graduate students.

This book evidences the seriousness and dedication with which Dr. Gibson and his fellow astronauts regard the scientific objectives of the Skylab mission. As one of the experimenters, I take this opportunity to express my personal thanks and appreciation for their collaboration and to wish them well on their great venture.

LEO GOLDBERG
Director
Kitt Peak National Observatory

MARCH 1972

Acknowledgments

A most pleasurable aspect of writing this book has been the stimulating and constructive suggestions that I have received from many individuals. Particular gratitude is expressed to Goetz Oertel, who offered a most illuminating review of the entire initial manuscript, and to R. Grant Athay, whose extensive comments on my discussions of the radiative properties of the solar atmosphere have significantly contributed to the work. I am also greatly indebted to those who have given me detailed reviews of certain sections: John Eddy (A Description of Solar Structure and Processes), Edward Frazier (Organized Velocity Patterns), Icko Iben (The Interior), and John Jefferies (Nonlocal Thermodynamic Equilibrium). I also thank those who have most kindly contributed comments on specific topics discussed in the text: Alfred Clark, Jr., Alexander Dessler, Franz Deubner, Owen Garriott, Frank Orrall, Sara Smith, John Thomas, Oran White, and George Withbroe. My special gratitude is given to Leo Goldberg for contributing the Foreword to this book and his continuous enthusiastic support.

EDWARD G. GIBSON

Contents

Symbols

A	area
$A(r)$	limb-darkening function
A_{rs}	rate of transitions from state r to state s by spontaneous emission per unit number density
$A_{\infty 1}{}^s$	rate for photo recombination from an ionized state to the ground state for an ion in the sth stage of ionization per unit number densities of ions and electrons
$\mathbf{a}$	acceleration
a, b	coronal flattening parameters
a_0	Bohr radius
$\mathbf{B}, B$	magnetic field
$B(r)$	limb-darkening function
$B_\odot$	total solar brightness
$\mathbf{B}_i$	magnetic field of incident electromagnetic wave
B_r, B_ϕ	magnetic field in the radial and azimuthal directions, respectively
$\mathbf{B}_s$	magnetic field of scattered electromagnetic wave
B_λ	Planck function (per unit wavelength interval)
B_ν	Planck function (per unit frequency interval)
C	constant
$\mathrm{Ca}\ H$	H line of calcium once ionized at 3968 Å
$\mathrm{Ca}\ K$	K line of calcium once ionized at 3934 Å
CF	observer correction factor
$C(\Delta t)$	time correlation function of the solar velocity field
C_p	specific heat at constant pressure
C_{rs}	rate of transitions from state r to state s by collisions per unit number densities of ions and electrons
C_v	specific heat at constant volume
$C_{1\infty}{}^s$	rate for transitions from the ground state to an ionized state for an ion at the sth stage of ionization per unit number densities of ions and electrons
c	speed of light in a vacuum
D_e	average equatorial diameter of coronal isophote
D_p	average polar diameter of coronal isophote
E	intensity of emission corona
$\mathbf{E}_i$	electric field of incident electromagnetic wave

E_s	energy of state s
$\mathbf{E}_s$	electric field of scattered electromagnetic wave
e	electron charge
$\mathbf{e}_r$	outward unit vector perpendicular to the limb of the sun
$\mathbf{e}_t$	unit vector tangent to limb of the sun in counterclockwise direction
$\mathbf{e}_\phi$	unit vector in azimuthal direction
F	intensity of F corona
F_m	magnetic force per unit volume
f	atomic oscillator strength (ch. 4)
f	frequency, radio range (ch. 6)
f	following spot(s) (ch. 2)
f_m	gyrofrequency
f_p	plasma frequency
G	gravitational constant
g	force of gravity per unit mass
g_s	statistical weight of state s
$g_\odot$	solar gravity at $1R_\odot$
H	atmospheric scale height
H	hydrogen
Hα	hydrogen Balmer-alpha line at 6563 Å
Hβ	hydrogen Balmer-beta line at 4861 Å
h	Planck's constant
h	height in the solar atmosphere above height of $\tau_{5000 \text{ Å}} = 1$
I	electric current
$\bar{I}$	specific intensity averaged over all wavelengths
IS	number of individual spots
$\mathbf{I}_\lambda, I_\lambda$	specific intensity at wavelength λ
$I_\lambda{}^\circ$	initial value of I_λ
J	total azimuthal quantum number
$\mathbf{J}$	electric current density
$\bar{J}$	specific intensity averaged over all wavelengths and directions
$\langle J \rangle$	J_λ averaged over the line absorption coefficient
J_λ	specific intensity averaged over all directions
j_λ	rate of radiant energy emission per unit mass, solid angle, and wavelength interval
$j_\lambda{}^c$	j_λ in the continuum next to the line
$j_\lambda{}^l$	j_λ in the line
K	intensity of K corona
K_r	K corona polarized in the radial direction
K_t	K corona polarized in the tangential direction
K_λ	intensity of K corona at wavelength λ
$K_\lambda{}^c$	K_λ in the continuum next to the line
$K_\lambda{}^l$	K_λ in the line

k	Boltzmann's constant
L	characteristic length
$L(r)$	luminosity at radius r
$L_\odot$	solar total luminosity
l	azimuthal quantum number
l_c	intensity at line center relative to continuum for coronal light
l_p	intensity at line center relative to continuum for photospheric light
$L\alpha$	Lyman-alpha line at 1216 Å
$L\beta$	Lyman-beta line at 1026 Å
M	mass inside solar sphere of radius r
M_J	total magnetic quantum number
$M_\odot$	solar mass
m	magnetic quantum number
m	particle mass (sec. 4.6)
m_e	electron mass
m_H	hydrogen atomic mass
m_s	projection of s on an arbitrarily chosen axis
m_l	projection of l on an arbitrarily chosen axis
N	number density
$\underline{N}$	number of atoms per unit area along the line of sight
$\overline{N}G$	number of spot groups
N_e	number density of electrons
N_H	number density of hydrogen
N_i	number density of ions
N_j	number density of state j ($j=$ an integer)
N_s	number density of atom with s electrons removed
n	total quantum number
$\mathbf{n}$	unit vector normal to a surface
n_r, n_θ, n_ϕ	quantum numbers corresponding to r, θ, and ϕ, respectively
P_g	period of gravity wave oscillation
P_r, P_θ, P_ϕ	linear momentum corresponding to r, θ, and ϕ, respectively
p	pressure
p	preceding spot(s) (ch. 2)
p_c	central pressure
p_d	fluid dynamic pressure
p_m	magnetic pressure
Q_{lu}	electron-atom collision cross section
R	projected radius
R_m	magnetic Reynolds number
R_{rs}	rate of transitions from state r to state s by absorption of radiation per unit number density
$R_\odot$	solar radius
r	radius

$\mathbf{r}$	position radius vector
r'	dummy variable of integration
S_λ	radiation source function
s	distance
T	temperature
T_b	brightness temperature
T_c	central temperature
T_d	T_b averaged over the solar disk
T_e	electron temperature
T^*	radiation temperature defined for NLTE source function
t	time
UT	universal time
u_s	partition function for sth stage of ionization
u, v, w	velocities in Cartesian coordinates
V	velocity
$\mathbf{V}$	macroscopic velocity
V_A	Alfvén velocity
V_{fast}	fast-mode wave velocity
V_{material}	material velocity
V_0	initial velocity
V_s	speed of sound
V_{slow}	slow-mode wave velocity
V_{wave}	wavefront velocity
V_g^{rms}	root-mean-square gas velocity
$V_{\text{turb}}^{\text{rms}}$	root-mean-square turbulent velocity
W	equivalent width
X	hydrogen mass fraction
X_{CN}	combined mass fraction of carbon and nitrogen
x, y, z	Cartesian coordinates
Y	helium mass fraction
Z	heavy-element mass fraction
z	positive charge on nucleus
ZS	Zurich sunspot number
α	angle between the direction of the incident electric field and the direction of the scattered electromagnetic wave
α	constant used in calculation of $\dot{\epsilon}_{\text{noise}}$
β_λ	reciprocal of emission scale height
Γ	constant in the boundary condition on pressure and temperature at the solar surface
γ	ratio of C_p to C_v
$\Delta\lambda_D$	Doppler width of line
$\Delta\lambda_M$	Zeeman wavelength split of lines
$\Delta\lambda_N$	natural width of line

δ	slip between fluid and magnetic field
ϵ	energy production rate per unit mass (ch. 3)
ϵ	coronal flattening index (ch. 6)
ϵ_{cc}	energy production rate per unit mass by the carbon cycle
ϵ_M	magnetic-moment/magnetic-field interaction energy
$\dot{\epsilon}_{noise}$	rate of acoustical noise energy generation per unit volume
ϵ_{pp}	energy production rate per unit mass by the proton-proton cycle
η	electron displacement from initial location
η_λ	ratio of $K_\lambda{}^l/K_\lambda{}^c$
θ	polar angle
κ	opacity
$\bar{\kappa}$	opacity averaged over flux
$\kappa\rho$	absorption coefficient for radiation
κ_λ	absorption coefficient at wavelength λ
Λ	energy-level perturbation parameter
λ	wavelength
λ_0	wavelength at line center
λ_p	wavelength corresponding to plasma frequency
μ	index of refraction (ch. 6)
μ	mean atomic weight
$\boldsymbol{\mu}$	magnetic moment
μ_0	magnetic permeability of a vacuum
μ_x	mean atomic weight of fully ionized hydrogen
μ_y	mean atomic weight of fully ionized helium
μ_z	mean atomic weight of fully ionized heavy elements
ν	frequency
ξ	$R/R_\odot$
ρ	density
$\boldsymbol{\varrho}$	vector from scattering center to observer
ρ_c	central density
ΣK_p	magnetic activity index
σ	Stefan-Boltzmann constant
σ	electrical conductivity (ch. 5)
σ_1, σ_2, π	split Zeeman line components
σ_T	Thomson cross section
τ_λ	optical depth at wavelength λ
τ°	initial value of τ
Φ	upward flux of noise energy
ϕ	angle, azimuthal
χ_s	ionization potential of atom which has s electrons removed
Ψ	scattered radiant power per steradian
Ω	angular momentum loss per unit mass of solar wind
ω	rate of solar rotation

ω	direction
ω_c	critical frequency

Subscripts:

ad	adiabatic
at	atmosphere
0	initial value
rad	radiation

Superscripts:

c	designates continuum next to line
l	designates absorption line
$\circ$	initial value

Physical Constants

Bohr radius:
$$a_0 = \epsilon_0 h^2 / \pi m_e c^2 = 0.529172 \text{ Å}$$
$$= 5.29172 \times 10^{-9} \text{ cm}$$

Speed of light:
$$c = 2.997930 \times 10^{10} \text{ cm/sec}$$

Electronic charge:
$$e = 1.60206 \times 10^{-19} \text{ coulomb}$$

Planck's constant:
$$h = 4.1354 \times 10^{-15} \text{ eV-sec}$$
$$= 6.62517 \times 10^{-27} \text{ erg-sec}$$

Boltzmann's constant:
$$k = 8.6164 \times 10^{-5} \text{ eV/K}$$
$$= 1.38044 \times 10^{-16} \text{ erg/K}$$

Electron rest mass:
$$m_e = 0.510976 \text{ MeV}$$
$$= 9.1083 \times 10^{-28} \text{ gram}$$

Proton rest mass:
$$m_p = 938.211 \text{ MeV}$$
$$= 1.67239 \times 10^{-24} \text{ gram}$$

Ratio proton mass to electron mass:
  $m_p/m_e = 1836.12$

Capacitivity of vacuum:
  $\epsilon_0 = 8.85434 \times 10^{-14}$ coulomb/cm-volt

Compton wavelength of electron:
  $\lambda_c = h/m_e c = 2.42626 \times 10^{-10}$ cm

Permeability of vacuum:
  $\mu_0 = 4\pi \times 10^{-9}$ volt-sec/amp-cm

Wien's displacement law constant:
  $(\lambda T)_{\max} = 0.289782$ cm-K

Solar Properties

Distance from earth:
  1 astronomical unit (AU) $= 1.496 \times 10^{13}$ cm
                           $= 214.94 R_\odot$

Gravity at surface:
  $g_\odot = 2.74 \times 10^4$ cm/sec^2

Luminosity:
  $L_\odot = 3.86 \times 10^{33}$ ergs/sec

Mass:
  $M_\odot = 1.991 \times 10^{33}$ grams

Radius:
  $R_\odot = 6.960 \times 10^{10}$ cm
       $= 0.6960 \times 10^6$ km
       $= 109$ earth radii

Understanding the Sun: Why, What, and How

1.1 MOTIVATION

Solar energy—it sustains every known living organism. The sun provides virtually all of the heat and light our planet receives. Thus, it has been, and remains, a major factor in shaping the course of our own evolution. Awareness of our physical dependence on solar energy stimulates a curiosity about the nature of its source. However, our desire to understand goes beyond curiosity. Gaining insight into the nature of the sun's structure and dynamics has significance in many areas.

The sun is a star, a very unique one for us because of our proximity to it. It is representative of many distant stars, but we are close enough to it to observe the details of its physical makeup. Theories of stellar structure and evolution are formulated and tested using the sun as a reference. In understanding the sun and stars we must understand processes that occur on the very small scale (microscopic) and the very large scale (macroscopic). To this end we use the sun as a gigantic astrophysical laboratory. The existing combinations of temperature, density, and very large characteristic lengths provide physical conditions far in excess of the capabilities of terrestrial laboratories. Thus, several fundamentally important areas of study with practical application are furthered by solar investigations. These areas include atomic physics, nuclear physics, plasma physics, and magnetohydro-dynamics.

The character of our environment is strongly dependent on the character of the radiation emissions from the sun. Biologically, we are very sensitive to high-energy solar radiation and particle emissions. Understanding of our own evolution, as well as the possibility of life forms elsewhere in the solar system, requires that we understand the past history of the sun's high-energy emissions. The major step that we are presently taking in exploring and utilizing space requires that we be able to predict the time of occurrence and the type of energy emissions of solar flares. In this way, adequate protective measures for flight crews can be designed and timely utilized. Even adequate design of unmanned spacecraft requires that the total solar radiation emission be well defined. The very thin protective layer of gas around the earth, our atmosphere, is also sensitive to the sun's radiation. An improved understanding of the characteristics of the energy our atmosphere receives in turn yields further insight into such variable terrestrial processes as weather, the chemistry of the upper atmosphere, the course of geological ages, and long-range radio communications that are influenced by the properties of the ionosphere.

Motivation for gaining knowledge is at best difficult to analyze. Even though the furtherance of science and practical applications have been mentioned here, the enjoyment received from studying inherently interesting phenomena should not be ignored. Solar structure and processes involve very large energies by our standards, very large physical dimensions as well as microscopic lengths, time scales ranging from nearly the age of the universe itself to seconds, extremely high temperatures of up to 10 billion degrees Kelvin, and dynamic and complex interactions between magnetic fields and matter nowhere encountered or reproducible in our own environment. The understanding of solar phenomena stimulates and exercises our intellect, making it an end in itself.

1.2 CENTRAL QUESTIONS

Current research in solar physics seeks answers to many very detailed questions. To make a given research effort feasible, the questions that it asks must usually be small in scope. However, almost all of them are part of much larger and broader questions summarized below.

Abundances

What is the relative abundance of the elements? That is, of what is the sun made? Certainly we need this information to make physical models of the sun and analyze observed phenomena. In addition, however, the knowledge of abundances, especially the ratio of helium to hydrogen, is of importance in understanding the evolution of our galaxy and the universe. A currently attractive theory for the beginning of our knowable universe, the "big bang" theory, asserts that approximately 13 billion years ago all matter and energy emerged from a high-density primordial fireball. The ratio of helium to hydrogen which would have resulted is not greatly different than that observed in the sun ($\approx 1/10$, by number), but the combined abundance of the heavier elements would have been much less than the solar value ($\approx 1/100$). Thus, it is further theorized that stars were formed from the original hydrogen and helium, the heavier elements and a relatively small amount of additional helium were formed in their interiors by nuclear fusion reactions, some of these stars subsequently exploded, and the sun and other nearby stars contracted from the explosion remnants. A second theory, the steady-state theory, assumes that matter is continuously being "created" everywhere and that the average density of matter remains constant as the universe expands. The ultimate acceptance or rejection of any cosmological model depends in part on the ability of the model to correctly predict the observed solar and stellar abundances. To be a decisive yardstick, these abundances must be known accurately.

Energy Generation

What are the basic thermonuclear processes responsible for the sun's luminosity? Our ability to understand the continuous flow of energy from the sun and stars depends upon our ability to comprehend the details of the nuclear reactions that convert mass into energy. In an extremely difficult experiment, neutrinos from the sun have been observed. Neutrinos are massless, chargeless particles that travel with the speed of light and interact so rarely with matter that almost all those generated in the core by nuclear reactions directly escape the sun. Thus, when the extremely difficult task of detecting the elusive neutrino is overcome, we can "see" all the way to the solar core. So far, the measured neutrino flux is significantly lower than the predicted value which calls for a modification of either our theories of stellar interiors or the experiment procedures and interpretation. The measured neutrino flux also sets an unexpectedly low limit on the helium abundance just considered.

Does the rate of energy generation by the sun change with time? Certainly we expect changes in the energy production rate on a time scale comparable to the age of the sun ($4\frac{1}{2}$ billion years). However, changes on a much shorter time scale cannot be ruled out. Is the solar constant really a constant?

Outward Energy Flux

How is the energy transported outward from the core, where it is generated, to free space and how are solar properties determined by this energy flow? The energy generated in the core diffuses toward the surface as radiation, except for the relatively small amount carried away by neutrinos. At a point close to the surface, most of this energy flux is transformed into turbulent convective bubbling motions of the gas and reaches the visible edge of the sun in this form. It then returns to the radiative form we observe. However, the turbulence also generates waves which propagate mechanical energy into the relatively thin atmosphere above and heat it to temperatures only slightly less than those in the core. Our understanding of this atmospheric heating and the resulting temperature structure is far from complete. The role of observed atmospheric structures, including spicules, the chromospheric network, and active regions, in the mechanical heating of the atmosphere is also largely unknown.

Solar Wind

How is the flux of particles leaving the sun generated and what is its relation to observed solar features? The energy source for the wind ultimately lies in the mechanical heating of the atmosphere, but the details of the energy conversion are not well understood. The relation between the observed nonuniformities of the solar wind are related to the large-scale magnetic fields and the resulting atmospheric structures. Again, the details of this relation are not well known. In addition to energy, the solar wind continuously transports angular momentum away from the rotating sun. The present and past values of this momentum loss are not accurately determined. Thus, the history of the sun's rotation and the effect on its own evolution are not well defined.

Solar Activity

What are the mechanisms which generate cyclic nonuniform activity on the sun? Energy is not emitted uniformly or steadily over the sun's surface, but rather "solar storms" are observed in which the local energy emission appears enhanced.

These storms, which may last for many months, are manifested by dark sunspots surrounded by plages (large areas brighter than average), prominences (large volumes of dense cool gas suspended above the surface), very nonuniform structures in the outer atmosphere, and a complex configuration of enhanced magnetic fields. The frequency of occurrence of this activity reaches a peak approximately every 11 years, but the magnetic fields return to the same general configuration only every 22 years. It currently appears probable that solar activity is caused by an interaction between magnetic fields and the nonuniform rotation of the sun. The sun's equator rotates faster than the poles and the shearing action on the gas contorts the fields into configurations that produce activity. Although this appears feasible, many details of the formation, maintenance, and dissipation of solar activity are yet to be understood.

Associated with solar activity but also major questions in themselves are: What is the past history and current distribution of magnetic fields throughout the sun? And what is the mechanism responsible for the faster rotation at the solar equator? Both of these are fundamental to our understanding of solar and stellar phenomena.

 ## Flares

What is the basic mechanism responsible for a flare? Although flares are really a form of solar activity, their practical importance and their intriguing dynamic nature warrant them special attention. Flares are manifested by an explosive release of high-energy radiation and, occasionally, particles from very localized areas of magnetically complex active regions. This release occurs sporadically and involves energies that are extremely large by our earthly standards. It is currently suspected that large solar magnetic fields accumulate and store energy in an unstable configuration. Return to a more stable and lower energy configuration is somehow triggered and energy is rapidly released. The details of the energy buildup, storage, and release are not known. Also of importance, but not understood, is the mechanism by which particles are accelerated to extremely high energies and released.

Our Progression Toward the Answers

It was only a half century ago that Sir Arthur Eddington speculated that the energy source for the sun and stars is the conversion of mass into energy as hydrogen undergoes fusion reactions to form helium. Since that time, especially in recent years, our knowledge and understanding of the sun has grown rapidly. This growth is attributed to increased observational and theoretical capabilities and increased interest in understanding solar phenomena from many sectors.

The objective of the solar observer is to measure the sun's radiation with high spectral and spatial resolution and, in some instances, high time resolution. Our atmosphere has always impeded his progress. It absorbs all the solar radiation it receives except in some relatively narrow wavelength ranges in the visible, infrared, and radio regions. Turbulent eddies within our atmosphere refract the sun's radiation and limit our ability to spatially resolve solar features. Also, the corona, the very tenuous outer atmosphere of the sun, can be observed only at times of solar eclipse. At other times when we try to observe it by covering up or occulting the sun's bright disk, light from the disk is scattered by the atmosphere and creates a background that overwhelms most of the corona's faint light. As observing platforms have become available on sounding rockets and orbiting spacecraft, the limitations of our atmosphere have been removed. Instruments can now measure the total solar spectrum; their spatial resolution is limited only by the defraction limit of their optics and pointing stability, and they can continuously observe the changing corona.

Significant strides in the improvement of ground-based technology have also been made. These include the development of the vacuum telescope which significantly decreases the atmospheric limitation on spatial resolution; improved spectrographic techniques giving greater spectral resolution; and improved sensors, both photoelectric and film, yielding improved resolution in space, wavelength, and time.

The availability of high-quality observations and an increased interest has spurred theoretical efforts. The growth of computer technology has permitted the calculation of more accurate but complex physical models. New theoretical tools, data, and understanding of basic phenomena have become available with the many significant developments in the fields of plasma physics, magnetohydrodynamics (MHD), nuclear physics, and atomic physics.

The current surge of interest and our rapidly expanding observational and theoretical capabilities make this an exciting time to take part in exploring the sun.

1.3 OUR METHODS AND APPROACH

In the following chapters we discuss our current knowledge of the sun and emphasize physical concepts. That is, the presentation of the observational results and photographs and the use of equations are all directed toward leaving the reader with a firm physical feel for the subject. This approach is based on the conviction that in order to either properly appreciate, observe, or theoretically analyze solar phenomena, one must have a clear mental picture of the physical world under consideration.

A broad overview of solar structure and processes is presented in chapter 2. The treatment is purposely kept basic so that people without advanced training in physics and mathematics can appreciate the subject. It also serves as a rapid orientation for those with more advanced backgrounds but unfamiliar with solar phenomena.

The quiet sun is discussed in detail in chapters 3 to 6. An equivalent treatment of the active sun would require another volume of at least the same length. Subjects having direct bearing on the central questions just discussed are emphasized. It is felt that it is both meaningful and valid to discuss the quiet sun as an entity by itself. It is a logical starting point for understanding all solar phenomena and can be used conceptually as a matrix into which active phenomena are introduced. The relatively short length of the solar cycle implies that activity is restricted to the sun's outer layers. The overall magnetic field of the active sun is completely reversed during a cycle and, because of the very high electrical conductivity of the solar gases, the field cannot appreciably penetrate the surface. Thus, treatment of the solar interior as a spherically symmetric body free of activity is a valid approach. In the sun's inner atmosphere, the photosphere and chromosphere, quiet and active regions can be observationally separated and we can again validly describe quiet-sun characteristics. However, in the outer atmosphere, the corona, the effects of activity are more widespread and have therefore been included in our description where it is required.

It is hoped that you will experience some of the same excitement and awe in understanding solar phenomena as I have found in describing them.

2

A Description of Solar Structure and Processes

2.1 CLASSIFICATION OF PHENOMENA

The description of the physical nature of solar phenomena and the understanding of their origins is aided by a division of these phenomena into two classes: quiescent and active.

In the quiescent model, the sun is viewed as a static, spherically symmetric ball of hot gases; that is, solar properties change with radius only and are uniform over any one spherical layer. Using this assumption, we investigate first the core of the sun and then progress through several distinct layers to an area many solar radii outside the sun's visible edge. Thus, the core, convection zone, photosphere, chromosphere, and corona are considered in their order of occurrence, which enables us to trace the generation of solar energy and the various modes of its transport outward. The unique physical characteristics of each layer are attributed to various manifestations of this outward energy flow. The model of the quiet sun which evolves will form a conceptual framework into which the characteristics of the active sun are introduced.

In contrast, solar activity refers to processes that occur in localized regions of the sun's atmosphere and within finite time intervals. The observable features of an active region form the basis of the study; these include sunspots, plages, filaments, and flares (fig. 2–1). The time scales for solar activity can be classified as slow (the time of growth to maximum of the solar cycle), intermediate (the development time of an active region), or fast (the rise time of a flare), and have magnitudes from many years down to seconds.

2.2 THE SOLAR CORE

An essential property of the sun is that it is massive (one-third million times as massive as the earth). Under its own gravitational attraction, solar material is compressed to such a high central density and temperature that nuclear reactions take place. These nuclear reactions are the source of the energy which is continuously radiated to space and which drives solar activity.

A relatively small core contains most of the mass and is almost entirely responsible for the sun's luminosity. For example, within the central sphere having one-fourth the solar radius (1/64 of the sun's volume), one-half of the solar mass is

7

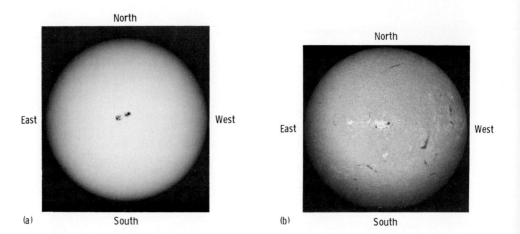

(a)

(b)

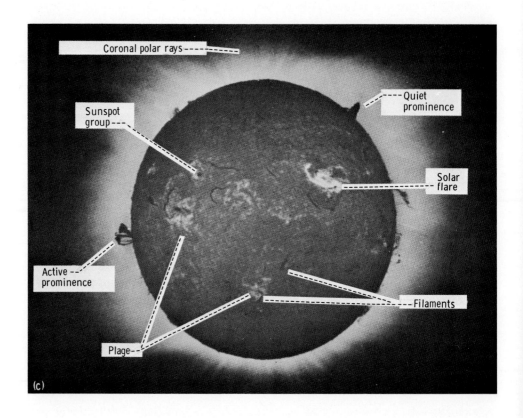

(c)

concentrated and 99 percent of the sun's emitted energy is generated. At the very center, the sun's temperature is 15 million degrees Kelvin, its pressure is approximately 250 billion atmospheres, and its specific gravity is slightly less than 160. Although the nuclei are a thousand times more densely packed than those of any metal, the high temperature keeps the material in a gaseous state. That is, a rigid lattice structure does not exist and electrons and bare nuclei still move about rapidly as free particles. The energy released in the core results from the fusion of hydrogen nuclei to form helium nuclei ($4\,^1\text{H} \longrightarrow \,^4\text{He}$) and, for every 1 gram of hydrogen entering the reaction, 0.007 gram is converted into energy. Hence, to generate continuously the observed luminosity of 4×10^{23} kW, this nuclear furnace devours mass at the rate of 5 million tons per second.

The core also contains almost all of the products of reaction or "ashes" of the nuclear burning. Correspondingly, there is a central depletion of hydrogen. In moving out from the sun's center to the surface, the fraction of hydrogen by mass increases, with 96 percent of the increase taking place in the first $\frac{1}{4}R_\odot$ ($1R_\odot = 1$ solar radius). The remainder of the sun is essentially a uniform mixture of hydrogen, helium, and approximately a 1-percent mixture of heavier elements. The hydrogen atoms are approximately 10 times more abundant than the helium atoms, and the atoms of the heavier elements appear in roughly the same abundance ratios as in the earth's crust. (C, N, O, Ne, Mg, Si, S, A, Ca, Fe, and Ni are the major contributors to the gas density.) These heavier elements are the products of nuclear reactions that may have been formed in the early moments of the "big bang" universe or in the interiors of stars formed earlier than our sun.

The energy that is generated in the sun's core is transferred toward the surface by radiation. Outward from the core, the temperature, pressure, and density decrease rapidly, as does the energy of an average photon. Photons are absorbed and re-emitted many times as they diffuse toward the surface. In this way, the energy flowing from the core in the form of high-energy gamma rays is changed to X-rays,

FIGURE 2–1.—The full disk of the sun. (a) White light (2155 UT), taken on October 21, 1971. Significant features which are evident here include the sharpness of the limb, the increased darkening near the limb, and the sharp contrast between the quiet uniform background and the sunspots at the center. Also evident is the lack of complex features relative to (b). (b) Hα (2120 UT). This photograph was obtained in the light of the Balmer-α absorption line of hydrogen (abbreviated Hα and here includes the light in about a $\frac{1}{2}$-Å wavelength increment centered at 6563 Å). In this photograph, taken 35 min before the photograph in (a), we observe light which originated higher in the atmosphere (the chromosphere) than if it had been taken in white light (the photosphere). The sunspots are partially marked by the complex structures of the chromosphere which includes fibrils (numerous small dark linear elements covering the disk), filaments (large dark linear elements), and plages (bright areas usually near sunspots). Note that limb darkening is evident here also. (c) Composite photograph. This includes the solar disk in Hα on July 16, 1959, prominences at the limb from a 1928 Mount Wilson spectroheliogram, and the solar corona during the eclipse of July 1963. ((a) and (b) are courtesy of E. Mayfield and E. Frazier, San Fernando Observatory of the Aerospace Corp.; (c) is courtesy of S. Smith and B. Nolan, Lockheed Solar Observatory.)

then to extreme ultraviolet (XUV) rays, to ultraviolet (UV) rays, and finally to the lower energy visible light which is most characteristic of the solar energy freely radiated to space. Figure 2–2 lists these spectral ranges and the variables used. However, the energy is not transported all the way to the surface by radiation only. At approximately $0.86R_\odot$, the gas properties have changed to such an extent that the gas above is convectively unstable and turbulent convection occurs. The general structure, physical properties, and modes of energy flow of the sun are given in figure 2–3.

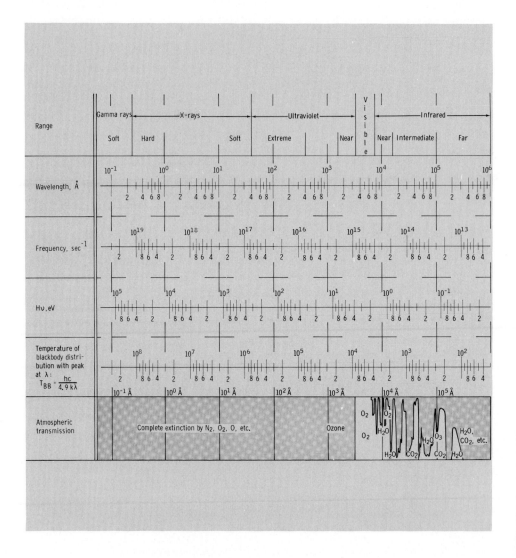

Figure 2–2.—Ranges of the electromagnetic spectrum.

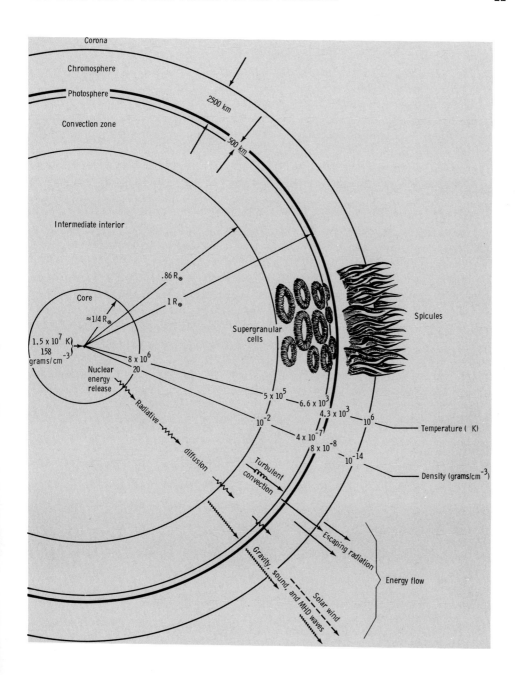

FIGURE 2–3.—Idealized general solar properties, structure, and modes of outward energy flow. The features shown are not to scale and provide a qualitative picture only.

2.3 THE CONVECTION ZONE

Temperature is the gas property that is primarily responsible for the establishment of a turbulent layer beneath the sun's surface. In the convection zone, the temperature has reached a value which is low relative to that in the core. This has two important consequences. First, a significant number of the free electrons in the gas are moving slowly enough that they can be captured into bound energy states by hydrogen and other nuclei to form atoms. Secondly, associated with the increase in the number of atoms, there is an increase in the opacity of the gas (it becomes less transparent to radiation) and a resulting increase in the temperature gradient. Photons are more easily absorbed by atoms, a greater resistance to the diffusion of radiation is offered, and a steeper temperature gradient results. Hence, an element of gas that moves slightly upward, cooling by expansion as it goes, also tends to be heated by the energy given up when electrons recombine with nuclei; therefore, its temperature does not drop as rapidly as it would otherwise (fig. 2–4). Because of this heating and the large temperature gradient in the surrounding medium, the element of gas is at a higher temperature and, more importantly, at a lower density then its surrounding medium. Thus, the motion upward is accelerated and turbulent convection results. This instability also is exhibited by an element that is initially moving downward. The convection cells that are formed are similar to thunderstorms in our own atmosphere. Throughout the convection zone, except immediately below the photosphere, the effect of the increased opacity is considerably stronger than the effect of recombination. The energetic boiling and bubbling at the top of this turbulent layer can be observed at the sun's surface.

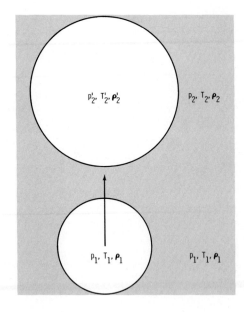

FIGURE 2–4.—Buoyancy of an upward-moving fluid element. The subscript denotes the initial conditions which are the same inside and outside of the fluid element. The subscript 2 denotes the conditions after the rise of the element, which is assumed to occur without heat transfer across the element's boundaries. Also, $p_2' = p_2$. If $\rho_2' < \rho_2$, the element will continue to rise because of buoyancy forces. In this case the atmosphere is convectively unstable.

The primary mode of energy transfer through the convection zone is direct transport, not radiation. Each element of rising gas carries its own parcel of energy directly to the surface. In addition to this mode of transfer, the powerful turbulence generates noise or "mechanical energy" which, as low-frequency sound waves, propagates through the photosphere and into the sun's outer layers. Although the amount of energy transported in this way is relatively small, it plays a major role in establishing the character of the outer layers of the sun. Gravity waves, generated in the low photosphere by overshooting convection cells, may also propagate a significant amount of nonradiative energy. Water surface waves, with which we are familiar, are a form of gravity waves.

Up to this point, our discussion has been based on theory only. The characteristics of the interior (core, intermediate region, and convection zone) are not visible to us and must be determined by calculations that are made to fit the observable features at the surface. From this point on, however, our primary source of knowledge will be observation rather than theory.

2.4 THE PHOTOSPHERE

In moving outward through the convection zone, the gas density, temperature, and pressure continue to decrease, and density becomes the important parameter. A layer is reached where a photon emitted outward has only a small probability of being reabsorbed or scattered. The photon then is more likely to escape into space through the transparent atmosphere above. It is this layer, called the photosphere (light sphere), which we actually see and which defines the very sharp visible edge of the sun. The temperature here is relatively low, and because the sun is in hydrostatic equilibrium, the scale height of the atmosphere is small and the density drops off very rapidly. Additionally, the density of the negative hydrogen ion (H−), which is responsible for most of the radiation emission and absorption at visible wavelengths, drops off even more rapidly. The sharp decrease in the density of H− with height, over and above the decrease of the total density, is related in chainlike fashion to the decrease of the electron density (H+e⇄H−) which is a very sensitive function of the decreasing temperature. In this way, most of the radiation we see is emitted from a very thin layer only about 100 km thick. This layer is 0.014 percent of $R_\odot$ or one-seventh second of arc as seen from the earth (1 arcsec = 726 km).

Some physical properties of the sun, defined at the thin visible surface of the photosphere, are the following. The radius is 0.696×10^6 km or 109 earth radii. The corresponding average angular diameter viewed from earth is 31′59″ or 1919 arcsec. The surface gravity is approximately $27g$, the pressure is about 0.01 atm, and the temperature at the top of the photosphere is approximately 4300 K. If it is assumed that the emitted radiation is in equilibrium and the Stefan-Boltzmann law (energy flux $= \sigma T^4$) is used to calculate an effective temperature for the whole emitting layer, a value of 5780 K results.

The energy which is radiated by the photosphere constitutes almost all of the

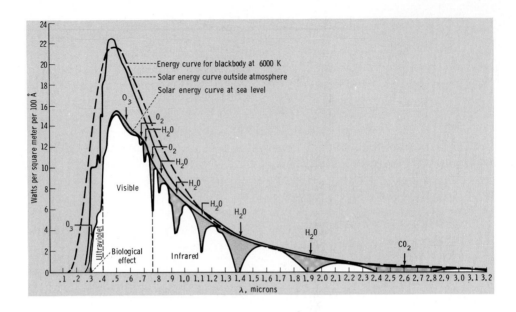

FIGURE 2–5.—Solar energy at the earth's orbit and the attenuation by the earth's atmosphere
(From Hynek, 1951; used with permission of McGraw-Hill Book Co.)

energy emitted by the sun into space and is centered in the visible spectrum.
Figure 2–5 illustrates the distribution of solar energy with wavelength. Also shown
are some of the absorbing regions of our own atmosphere. It has been calculated
that approximately half of the solar energy received at the earth's surface is in the
visible range. Thus, it is not surprising that our eyes have developed sensitivity in
the visible spectrum rather than in another range. An important feature of the
solar spectrum not shown in figure 2–5 is the presence of Fraunhofer absorption
lines, named after their discoverer. They appear as sharp dips in the intensity-
versus-wavelength curve (fig. 2–6).

FIGURE 2–6.—Hα absorption line. The circles
represent the mean profile at the center of
the quiet solar disk as observed on December 21, 1962. The solid triangles are observations made in 1960. The absorption
at −2.3 Å is a blend of Si I absorption
line and absorption by terrestrial water
vapor. Hα is an exceptionally strong line.
Most Fraunhofer lines are weaker and are
formed entirely below the temperature
minimum in the photosphere. (Courtesy of
O. White, Sacramento Peak Observatory,
Air Force Cambridge Research Laboratories.)

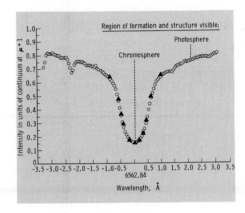

Each atom in the solar atmosphere will preferentially absorb and reemit radiation at certain discrete wavelengths or lines in the spectrum. The probability that a photon emitted in the photosphere will be reabsorbed before escaping to space will be greater, the closer its wavelength is to one of these discrete wavelengths. Most Fraunhofer lines are relatively weak, with respect to the hydrogen Balmer-alpha line (Hα), and originate entirely from regions below the temperature minimum. Thus, radiation escaping the photosphere at the center of most lines will be characteristic of the higher cooler layers; hence, lower in intensity. Conversely, the radiation off line center, where the atmosphere is more transparent, will have originated in the lower hotter layers and will be more intense. These characteristics provide a useful tool for determining how the properties change in the solar atmosphere with height. We can "see" down to a given layer by correctly choosing the wavelength at which to make our observations. The hydrogen Balmer-alpha line at 6563 Å (Hα), which is emitted when a hydrogen atom drops from its second to its first discrete level of excitation, is commonly used for observation. It is a natural wavelength for observation because it occurs in the visible spectrum and because hydrogen is by far the most abundant element in the solar atmosphere. Figure 2–1 (b) is a photograph taken at the center of the Hα absorption line and is characteristic of the chromosphere, the layer above the photosphere. The atmospheric fine structure that can be seen here is far more detailed than if the picture had been taken far from line center or had included the total visible spectrum, as in figure 2–1 (a). Use of a narrowband filter on the core of a strong line allows us to observe the very nonuniform chromospheric structure.

In the photosphere, a surprising phenomenon occurs. One would expect that, because the layers above the photosphere absorb only a small amount of energy from inside and are free to release this energy by radiation, the temperature would continue to decrease as we move outward. However, at the top of the photosphere, the temperature reaches a minimum and then actually increases outward to a coronal value of approximately 10^6 K, a temperature approaching that found in the core. This is demonstrated by the transition from the darkening at the edge of the sun evident in white-light photographs, which is characteristic of photospheric emission (fig. 2–1 (a)), to the limb brightening seen in much shorter wavelength photographs, which is characteristic of the atmosphere above (fig. 2–7). When we observe closer to the limb, the radiation we see originates from higher layers because of the increase in the number of atoms along our line of sight. As was previously implied, the mechanism responsible for the additional energy input to the outer atmosphere is the wave generation by the convection zone below. A small but significant amount of nonradiative energy in the form of waves passes through the photosphere and is dissipated in the chromosphere and corona, thereby elevating their temperatures.

Contrary to this line of reasoning, however, is the limb darkening (fig. 2–1 (b)) and absorption (fig. 2–6) observed in Hα. If the temperature increases with height in the chromosphere, where the cores of strong lines like Hα are formed, why do we not observe limb brightening and observe emission rather than absorption lines?

FIGURE 2–7.—X-ray photograph of the sun made on November 4, 1970. This excellent photograph illustrates the very non-homogeneous detailed structure of the solar gas and magnetic field in the lower corona. The gas density and temperature is controlled by the magnetic field and the emission outlines the magnetic lines of force and tends to be strong where the field is strong. Limb brightening, enhanced emission from active regions, and loops or arches of emitting gas that connect areas on the surface of opposite magnetic polarity are evident. (Courtesy of Solar Physics Group, American Science & Engineering, Inc.)

The answer lies in a fundamental difficulty often encountered in analyzing the solar atmosphere—the lack of thermodynamic equilibrium. The high-temperature chromospheric gas is immersed in the relatively low-temperature photospheric radiation and the concept of a single temperature that describes both gas and radiation properties is no longer applicable; hot gas and bright radiation do not necessarily correspond. The population of the energy levels of the atoms and ions do not correspond to the thermodynamic equilibrium population at the gas temperature. Analysis reveals that, for many lines, the ratio of the densities of the emitters to the absorbers is much lower than the corresponding case of thermodynamic equilibrium at the gas temperature. Thus, strong absorption at the centers of lines formed in the chromosphere can often result.

An obvious indication of the underlying hydrogen convection zone and the most notable feature of the photosphere is granulation. In a high-resolution white-light photograph, granulation is clearly evident, resembling a pattern of corn kernels (fig. 2–8). In reality, the photosphere is the top layer of the seething, bubbling convection zone. Large cells or fluid elements well up to the surface, radiate away their excess heat, and split apart as the cooler gases flow back down around their outside edges. These cells have an average angular size of a little over 2 arcsec (1800 km), a characteristic lifetime of 10 min, and a temperature difference from center to edge of at least 100 K. Convection patterns of a similar appearance can be

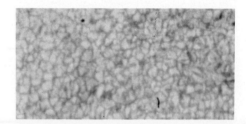

FIGURE 2–8.—White-light granulation. (Courtesy of R. Danielson, Project Stratoscope of Princeton University, sponsored by ONR, NSF, and NASA.)

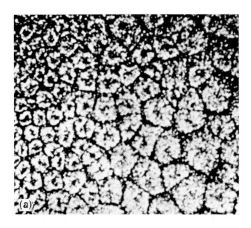 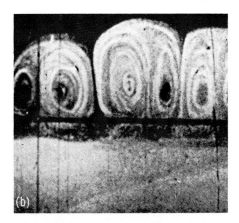

FIGURE 2–9.—Convection cells. (a) Convection cells in a thin layer of oil. Heat is added at the bottom of a thin layer of oil, carried upward by the flow at the center of each cell, and liberated to the air. The cooler oil sinks back down at the edges of the cells. This process has been made visible by the addition of fine aluminum powder. (b) A cross section of convection cells in smoke. Heat is added by passing electrical current through the horizontal wire at the center of the picture and convection cells above the wire are formed. (From Kiepenheuer, 1959; copyright 1959 by the University of Michigan Press.)

generated in a thin layer of oil (fig. 2–9) and within the earth's atmosphere (fig. 2–10).

A larger and somewhat more difficult to observe pattern of photospheric motion is supergranulation, which is also thought to be of convective origin. Using the Doppler effect, one can detect the mainly horizontal motion from center to edge within a supergranular cell (figs. 2–11 and 2–12). Supergranulation cells are approximately 18 times larger than granulation cells ($2\frac{1}{2}$ earth diameters), and they last

FIGURE 2–10.—Cumulus cloud formations resulting from convection cells in unstable air. Note the resemblance to solar granulation. The photograph was taken by Astronauts L. G. Cooper and C. Conrad, Jr., from the Gemini 5 spacecraft off the coast of Baja California, Mexico. (NASA MSC, S–65–45455.)

FIGURE 2–11.—Hα canceled velocity spectroheliogram made by Leighton's method. Spectroheliograms are made using a spectroheliograph in which the entrance slit is mechanically
moved across the image of the sun while the exit slit is moved over stationary film. In this
way a photograph of the sun can be made using only the light within a very small wavelength
increment. This picture was made from the photographic cancellation of two spectroheliograms, one made on the red side of Hα line center (Hα+Δλ) and the other made an equal
distance from line center but on the blue side (Hα−Δλ). For the one made on the red side,
regions moving away from the observer will appear darker because the light from the region
will be Doppler shifted toward the red. That is, the light observed at Hα+Δλ will have
originated closer to the absorption line center and therefore will be darker. The same will be
true for regions moving toward the observer seen at Hα−Δλ. The photographic differences
between receding and approaching velocities can be enhanced if the spectroheliogram made
at Hα−Δλ is photographically reversed (positive to negative) and added to that made at
Hα+Δλ. Now regions having no velocity relative to the observer will appear gray, those
moving away will appear dark, and those approaching will appear light. Leighton's method
proved so sensitive that it was necessary to introduce a special correction to eliminate the
effect of solar rotation (≃2 km/sec, corresponding to a Doppler shift of 0.04 Å). The above
picture is a result of applying this procedure to Mount Wilson photographs. The center of the
sun appears gray showing that no large-scale vertical pattern exists. However, as we observe
closer to the limb, pairs of bright-dark elements became pronounced. They are the same size
as the chromospheric network. The dark elements of each pair are always closer to the limb
showing that the mainly horizontal flow is away from the center of each pair (convection
cell). (Courtesy of R. Leighton, Mount Wilson and Palomar Observatories.)

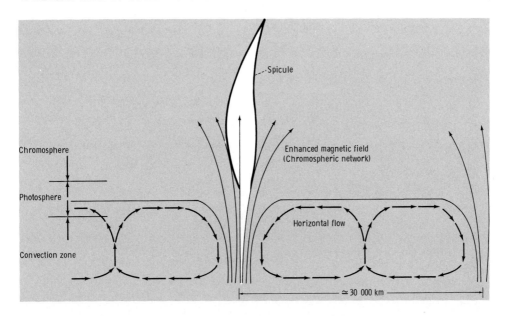

FIGURE 2–12.—Supergranulation. The flow of ionized gas from the center to the edges in supergranulation cells carries magnetic fields to the cell boundaries and a network of enhanced fields results. Spicule location coincides with this network.

roughly 120 times longer. Because of its size, supergranulation has a more deeply rooted pattern of motion. This motion may be caused by larger and thicker convection cells induced by the helium ion recombination which occurs in a much lower layer than the recombination of hydrogen ions.

The disturbances created by the convection zone are also responsible for a rhythmic rising and falling of the solar atmosphere with a period of approximately 5 min. These vertical oscillations are observed to vary harmonically across the surface as well, with a spatial wavelength of 5000 km or less. The observed change in phase in the vertical direction is negligible, suggesting that the oscillations are standing waves trapped in the photosphere and in the chromosphere around the temperature minimum. Both outward-propagating low-frequency sound waves generated in the convection zone and gravity waves excited by the underlying turbulence are under consideration as the basic cause for the oscillations. An artist's conception of the solar atmosphere is shown in figure 2–13.

2.5 THE CHROMOSPHERE

For a few seconds before and a few seconds after totality during an eclipse, a bright pink flash appears at the limb. This flash gives visibility to the chromosphere or "color sphere," the normally transparent layer above the photosphere. Its color is attributed to the dominance of the red-line Hα in the emission spectrum. Because the chromosphere is just above the temperature minimum, the density in its lower

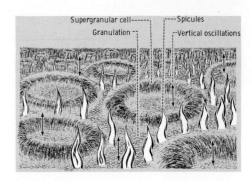

FIGURE 2–13.—The solar atmosphere.

portion continues to decrease very rapidly with height. A large density decrease (a factor of 10^{-4}) across the chromosphere results and, as in the photosphere, this large density change can be used as a key to our understanding. The chromosphere can be viewed as the froth on top of the turbulent and relatively dense photosphere, a froth that is closely coupled by magnetic fields to the underlying dynamics.

As the low-frequency sound waves generated in the turbulent convection zone move into the chromosphere, two important changes occur. Because of the rapid density decrease, the sound waves are accelerated to shocks. The amplitude of the material velocity in a wavefront must increase if the flux of energy $1/2\rho V^2_{material} V_{wave}$ is to remain nearly constant, similar to the effect produced by the cracking of a whip. These higher velocity pulses of fluid motion lead to more energetic collisions between the fluid particles and, thus, a stronger heating of the fluid as the waves pass through it. Second, the decrease in density leads to a relative increase in the ability of the magnetic fields to carry the energy flux in the form of waves (MHD waves). These waves traveling through the field also induce vibrations of the charged particles, electrons and ions, and energy is again deposited in the fluid as these particles collide with each other or with the uncharged particles. The combination of these two mechanisms results in the chromosphere being heated from 4300 K at its base to near-coronal values in less than 3000 km. The gravity waves, generated in the photosphere by the motion of overshooting convective cells, also can couple with magnetic fields and may provide another source of atmospheric heating. Regardless of the details of energy source, kinetic energy in the form of a coherent and directed wave motion (either of the entire fluid or of just the charged particles) is converted by particle collisions into the kinetic energy of random particle motion that we call heat.

The density decrease also causes the kinetic energy of fluid motion to become small relative to the energy stored in the magnetic field, which does not decrease rapidly with height. The ability of a magnetic field to store energy can be visualized as follows. When increasing the strength of a magnetic field by increasing the current which produces it, electrical energy must be expended to overcome the inductive effects that resist the current change. This energy can be pictured as being deposited in the magnetic field, the energy density being proportional to the square of the field strength. The stored energy will manifest itself by inducing currents and forces when the solar material, which has a high electrical conductivity, tries to move perpendicular to the magnetic lines of force. Because of the density decrease, the situation changes from that in the photosphere, where the fluid motions overpower the magnetic field and push it about at will, to that in the upper chromosphere, where the motion of the completely ionized gas is confined and organized by the magnetic field. In particular, the horizontal outward motion in the supergranular cells carries magnetic fields to the cell edges where the shear in the fluid flow enhances the field strength. This produces a network of magnetic fields which extends up into the chromosphere (fig. 2–12). It has been established that this chromospheric network coincides with the network of high temperatures and either bright emission or dark absorption features seen in many Fraunhofer

FIGURE 2–14.—Hα line-center spectroheliogram made on August 27, 1963. The network of bright emission in quiet regions can be detected, but is much more evident in figure 2–15. (Courtesy of Mount Wilson and Palomar Observatories.)

FIGURE 2–15.—Ca II spectroheliograms made on August 27, 1963. (a) Violet side of Ca II line
at 3934 Å. The network of bright emission is much more evident in this spectroheliogram
made slightly on the violet side (K2V) of the absorption line of Ca II (calcium ionized once)
at 3934 Å (referred to as the Ca K absorption line). (Courtesy of Mount Wilson and Palomar
Observatories.)

absorption lines characteristic of the chromosphere (figs. 2–14 and 2–15). This
network of higher temperatures is a consequence of the enhanced magnetic fields
which facilitate the upward transport of mechanical energy and the dissipation
mechanisms of the MHD waves discussed previously.

The chromospheric network is also the location from which brilliant jets of
luminous gas rise to approximately 10 000 km and then fade in 2 to 5 min. These
flames or spicules (spears) are evident in photographs of the limb, where they

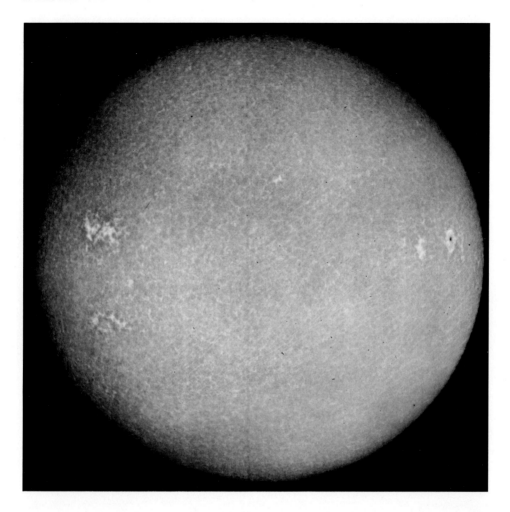

FIGURE 2–15 (concluded).—Ca II spectroheliograms made on August 27, 1963. (b) Violet side of Ca II line at 8498 Å. In this spectroheliogram made slightly on the violet side (−0.36 Å) of the absorption line of Ca II at 8498 Å, the network is again evident but to lesser degree than in K2V. (Courtesy of Mount Wilson and Palomar Observatories.)

appear to be densely packed because of line-of-sight superposition. Hence, the term "burning prairie" has been applied to the chromosphere (fig. 2–16). By observing in Hα but slightly to the red side of line center, we can easily see the spicules in absorption against the relatively bright solar disk, and their sparseness and similarity to the network are evident (fig. 2–17). They, too, lie along the chromospheric network and undoubtedly their origin is strongly related to the presence of magnetic fields. It may be that spicules provide the primary path for material and energy flows into the corona, or they may be nonrelated, but dynamic, side effects.

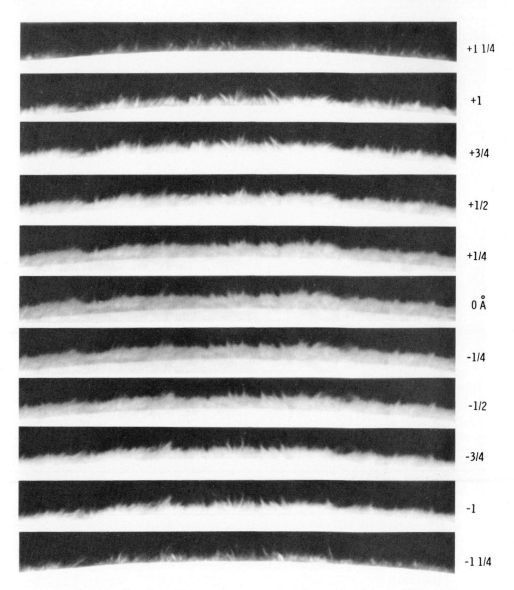

+1 1/4

+1

+3/4

+1/2

+1/4

0 Å

−1/4

−1/2

−3/4

−1

−1 1/4

FIGURE 2–16.—Spicules at the limb observed in Hα. This remarkable series of photographs was
made by Dunn using the Sacramento Peak vacuum telescope to reduce the effects on seeing
of turbulence in the earth's atmosphere and thereby obtain relatively high resolution. Individual spicules are easily resolved. At line center the overlapping of many spicules along
the line of sight gives the appearance of a diffuse chromospheric limb above the inner sharp
photospheric limb. If all light outside of a narrow passband centered at Hα could be filtered
out, only this outer diffuse limb would be visible. There is not a one-to-one correspondence
between features seen in the red and violet wings of Hα (±1.0 Å) which illustrates the Doppler
effects of motion along our line of sight in the spicules. (Courtesy of R. Dunn, Sacramento
Peak Observatory, Air Force Cambridge Research Laboratories.)

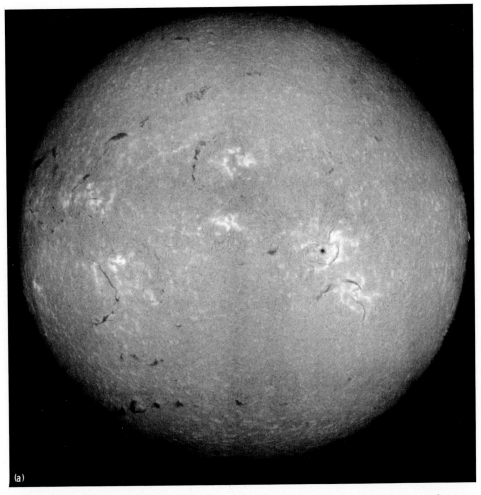

FIGURE 2–17.—Spectroheliograms made on July 23, 1961. The photographs illustrate the correspondence between the chromospheric network and the spicule grouping. Although an exact
correspondence cannot be made by visual inspection, the equality of the general scales of the
network and spicule pattern is evident. Also, the location of a well-formed network (*b*) and
a well-ordered spicule pattern (*c*) shows good correspondence. The network can also be seen
at Hα line center (*a*) in quiet regions as faint brightenings called flocculi which lie at the bases
of the spicules. (*a*) Hα line center. (Courtesy of Mount Wilson and Palomar Observatories.)

2.6 THE CORONA

In the region above the chromosphere, we encounter very low densities and a
correspondingly more difficult task of observation. Relative to the disk of the sun,
the corona's intensity in white light is lower by a factor of at least 10^{-6}, a brightness
roughly equivalent to that of a full moon. Direct observation by earthbound
coronagraphs (telescopes which occult the sun's disk) can yield only partial informa-

FigURE 2–17 (continued).—Spectroheliograms made on July 23, 1960. (b) Violet side of Ca K line center (K2V). (Courtesy of Mount Wilson and Palomar Observatories.)

tion about the white-light corona out to many solar radii because the background sky intensity, produced by light scattering in our atmosphere, overwhelms the corona's faint light. There are several ways of overcoming this difficulty.

The conventional and time-honored method of observation is to wait for a total eclipse, which occurs roughly two times every 3 years, and to let the moon do the occulting. Fortunately, the moon is almost the same angular size as the sun. The advantage gained in this case is that direct rays from the disk are no longer scattered by the ambient atmosphere and the intense background light is not produced. Thus, the white-light corona can be observed out to a much larger radius (fig. 2–18). However, the life of the corona observer employing this method is not

FIGURE 2–17 (concluded).—Spectroheliograms made on July 23, 1961. (c) 0.7 Å to the red side of Hα line center. (Courtesy of Mount Wilson and Palomar Observatories.)

an easy one. Expeditions carrying several tons of equipment usually must travel to remote sites on the earth to observe a total eclipse. When totality arrives, he will be able to take data for a maximum of only a few minutes, weather permitting.

A second method of observing the white-light corona out to several solar radii employed recently involves momentarily lifting a coronagraph above the major portion of our atmosphere on a sounding rocket. The background of scattered light is greatly reduced and the light from the photosphere and chromosphere can be effectively occulted within the instrument. This method is useful, but its natural extension, flight of a coronagraph on an orbital spacecraft, will rapidly exceed the few hundred minutes of observation time that has been available from total eclipses during the last century.

FIGURE 2–18.—The solar corona at sunspot minimum. This photograph was made at the eclipse of June 30, 1954, and shows a corona that is almost spherically symmetric except for the band of enhanced electron density around the equator which results from the small amount of activity present. The exposure time was 50 sec. (Courtesy of A. Wallenquist, Uppsala Observatory.)

The light seen from the white-light corona originates in three distinct ways. The first component of coronal light, the K corona (from the German Kontinuierlich, meaning "continuous"), is responsible for most of the light we see within the first $1.3R_\odot$ from the surface (fig. 2–19). This light is the continuous spectrum emitted by the photosphere and scattered toward the observer by the free coronal electrons (fig. 2–20). The Fraunhofer lines do not appear because the Doppler shift given each photon of light as it is scattered by a rapidly moving electron is large relative to the width of the lines. Therefore, the lines become very broad and overlap so that they are no longer discernible. The F corona, on the other hand, is a compo-

FIGURE 2–19.—The three components of coronal light. The dominant component from 1.0 to $2.3R_\odot$ is the K corona shown here for solar maximum. The F corona is dominant from this radius outward. The E corona makes a relatively small contribution when the total emitted energy in the visible spectrum is considered, as was done for this figure, but for lines of emission over limited wavelength intervals it can be large relative to the other two components. This figure illustrates that even to see out to only $1.2R_\odot$ to $1.3R_\odot$, optimum viewing conditions are required (pure blue sky). Also, we are limited even during an eclipse by the radiance of the background sky which, for the upper limit on the radiance shown here, would limit the observation of the F corona to approximately $4R_\odot$. The lower limit on the sky radiance at midtotality of 3×10^{-10} $B_\odot$ would permit observation well beyond $4R_\odot$. (After van de Hulst, 1953.)

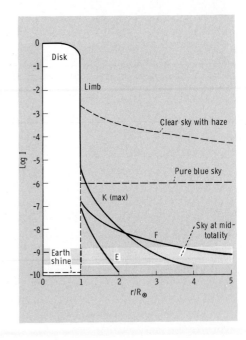

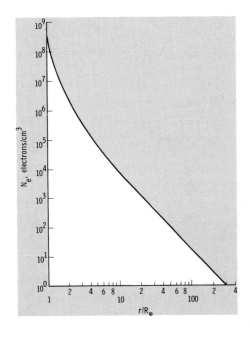

FIGURE 2–20.—Representative coronal electron densities at the solar equator and sunspot minimum. The values shown for $30R_\odot$ outward are uncertain. At sunspot maximum these densities are approximately a factor of 2 higher. The values used in making this plot have been given by Newkirk (1967).

nent which arises from the photospheric light scattered by relatively heavy, slow-moving solid particles between the earth and sun in the plane of the ecliptic and does show the Fraunhofer lines. This is the same mechanism responsible for the zodiacal light and, in fact, the F corona is sometimes referred to as the "inner zodiacal light." The third component, the E corona, is the light of the lines emitted by ions of the coronal gas. Relative to the electrons, the thermal motion of the ions is slow and the emission lines are also not washed out by large Doppler shifts like the Fraunhofer lines of the K corona.

It is not precisely correct to use the concept of temperature to gage the energy state of the coronal gas. Because the coronal gas is transparent to almost all of its own radiation and is therefore not a closed system, it is not in thermodynamic equilibrium. Many methods exist to define the temperature of the coronal gas. Most of these methods yield approximately the same value and have established that each particle in the corona has a very high average energy.

One method is to deduce a temperature from the hydrostatic scale height of the radial density change, the temperature (average particle energy) being proportional to this height. Another method uses observations of the intensity of the radiation at radio wavelengths to directly determine the gas temperature. Although the corona is transparent to visible light, it is opaque to radio waves having wavelengths greater than approximately 2 meters. The electron gas is of sufficient density to be a good absorber and emitter of radiation in this range. Thus, the electron gas and the radiation of radio wavelengths can be assumed to be at the same temperature. A third method is to observe the high degree of ionization of the coronal atoms and then to calculate the temperature (average electron energy) that must exist to achieve balance between the ion production and removal mechanisms. Illustrative of this high ionization is Fe XVII, iron ions which have been stripped of 16 of their 26 electrons and which contribute many high-energy emission lines to the E corona. Lastly, a temperature (average ion speed) can be obtained from the measured Doppler width of the coronal ion-emission lines. These methods confirm that an effective temperature of 10^6 K exists, 1.5×10^6 K being a nominal value for the inner corona. Even though this temperature is very high, the total amount of energy in the corona is small. The average energy per particle is large, but the energy density is low because of the extremely low particle density, 10^5 particles/cm³ at $4R_\odot$ compared to 10^{19} particles/cm³ at sea level in the earth's atmosphere. Also, because of this low density, the energy emitted by the corona is only about 10^{-3} of that of the chromosphere.

Because the corona's high temperature and degrees of ionization cause much of the emitted radiation to fall into the higher energy X-ray and XUV ranges where the photosphere and chromosphere appear relatively dark, a coronagraph is not required when observing in these spectral regions. Areas of locally higher density of the inner corona can be seen directly against the relatively dark photospheric disk (fig. 2–7).

The corona is not static, as so far implied, but is expanding under its own pressure gradient against the solar gravity and into the vacuum of space. The resultant flow, termed the "solar wind," reaches the earth with a supersonic velocity of roughly 400 km/sec, a density of only a few particles per cubic centimeter, and a temperature of about 10^5 K. The earth-sun distance of $215R_\odot$ is covered by the flow in approximately 5 days, in contrast to the 8 min it takes visible light to reach us. Close to the sun (less than approximately $3R_\odot$), the geometry of the flow is controlled by the magnetic-field structure. However, because of the decrease of the magnetic pressure relative to the gas-dynamic pressure, the fields are contorted and strung out into the solar system by the wind outside of the region close to the sun. Hence, the earth is actually immersed in the sun's outer atmosphere, although this atmosphere is extremely tenuous.

In summary, we have seen that the sun's energy is generated in the core and that almost all of it is released into space by the relatively thin photosphere. The convection zone also converts a small amount of the energy from the core into mechanical form which, together with the sharp drop in density, is responsible for the very high temperature of the sun's outer atmosphere. Each layer has been seen to have its own distinctive character even though the layers overlap and merge into one another. We can now introduce into this model the dynamic features of solar activity.

2.7 THE SOURCES OF ACTIVITY

The sun's energy source is nuclear fusion in the core. Because this energy is released at a steady rate, one might expect a spatially uniform and steady release of radiation at all wavelengths over the entire solar sphere. However, over short periods of time and from certain locations, the intensity fluctuates rapidly with large increases occurring at the shorter wavelengths. Thus, there are physical entities which continually perturb our spherically symmetric and steady-state model of the sun and cause the localization of energy release in space, time, and wavelength. The subtle complexities of the physical situation make cause and effect difficult to distinguish. However, at the risk of being enticed by currently attractive theories, we make the simplifying assumptions that the major perturbing factors are the sun's large-scale magnetic field and its differential rotation.

The sun is observed to have a general magnetic field like the large-scale dipole field of the earth. A weak field of approximately 1 gauss, compared with the earth's 0.6-gauss field, dominates the northern polar region above 50° solar latitude, and a roughly equivalent field of opposite polarity dominates the corresponding region of the southern hemisphere. However, a precisely defined axis and symmetry are lacking. Also, this general field does not arise from a dipole within the sun. Rather, it is the net result of the summation of many small surface fields.

The rotation of the sun is in the same direction as that of the earth. In fact, the rotations of the sun and nearly all the planets, as well as each planet's revolution about the sun, are in the same direction. Unlike the earth, the sun does not rotate as a rigid body. The equatorial region rotates faster than the poles. In the photosphere, the sidereal rate of rotation ω is given approximately by (Howard and Harvey, 1970)

$$\omega = \frac{1}{26} \left(1 - \frac{1}{8} \sin^2 \theta - \frac{1}{6} \sin^4 \theta \right) \qquad \text{rotations/day} \qquad (2\text{-}1)$$

where θ is the solar latitude (fig. 2-21(a)). Hence the period of rotation varies from 26 days at the equator to almost 37 days at the poles. The corresponding synodic periods of rotation observed from earth are 27 days at the equator to nearly 41 days at the poles. This rotation rate is obtained from observed Doppler shifts of photospheric lines and is approximately 4 to 5 percent less than the rotation rate of sunspots. Sunspots, in turn, rotate slightly slower than the observed magnetic fields, filaments, and the K corona, except at the equator where these rates are approximately equal.

This nonrigid rotation may result from the solar interior's rotating much faster than the surface, producing a higher shear stress at the equator. A basis for this speculation is that, if the solar system had condensed from a rotating gaseous cloud, the sun should have 200 times the angular momentum it would have if it rotated with only its observed surface velocity. Also, very careful measurements by Dicke (1970) indicate that the sun has an oblateness of 5×10^{-5}, which could be accounted for by the centrifugal forces of a rapidly rotating solar core. If a rapidly rotating core exists, it would also be a major source of the angular momentum carried away from the sun by the solar wind.

Differential rotation has also been attributed to nearly horizontal waves which form an eddy flow pattern on the solar surface. These waves, called Rossby waves, have the characteristic of transporting elements of fluid with higher than the average ambient angular momentum toward the equator and thereby inducing a

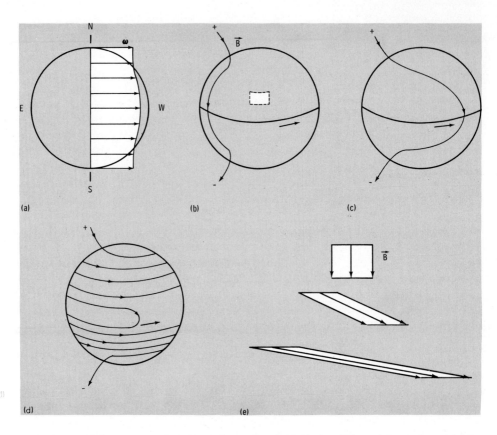

FIGURE 2–21.- -Enhancement of surface solar magnetic fields by differential rotation. (*a*) The general variation of angular velocity with latitude. Starting with a frozen-in longitudinal magnetic-field line as shown in (*b*), differential rotation will wind it up as shown in (*c*) and (*d*). (*e*) The effect on the surface fluid element denoted in (*b*). The field lines are moved closer together under the shearing action of differential rotation and the field strength thereby increased. ((*b*) to (*d*) are after Livingston, 1966.)

differential rotation. Rossby waves in the earth's atmosphere are thought to be the cause of the jet streams observed at midlatitudes. A possible source of energy for solar Rossby waves is found in the convection zone. The smaller eddies of convective motion may feed kinetic energy into the larger eddies of Rossby waves by nonlinear processes. This is opposite to frictional decay in which larger eddies break down into progressively smaller ones and finally to heat. A second possibility is that the large-scale eddies are driven by a difference in temperature between the equator and poles. Because it is the "effective" gravity (gravity plus rotational forces) which influences the characteristics of solar convection and the accompanying heat flux and because this effective gravity varies from equator to pole, a temperature difference could result. Regardless of its origin, differential rotation, through its interaction with the general solar magnetic field, is most likely the motor which drives solar activity.

The term "interaction," also briefly alluded to in the discussion of the chromospheric network, requires clarification at this point. Lines of magnetic force are imaginary concepts used to promote an intuitive understanding of a physical situation. They arise from the flow of electric current and are pictured as endless loops which close on themselves and along which a compass needle would aline itself. The strength of a field is proportional to the number of lines running through an element of fluid. If these lines are frozen into the element (which is then expanded, twisted, or otherwise made to change its cross-sectional area), the density of lines and field strength change accordingly. In reality, the solar material and its magnetic field are so closely coupled to one another that in almost all cases the field can be considered "frozen in." The property responsible for this strong coupling is the high concentration of charge carriers (electrons and ions). The resulting high electrical conductivity ranges from approximately that of sea water to that of mercury, a change of a factor of approximately 10^4. The term "plasma" is used here to refer to a gas that has a large-enough concentration of charge carriers to shield itself from external electric fields and prevent the accumulation of large-scale net charge. When an element of solar plasma moves perpendicular to a magnetic field, a current, a secondary magnetic field, and a force are induced in a direction that opposes the change in the lines of force as seen by this element. This current is proportional to the conductivity and the relative velocity between field and plasma. Hence, if the conductivity is large, only small relative velocities perpendicular to the field are possible and the field and plasma will behave as if they were frozen together. If the plasma kinetic energy density is much larger than the energy density of the field, the plasma can move and contort the field without restriction. However, if the reverse is true, the plasma is constrained to move parallel to the lines of force which then define the fluid streamlines. As seen in the case of supergranulation and the chromospheric network, both situations occur in the solar atmosphere.

The general magnetic field, frozen into the surface and initially running from pole to pole, is distorted by differential rotation as shown in figure 2–21. By this shearing action on the field, the density of lines can be increased significantly. These greatly enhanced fields and their gradients are intimately related to the production of solar activity. The range of time scales of this activity is wide; the 11-year solar cycle has been the largest clearly detected.

2.8 THE SOLAR CYCLE

The most straightforward and conventional way to follow the solar cycle is to observe how the number of spots that appear on the sun change with time. Sunspots are cooler than the surrounding photosphere and appear as relatively dark, sharply defined features in white-light photographs (fig. 2–1(a)). The number of spots on the disk is defined in a somewhat arbitrary manner by

$$ZS = CF(IS + 10 \, NG) \tag{2-2}$$

where ZS is the Zurich sunspot number, IS is the number of individual spots, NG is the number of spot groups (the factor of 10 is somewhat arbitrary), and CF is a correction factor assigned to an individual observer to account for variation in equipment, atmospheric conditions, and observer enthusiasm. The obvious cyclic nature of the sunspot number is evident in figure 2–22 where the average period is 11.0 years. Over the last four cycles, this period has averaged 10.4 years (fig. 2–23). There is a good indication of a long-term cycle of approximately 80 years superimposed on the solar cycle. Also evident is that the rise from minimum to maximum is shorter than the decline, the rise taking only about 4 years over the past few cycles. Hence, from the maximum in late 1968, we would expect a minimum in 1975 followed by another maximum in 1979.

A plot of the daily Zurich sunspot numbers reveals a behavior with a shorter time scale than is apparent from the yearly averages (fig. 2–24). A 27-day cyclic variation is evident and can be attributed to solar rotation. Some large spot groups will last for more than one rotation and, to a degree, spots have preferred meridians for recurrence. In addition to this, however, there appears to be a sizable but random short-term fluctuation in the number of sunspots.

Another clue about the physical nature of the solar cycle is found by observing

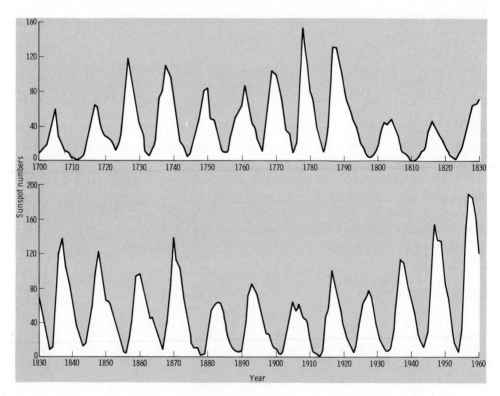

FIGURE 2–22.—Variation of sunspot number with time. (Courtesy of M. Waldmeier, Swiss Federal Observatory.)

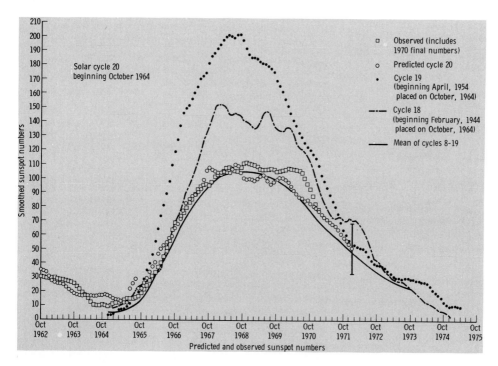

FIGURE 2–23.—Solar cycles 8 to 20. (From Solar-Geophysical Data, July 1971, No. 324–I, National Oceanic and Atmospheric Administration.)

the change with time in the latitude of the regions in which the spots break out. Generally, at the start of the cycle, these regions are at ±40° latitude, and they progress down to ±5° just as the next cycle is beginning. A diagram depicting this behavior (Maunder's "butterfly" diagram) is shown in figure 2–25.

The real key to understanding the cycle, however, is found in a study of the cyclic and symmetric variations of sunspot and polar magnetic fields. The umbra, the relatively dark cores of sunspots, are observed to be the locations of strong, approximately vertical magnetic fields. The majority of spots first occur in bipolar groups where the preceding spot p or group of spots, with respect to solar rotation, have the polarity opposite to that of the following spot f or group of spots (fig. 2–26). The preceding spots in the northern hemisphere almost always have the same polarity over one cycle and the opposite distribution of polarities is usually found in the southern hemisphere (fig. 2–27). Also, the weak polar magnetic fields are of the same polarity as the preceding spots of that hemisphere. A truly remarkable feature is that, with each new cycle, there is a reversal of sunspot polarities. It also appears that this is sometimes, but not always, followed by a reversal of the polar fields at about solar maximum. When the new high-latitude spot groups break out at the beginning of a cycle, they will be opposite in polarity distribution to the few spot groups from the previous cycle that may exist close to the equator. Thus, the

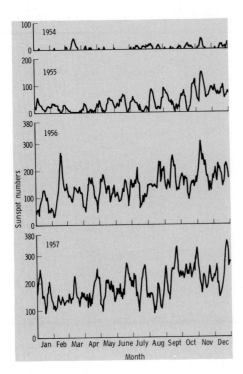

FIGURE 2-24.—Monthly variation of sunspot number. (Courtesy of M. Waldmeier,
Swiss Federal Observatory.)

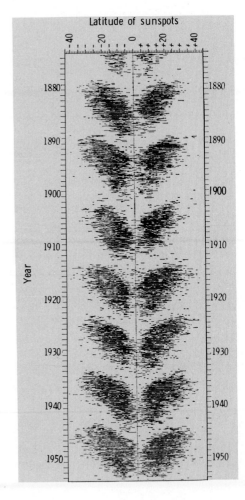

FIGURE 2-25.—Maunder's butterfly diagram. Time is shown on the vertical axis
and the latitudes of sunspot occurrence
are on the horizontal axis. The shift in
sunspot location from high latitudes to
low latitudes during the course of a cycle
is evident. It is seen that spots of the
previous cycle are usually still present
close to the equator when spots of the
new cycle break out at higher latitudes.
This figure is an excellent illustration of
the periodic and repeatable nature of sunspot distributions. (From Kiepenheuer,
1959; copyright 1959 by the University of
Michigan Press.)

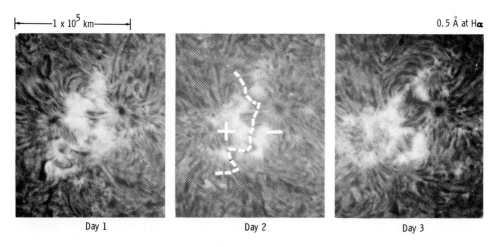

FIGURE 2–26.—Sunspot polarity. The preceding spot on the right of this young bipolar region has an opposite polarity to the following spot on the left. The polarities are shown in the central frame. The following spot will usually be replaced by plage as the region decays, which is well illustrated in this 3-day sequence. (Courtesy of S. Smith and B. Nolan, Lockheed Solar Observatory.)

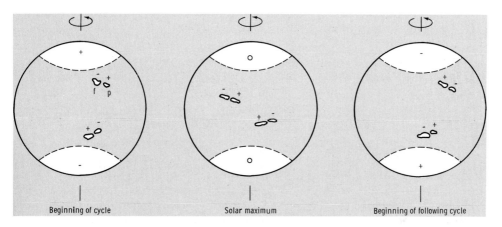

FIGURE 2–27.—Idealized reversal of polar and sunspot polarities with advancement of the solar cycle.

time required for the sun to return to the same general magnetic configuration of spots and polarities is actually two cycles, or 22 years.

A comprehensive model which explains the solar cycle has been advanced by Babcock (1961) and expanded by Leighton (1964 and 1969). It is useful to examine briefly this model in order to provide a coherent understanding of the many features of solar activity.

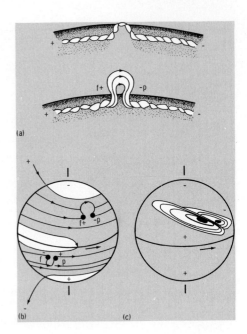

FIGURE 2–28.—Formation of the bipolar sunspot magnetic-field configuration. (a) Enhanced flux lines twisted by convective motions below the photosphere. (b) Spots formed by buoyant magnetic field. (c) Eroded and stretched magnetic fields of spot groups. (After Livingston, 1966.)

In a period of just 11 years, changes in magnetic fields, which tend to be frozen into the solar plasma, could penetrate only slightly below the surface of the sun. Thus, the general solar magnetic field is not appropriately represented by a bar magnet at the center of the sun, as in the classical picture, but is more correctly depicted as a field existing only in the outer shell (fig. 2–21(b)). As previously noted, differential rotation will tend to wind up initially meridional lines of force. Also, if the solar interior is rotating at a different speed than the surface, the field is again increased in strength. The convective motions below the photosphere can twist the tubes of enhanced flux lines into ropelike structures which further increase the density of lines (fig. 2–28(a)). Kinks in these ropes of flux by small-scale turbulence can produce even greater field strengths within small regions. When the field strength (hence, the magnetic pressure) becomes large enough, the field becomes buoyant, wells up through the surface, forms spots, and fans out into a loop configuration with preceding and following fields (fig. 2–28(b)). This critical point is reached first in the ±40° latitude regions where the rate of shearing of the fields is greatest. Leighton has shown that if the interior is rotating faster than the surface, consistent with the theory of Dicke which accounts for solar oblateness, the field strength at latitudes lower than the eruption is increased, whereas that at higher latitudes is decreased. Thus the zone of eruption propagates toward the equator. This model of the cycle is supported by the observations; Maunder's butterfly diagram, the distribution of the polarities of the spots, and the weak polar fields are accounted for. This model also correctly predicts that the following spots will be at a slightly greater latitude than the preceding ones. Lastly, the reversal of polarity distribution with advancement of the 22-year cycle can be accounted for as described in the following paragraph. Other details not discussed here are also predicted correctly by the Babcock-Leighton model.

The decline of solar activity and the polarity reversal are attributed to the random horizontal surface motions of the relatively thick supergranular cells into which the deep-rooted magnetic fields can be considered frozen. When we follow an element of fluid and its frozen-in magnetic field, we see that it moves in a random direction as part of the flow in a supergranular cell. After a day or so, the cell breaks up and the fluid element moves off in another random direction as part of a new cell. In this way, it engages in a "random walk" and can diffuse over the solar surface. Thus, the strong magnetic fields of spot groups are gradually eroded away by these motions, in addition to being stretched out by differential rotation (fig. 2–28(c)). Because the following spot is slightly closer to the poles, there is a preferential diffusion of the following field into the polar region. About halfway into the solar cycle, enough of this flux of opposite sign has diffused into the polar region to reverse its polarity. This also causes a reversal in the slope of the lines of force next to the polar region (fig. 2–29). As the polar field increases in strength because of continued diffusion, this reversal of slope spreads toward the equator. At every point where the slope has reversed, differential rotation no longer increases field strength but starts to unwind the lines of force. After 11 years, the magnetic fields have completely reversed themselves everywhere. When viewed in this manner, solar activity appears to be a relaxation process which continually repeats itself.

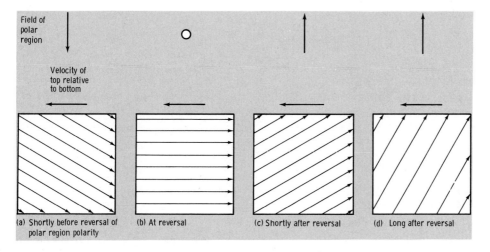

FIGURE 2–29.—Slope reversal and subsequent strength decrease of the magnetic field frozen into an element of solar plasma adjacent to the northern polar region. The reversal of the sign of the polar magnetic field reverses the slope of the field lines, (a) to (c). From this point on to the beginning of the next cycle, the differential rotation will decrease the field strength rather than increase it (d).

Magnetic energy is built up and stored as the lines of force wind up and then it is released through solar activity, the most violent release coming in the form of solar flares. This is distinct from a resonance process where the energy is continuously converted back and forth between two forms but never released, as in the oscillation of a pendulum. Also, the details of the generated fields are nearly independent of the details of the fields of the previous cycles. Thus, the fields we observe today are the product of the conditions existing over the past cycle or two; the memory of early solar fields has been completely erased.

We now turn to the various manifestations of solar activity in an active region, each of which has a magnetic origin.

2.9 THE ACTIVE REGION

An active region, sometimes called a center of activity or, more descriptively, a solar storm, encompasses many diverse but related phenomena: spots, plages, filaments, prominences, coronal activity, and flares. An active region at "storm maximum" is shown in figures 2–30 and 2–31. The primary, if not the essential, event in the formation of an active region is the creation of a magnetic disturbance. This one element is common to all of the above phenomena.

The strongest solar magnetic fields are found in the relatively dark, roughly circular umbra of a sunspot (fig. 2–32). Approximately vertical fields of up to 4000 gauss, almost as large as a strong alnico magnet, covers regions comparable to the size of the earth. Their lower effective temperature ($\gtrsim 4000$ K) and resulting darkness relative to the surrounding photosphere is attributed to a partial suppression of the convection of thermal energy through the upper layers of the convection zone by the strong magnetic fields. Also, because the magnetic pressure is a significant fraction of the total pressure, the gas in the umbra is less dense and more transparent than the surrounding photosphere. The decreased temperature also contributes to the greater transparence. Thus, we see to a greater depth in a spot which gives the illusion of a depression in the umbra when observed near the limb (Wilson effect). The penumbra, about $2\frac{1}{2}$ times the diameter of the umbra, is the lighter surrounding region composed of many radial filaments where the field is nearly horizontal. It has been suggested that the lighter areas between the darker filaments are convection rolls; that is, relatively hot tubes of gas that are convected up through the radially directed horizontal magnetic field. The displacement of the field is minimal because these tubes are parallel to the field lines. An outward flow of gas from the umbra to approximately twice the penumbra radius has been observed. This flow, termed the "Evershed flow," has a maximum velocity of about 2 km/sec. Strong localized vertical magnetic fields which do not result in fully developed sunspots are also possible. Pores, which are small dark regions resembling small sunspot umbra with no penumbra, are observed. Magnetic knots, small regions of concentrated field lines, are also seen. These knots have vertical fields of approximately 1000 gauss, are confined to areas of 1 to 2 arcsec in size, and are located in intergranular spaces, usually within active regions. Sometimes there is a

⊢ 1×10^5 km ⊣

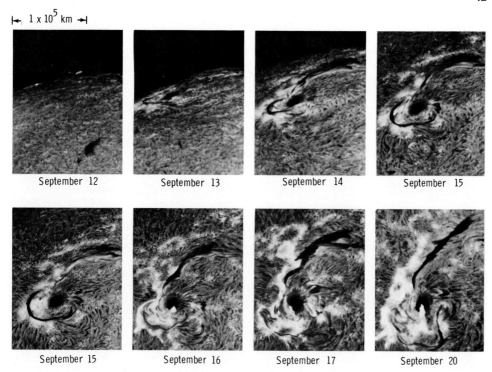

| September 12 | September 13 | September 14 | September 15 |

| September 15 | September 16 | September 17 | September 20 |

FIGURE 2–30.—Changes in an active region. The above series of photographs shows the 8-day history of an active region from the time it first appeared on the limb. These photographs differ from a spectroheliogram in that an optical filter of $\frac{1}{2}$-Å bandpass centered at Hα was used rather than a spectrograph to exclude all light except Hα from reaching the film. Pictures made in this way are termed "filtergrams." The bright regions seen at the limb on September 12 are prominences which appear as filaments seen against the disk on succeeding days The preceding sunspot is visible even in this narrowband Hα photograph. The general brightening in the region is plage. Major flares occurred on September 16 and 20. (Courtesy of S. Smith and B. Nolan, Lockheed Solar Observatory.)

slight darkening in the continuum radiation from a knot and the Fraunhofer lines are slightly weakened.

Another indication of magnetic activity is the presence of plages (the French word for "beaches"), which usually appear before and outlive the spots. Plages usually appear as broad areas of intensified brightness in Hα and many other wavelengths. In Ca K, the brighter regions approximately coincide with the enhanced vertical magnetic fields that surround spots in the photosphere (fig. 2–33). Thus, plages have been used to define the extent of the active region. Essentially, plages are incandescent regions of gas with a higher density than the surrounding atmosphere and a hotter overlying corona. It may seem paradoxical that spots are darker and plages are brighter than the surrounding medium when both are caused by

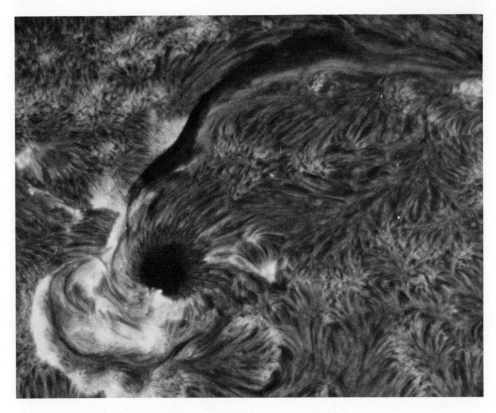

FIGURE 2–31.—An active region seen on September 17, 1966. Filaments, plage, a spot, and fibril structure are all evident. A counterclockwise cyclonic pattern to the fibril structure next to the spot is barely detectable. (Courtesy of S. Smith and B. Nolan, Lockheed Solar Observatory.)

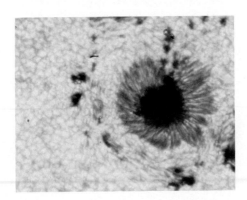

FIGURE 2–32.—Sunspots. (a) A leading sunspot and surrounding granulation seen in white light. The umbra and penumbra are nearly symmetric. (Courtesy of R. Danielson, Project Stratoscope of Princeton University, sponsored by ONR, NSF, and NASA.)

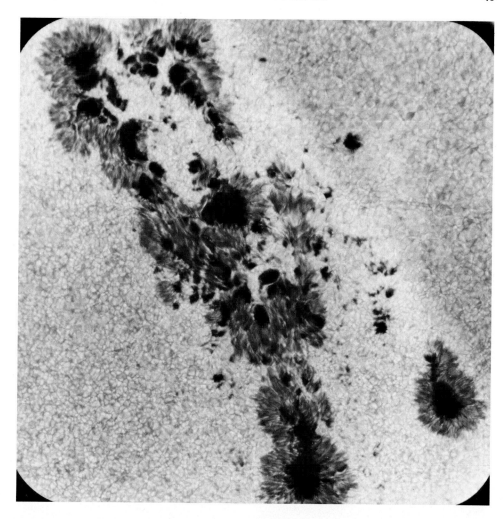

FIGURE 2-32 (concluded).—Sunspots. (b) A complex spot group. The complexity which a spot group can attain is well illustrated by this high-resolution photograph made on November 15, 1970. Note that the granulation pattern is visible right up to the edges of the spots. (Courtesy of R. Dunn, Sacramento Peak Observatory, Air Force Cambridge Research Laboratories.)

enhanced magnetic fields. The difference is that the spot fields are strong enough to appreciably inhibit the large convective flow of energy from below but the plage fields are not. However, the plage fields do enhance the relatively smaller flow of mechanical energy originating as noise in the convection zone and its dissipation in the solar atmosphere. In this way, plages are similar to the chromospheric network. In fact, the network in a plage usually has a higher contrast in addition to a larger characteristic length. The increased dissipation of mechanical energy and the

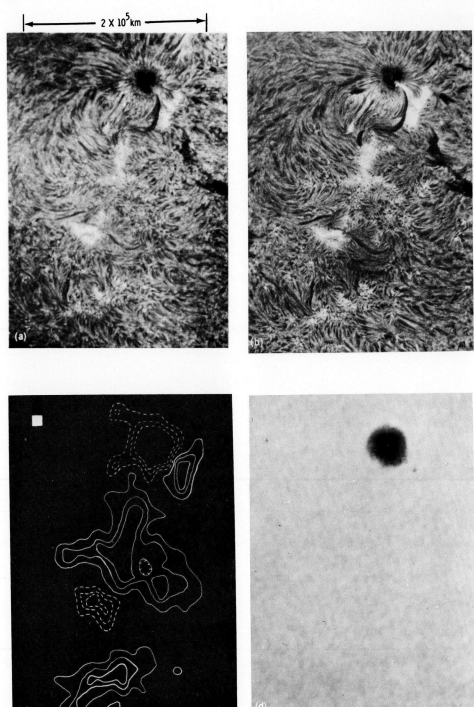

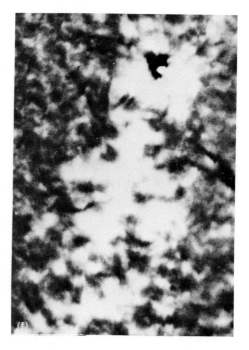

FIGURE 2–33.—An active region observed on September 6, 1966, in several wavelengths. (a) Filtergram at $H\alpha - \frac{1}{4}$ Å ($\frac{1}{4}$ Å to the violet side of $H\alpha$ line center). (b) Filtergram at $H\alpha$ line center. The plage in $H\alpha$ is best seen at line center. The plage of the following magnetic field (the cross at the center of the picture) is usually more pronounced than the plage of the preceding magnetic field or the sunspot (c). (c) Isogauss contours. These lines of equal magnetic-field strength for the magnetic-field component along the line of sight, the longitudinal component, were made by the Mount Wilson magnetograph using the 5250-Å line. Dotted and continuous lines are of opposite polarity. The circular field structure of the spot is evident. Also, the regions of high longitudinal magnetic-field strength appear as relatively bright areas in the previous two $H\alpha$ pictures and the brightening tends to be most pronounced where the magnetic-field gradient is largest (lower right of sunspot). (d) White light. Note that there is a spot only for the preceding magnetic field. (e) Filtergram at $H\alpha + \frac{1}{2}$ Å. The dark fibril structure is most enhanced here. The network of enhanced dark fibrils will usually outline the magnetic field of the active region. (f) Wideband Ca K spectroheliogram (K232) made at Mount Wilson. There is excellent correspondence between the contour of the bright regions seen here and the isogauss contour (c). (All figures are courtesy of S. Smith and B. Nolan, Lockheed Solar Observatory.)

FIGURE 2–34.—Structure of X-ray plage immediately following the March 7, 1970, eclipse. The photograph was made from a sounding rocket. Magnificent detail for an X-ray photograph of active region plage (low atmospheric brightening) and their interconnections (arches joining plage) is seen here. The resolution is especially good at disk center. The exposure was made using a Parylene filter and an exposure time of 11 sec. The moon can be seen at the eastern limb. The loop structure above active regions is noteworthy. Close examination reveals connections between the preceding magnetic regions of the northern hemisphere with those immediately across the equator in the southern hemisphere, a further verification of the Babcock-Leighton theory. (Courtesy of the Solar Physics Group, American Science & Engineering, Inc.)

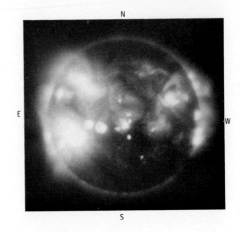

accompanying contrast in brightness of the plage area become more apparent as we observe at shorter wavelengths and correspondingly higher altitudes (fig. 2–34).

Several terms are used to describe regions of enhanced emission observed at various wavelengths. Relatively bright regions that are observed in white light or the continuum are located in the photosphere and are called photospheric faculae. They are best seen close to the limb and roughly coincide with overlying chromospheric faculae observed in strong Fraunhofer lines (fig. 2–35). Chromospheric faculae and plages are generally regarded as synonymous and as manifestations of active regions. Sometimes the wavelength at which the brightening is observed is explicitly stated; for example, Ca K plage or Hα faculae. The terms "flocculus" and "flocculi" usually refer to the brightening observed at the bases of spicules along the chromospheric network (fig. 2–17(a)). However, the term "bright flocculi" is also sometimes used to designate a region of plage.

The existence of strong, large-scale magnetic fields in an active region also plays a major role in the production of prominences. One type of prominence, the long-lived quiescent type, is shown in figure 2–36. Not all of the material which enters the corona through the chromosphere eventually leaves the sun in the solar wind, especially during periods of peak activity when flare puffs, surges, and sprays (discussed later) sporadically eject material from the surface. This material will sometimes condense into regions of locally higher density and lower temperatures and rain back down toward the photosphere. Because this plasma is highly ionized, it will flow along the field lines, outlining them and producing some graceful and elegant structures (fig. 2–37). Where the magnetic-field lines are parallel to the surface, they can also provide a means of support for this higher density plasma

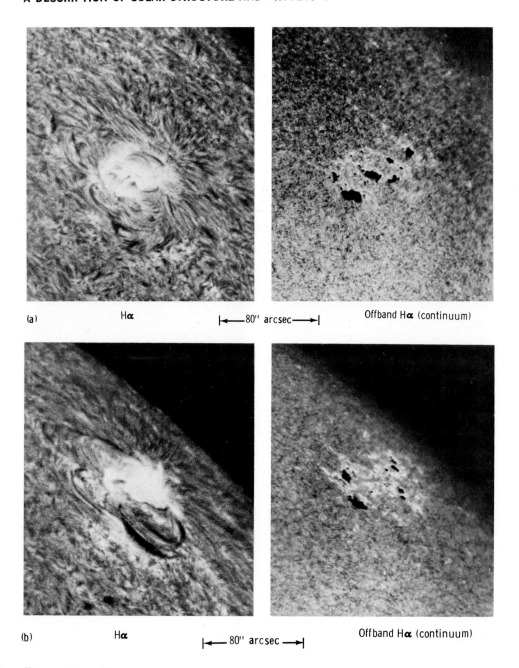

(a) Hα |←—80'' arcsec—→| Offband Hα (continuum)

(b) Hα |←— 80'' arcsec —→| Offband Hα (continuum)

FIGURE 2–35.—Photospheric faculae. The increased emission within an active region seen at the limb from the photosphere (shown here by offband Hα) is termed "photospheric facula." Comparison of (a) taken on October 7, 1964, and (b) taken on October 8, 1964, shows that the photospheric facula is best seen when the active region is very close to the limb. (Courtesy of S. Smith and B. Nolan, Lockheed Solar Observatory.)

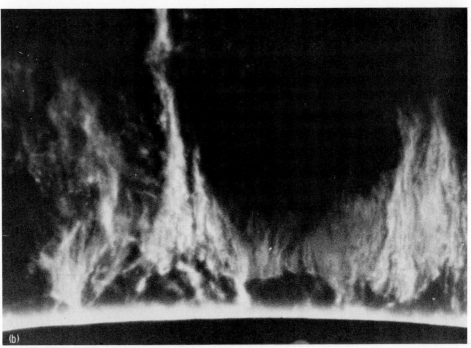

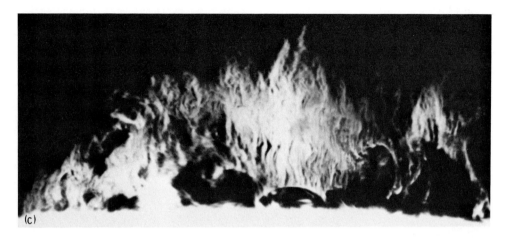

FIGURE 2–36.—Quiescent solar prominences of the hedgerow type seen in Hα with a filter. The material raining down from the corona is slowed and supported by horizontal magnetic fields. In (a), (b), and (c), it is seen that the prominence structure is not uniform but is composed of many small filaments. The chromosphere is seen just above the edge of the occulted sun. (Courtesy of R. Dunn, Sacramento Peak Observatory, Air Force Cambridge Research Laboratories.)

against the pull of solar gravity. The weight of the material causes the field lines to dip, giving the plasma a stable means of support (fig. 2–38). Quiescent prominences of this type are often long lived, up to 6 to 10 solar rotations, and remain long after other manifestations of an active region have disappeared. The wide range of possible magnetic-field structures and sources of condensed material has led to a wide variety in the forms, sizes, and lifetimes of the observed prominences.

A filament is nothing but a prominence seen against the disk. A prominence is visible in Hα at the limb because of its higher density (approximately 10^2 greater than the ambient corona) and its lower temperature (approximately 10^{-2} lower

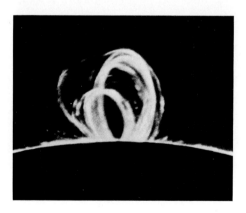

FIGURE 2–37.—A loop prominence. Plasma flowing from the corona to the chromosphere outlines the magnetic-field structure. (Courtesy of R. Dunn, Sacramento Peak Observatory, Air Force Cambridge Research Laboratories.)

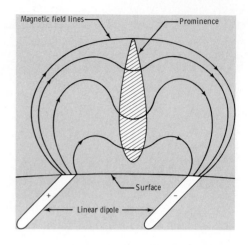

FIGURE 2–38.—Magnetic support of a linear prominence. The support of the locally higher density material of a prominence can be pictured as a result of the magnetic-field line deformation. The lines of force are analogous to rubberbands which increase their support when stretched downward by higher density material. More correctly, however, the support is a result of the force of an electric current flow perpendicular to the solar magnetic field ($\mathbf{J} \times \mathbf{B}$) and the current in turn produces a magnetic field which distorts the original one.

than the corona), which means that a relatively greater quantity of Hα-emitting nonionized hydrogen atoms are present along the line of sight. However, when seen against the relatively intense Hα light of disk, a prominence acts as an absorber and appears as a dark filament. A good illustration of the transition of a prominence to a filament as it rotates over the limb is seen in figure 2–39.

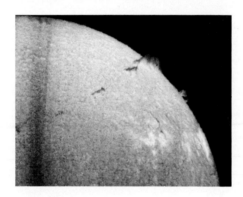

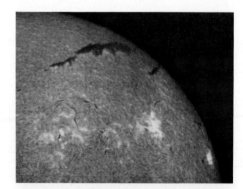

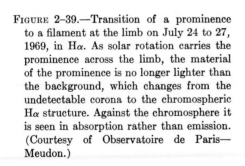

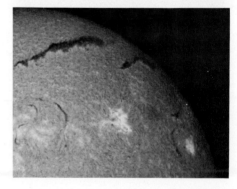

FIGURE 2–39.—Transition of a prominence to a filament at the limb on July 24 to 27, 1969, in Hα. As solar rotation carries the prominence across the limb, the material of the prominence is no longer lighter than the background, which changes from the undetectable corona to the chromospheric Hα structure. Against the chromosphere it is seen in absorption rather than emission. (Courtesy of Observatoire de Paris—Meudon.)

When discussing the chromosphere, we noted that it resembles a light froth on top of the photosphere and that, because of its relatively low density, the magnetic field defines its structural nonuniformities. This is especially true in an active region where we can use the observed structure in the Hα to infer the general magnetic-field configuration. That is, with fair accuracy we can usually detect the neutral lines, polarities, location of steep gradients of the vertical field, and the general direction of the horizontal field (fig. 2–40). Visual analysis of the chromospheric field structure of this type helps to develop an "observational feel" for the complexities of an active region.

We now consider an idealized correspondence between the features of an active region and magnetic neutral lines. A most obvious indication of magnetic neutral lines is the path traced by a quiescent prominence or filament. Because the field is horizontal in a filament and reverses its vertical direction in passing through it (fig. 2–38), a filament lies along the dividing line between regions of opposite polarity. Fibrils, the numerous small grasslike structures seen in Hα, tend to be alined with the horizontal magnetic field and thus act like iron filings in outlining the field structure. They clearly outline a filament channel. This is a region that contains the neutral line and is an extension of the field structure supporting a filament, but in which no filament is observed. Close to the neutral line in a filament channel, the horizontal field rapidly assumes a small angle relative to the line (a shear), as it usually does adjacent to a filament. Arch filaments, like fibrils, also follow horizontal lines of force. They are relatively short lived and often arch from one region of plage to another of opposite polarity. Thus, they are opposite in character to quiescent filaments. Lastly, plage corridors or dark lanes between bright plage also delineate the magnetic neutral line. Because the increased vertical field strength in a plage enhances the generation and propagation of the wave energy that heats the atmosphere, regions of low vertical field strength receive less nonradiative energy from below and appear relatively dark. A very narrow plage corridor between bright plage indicates a high horizontal gradient in the vertical field. Once the neutral lines are located, the spots can be used to define the polarities of the outlined regions. For the current solar cycle, the fields of the leader spots are negative or inward directed in the northern hemisphere and positive in the southern hemisphere. Leader spots are easily recognized because they lead a spot group in rotational motion (that is, they are located on the western side) and are relatively large, symmetric, and long lived.

So far we have described the active region statically. However, like the solar cycle, it is a dynamic process. Its characteristic time of formation of 10 days is intermediate between the rise time of 4 to 5 years for the solar cycle and the rise time of seconds to minutes for a solar flare, which we consider in the next section. An active region has the characteristic of a relaxation process and follows an orderly and fairly predictable development. In an idealized development of an active region, the first visual evidence of a magnetic disturbance is a systematic alinement in the Hα fine structure and the appearance of a small plage in the space between several supergranules. This is usually followed by the formation of spots,

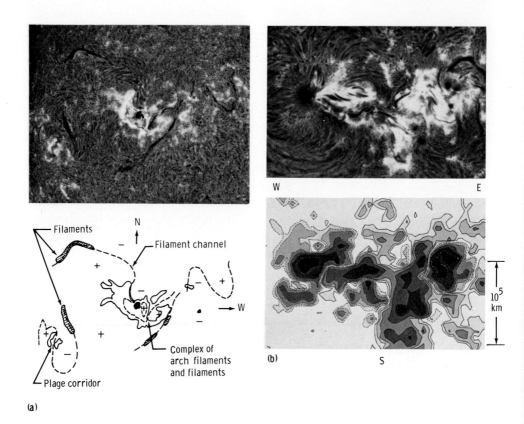

FIGURE 2–40.—Magnetic neutral line location and field polarities inferred from Hα structure. (a) The correspondence between magnetic neutral line locations (dotted lines) and quiescent filaments, arch filaments, filament channels, plage corridors, and/or fibril direction is well illustrated here (taken August 7, 1968). (Courtesy of P. McIntosh, Environmental Research Laboratories, National Oceanic and Atmospheric Administration.) (b) The filtergram (0.5 Å at Hα) at the top corresponds to the Mount Wilson fine-scan magnetogram at the bottom (taken June 2, 1967). Dashed lines are negative polarity and solid lines are positive polarity. Except in the immediate vicinity of the large sunspot on the western side of the region, the filaments lie approximately along the dividing lines of opposite polarity. Close to the spot and in areas of bright plage, this general rule is violated and short arch filaments appear to join rather than divide areas of opposite polarity. Also noteworthy is that this spot, seen here in Hα, has a well-developed and ordered fibril structure around it which is a continuation of the radially directed penumbral structure. (Courtesy of S. Smith and B. Nolan, Lockheed Solar Observatory.)

first the preceding one and then the following one. Prominences and flare activity appear as the region builds toward maximum activity in 10 to 15 days. After one rotation, almost all the spots except the preceding one have disappeared, the plage and filaments continue to increase in size because of the stretching action of differential rotation and supergranular diffusion, and flare incidence has greatly decreased. After two rotations, the plage is decreasing in brightness and it usually disappears by four rotations. At that time the single remaining filament has been drawn out to maximum extent, lying in a nearly east-west direction. The filament migrates poleward as it decreases in length and dissipates, but it may be visible for 6 to 10 rotations after the birth of the active region. Thus, the development of the various components of an active region is directly related to the dynamics of formation and dissipation of a bipolar magnetic region.

2.10 THE ACTIVE-SUN CORONA

Characteristics of the inner corona, which are extensions of chromospheric features, are illustrated in the X-ray photographs shown in figures 2–7 and 2–34. The emission of radiation is very nonuniform and numerous loop structures are evident. Because the magnetic field controls the plasma structure, these loops of emitting plasma allow us to observe the three-dimensional characteristics of the field and the manner in which magnetic flux links regions of opposite polarities. As expected, flux links the opposite polarities of an active region. Flux also sometimes links the following polarity of one active region with the preceding polarity of the next or adjacent region. Perhaps the most important observation is that the preceding polarity of a region can be linked by flux which crosses the equator to the preceding polarity of a region in the opposite hemisphere. Thus, once a bipolar magnetic configuration breaks through the solar surface, there is a severing and reconnection of field lines. According to the Babcock-Leighton model, flux linkage of preceding polarities across the equator must occur as the following polarities diffuse toward the poles and the total solar magnetic-field configuration is reversed over a solar cycle (figs. 2–27 and 2–28).

Because of the two perturbing factors, solar rotation and locally strong magnetic fields, the outer corona of the active sun differs substantially from the spherically symmetric steady-state outer corona previously described. The coupling between the surface-rooted coronal magnetic fields and the coronal plasma causes the corona to rotate (out to a few $R_\odot$) with the same angular velocity as the sun, like a rigid body. However, with increasing solar radius, the energy of the fields drops off more rapidly than the energy in the plasma. Hence, a point is reached ($\approx 3R_\odot$) where the solar wind assumes control of the dynamics. The fields at this point are not able to increase the angular momentum of the outward-moving plasma and are strung out into space, forming a spiral structure like that of a rotating garden hose (fig. 2–41).

Two other large-scale alterations must be made to our previous picture of the corona. These are in the density, which increases by a factor of approximately 2 at the equator from solar minimum to solar maximum, and in the temperature, which increases approximately 20 percent from minimum to maximum. Perhaps the most noticeable and interesting change, however, is the structural asymmetries arising from the locally strong magnetic fields that are so evident in the inner corona. These fields not only control the details of the plasma flow inside a few $R_\odot$

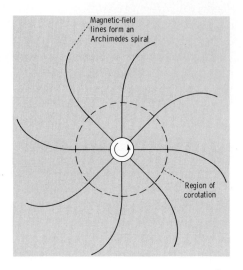

FIGURE 2–41.—General structure of the coronal magnetic field.

but are also ultimately responsible for increases in local plasma density and temperature. Most noteworthy of this type of coronal activity are coronal condensations, local enhancements in plasma density and temperatures which occur low in the corona over spot groups. They are observed in emission lines, and sometimes in white light, and appear as looplike structures or bright knots. Their characteristic size is a few ten thousand kilometers and their lifetime is on the order of hours to days (sporadic) or significantly longer (permanent).

A coronal photograph that exhibits a wide variety and abundance of detailed structure, which is also attributable to magnetic-field nonuniformities, is shown in figure 2–42. The nature of various coronal structures can be illustrated by the classification of the features seen in this picture. A streamer is a structure which appears bright relative to the background corona and which extends far outward, usually over $1R_\odot$. Helmet streamers are seen in figure 2–42 in the southeast and southwest quadrants and were observed to overlie prominences. Arches and the lack of material over the prominences are evident in the bases or domes of these streamers. Some streamers appear to be drawn out into very thin structures extending large distances into the corona. These rays are seen in the northwest quadrant. A ray covering a wide longitude is termed a "fan." Narrow streamers appearing at the poles are called "polar plumes" and usually outline the general dipole solar field. Very faint polar plumes are visible at the south pole in the negative of the original photograph of figure 2–42; faint details are lost in the conversion from the negative to the positive print. Thus, the corona of the active sun contains a wealth of detail controlled by the complex magnetic-field structures and differs considerably from that associated only with the chromospheric network of the quiet sun.

FIGURE 2-42.—The solar corona observed during the November 12, 1966, eclipse. This impressive picture of the corona was made by a team from the High Altitude Observatory headed by Gordon Newkirk, Jr., at Pulacayo, Bolivia (altitude of 13 000 feet). A neutral density filter which had a radial gradient covering a range of 10^4 in transmission was placed in the focal plane. This filter compensated for the rapid decrease of coronal brightness with increasing radius and allowed faint features in the outer corona to be observed without overexposing the chromosphere. The exposure time was 10 sec and the effective wavelength was 6400 Å using Kodak Linagraph Shellburst 70-mm film. The overexposed image of Venus is seen in the northeast quadrant. (Courtesy of G. Newkirk, Jr., High Altitude Observatory.)

2.11 SOLAR FLARES

All of the solar activity so far discussed changes slowly enough that a static or a steady-state description is appropriate. This is not true for the violence of a solar flare. In essence, a flare is a highly concentrated explosive release of energy within the solar atmosphere, followed by a gradual leveling off and decay of material motion and temperature. As seen in Hα, a small starlike brightening within a plage area occurs, followed by a rapid spread along preferred routes until, in a matter of minutes, the brightening covers areas that can be as large as approximately

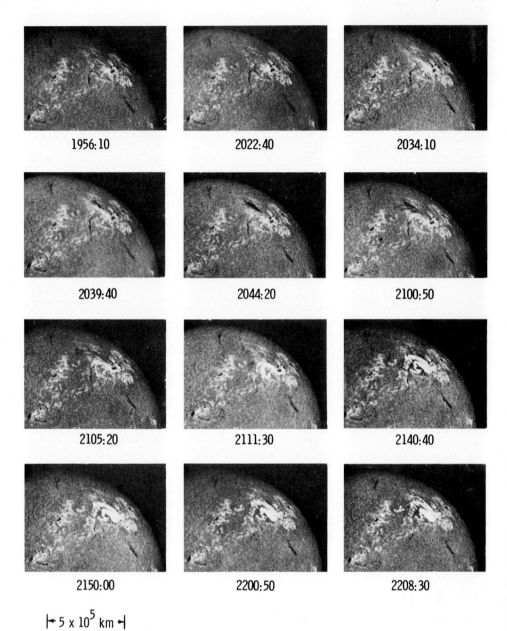

1956:10   2022:40   2034:10

2039:40   2044:20   2100:50

2105:20   2111:30   2140:40

2150:00   2200:50   2208:30

$\vdash$ 5 x 10^5 km $\dashv$

FIGURE 2–43.—Flare development. The long complex rise to maximum of the exceptionally large flare (of importance 3+) shown here started with brightening in very localized areas. The brightening continued to spread until it overwhelmed much of the complex structure of the active region. This series of filtergrams was made at Hα line center with a 0.5-Å passband, May 10, 1959; universal time is given for each frame. (Courtesy of S. Smith and B. Nolan, Lockheed Solar Observatory.)

1 sq arcmin (figs. 2–43 and 2–44). This brightening will gradually decay in about 1/3 to 3 hours. When observed in X-rays (fig. 2–45), flares can exhibit rise times on the order of seconds. The solar radio emissions at centimeter wavelengths are also enhanced during a flare with the initial rise either slightly leading or slightly following the rise at X-ray wavelengths (fig. 2–46). Radio bursts at meter wavelengths, which have distinctive characteristics, are also observed and have been classified into several different types. Lastly, in some cases electrons having velocities approaching the speed of light, as well as clouds of high-energy protons, are simultaneously ejected from the flare area.

The energy released by a flare is usually very much smaller than the total energy of enhanced emission from an active region over its lifetime. However, for

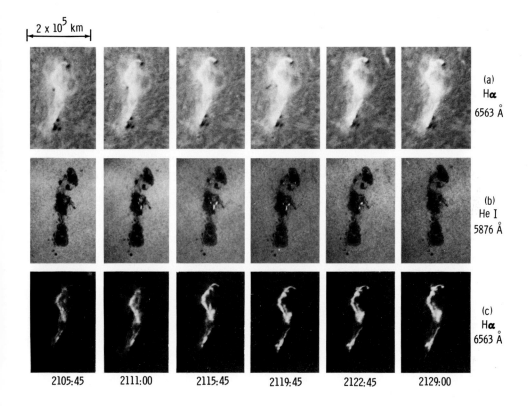

2 x 10⁵ km

(a) Hα 6563 Å

(b) He I 5876 Å

(c) Hα 6563 Å

2105:45 2111:00 2115:45 2119:45 2122:45 2129:00

FIGURE 2–44.—Flare bright points (February 11, 1970). The development of a flare in Hα as it is usually seen is shown in figure (a). In figure (b), very localized brightenings or hot spots are evident. The overexposed areas of Hα shown in figure (c) display these bright points although they cannot be clearly separated from the surrounding emission. A video system, which has a wider dynamic range than film, can be used to observe both these bright points and the relatively faint background structures by varying the intensity. (Courtesy of S. Smith and B. Nolan, Lockheed Solar Observatory.)

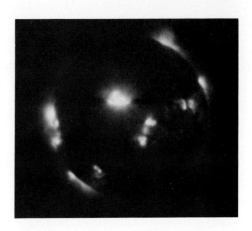

FIGURE 2–45.—X-ray photograph of the sun taken on June 8, 1968, by an X-ray telescope mounted on a sounding rocket. A flare is seen slightly to the upper left of sun center. Regions of X-ray plage are also evident, especially close to the limb. (Courtesy of W. Reidy, American Science & Engineering, Inc.)

very large flares these two energies can be approximately equal. The very large flares, which occur only a few times per solar cycle, can release up to 10^{32} ergs, the equivalent energy release of a 2-billion-megaton TNT bomb. Although one might first suspect nuclear processes as a source of this energy, the atmospheric density is much too low for fusion to take place, and evidence now points to the energy stored in locally strong magnetic fields.

Flares generally tend to occur in active regions where the magnetic fields are strong, complex, and in a highly stressed and unstable configuration. Indicators of these conditions are the presence of bipolar fields whose polarities are opposite than normal (reversed from fig. 2–27), a very twisted and kinked magnetic neutral line, growth of new fields in or near old ones, large Hα plage intensity and size, and strong observed fields and gradients. A flare is sometimes preceded by the expansion and breakup of a nearby filament, indicating a changing magnetic-field configuration. Once a flare is triggered, it often spreads rapidly along routes adjacent to the

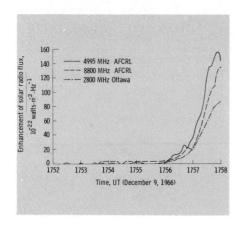

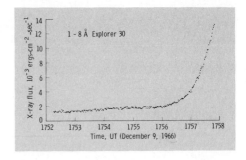

FIGURE 2–46.—Initial rise of flare-enhanced solar radio emission and solar X-ray emission. (From Donnelly, 1968.)

$\longleftarrow 1 \times 10^5 \text{ km} \longrightarrow$

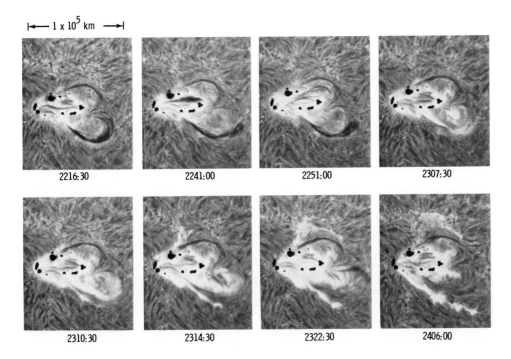

FIGURE 2–47.—Flare development relative to sunspots. This sequence of Hα filtergrams shows a flare development with the sunspots superimposed (July 6, 1965). The spot group is a complex one and the magnetic-field gradients are correspondingly large. It is seen that the brightening is centered along the lower chain of spots. (Courtesy of S. Smith and B. Nolan, Lockheed Solar Observatory.)

neutral line as the field relaxes to a less stressed configuration (fig. 2–47). However, the forces which caused the original buildup of magnetic energy and instability can continue to operate and subsequent flaring many times occurs in the same location. In this way a flare, like the solar cycle, can be thought of as a relaxation process. The field and its gradient build up, a dynamic release of energy occurs, and a few similar cycles may follow. Thus, flares are also very closely related to solar magnetic activity. In fact, the average incidence in terms of the number of flares per day, of importance 1 or greater, is roughly ZS/25, where ZS is the Zurich sunspot number. Hence, we could expect eight or nine flares per day at the peak of the current maximum but less than one per day at the minimum in 1975. The term "importance" is used to classify flares and subflares according to their visible areas and brightness seen in Hα, as shown in table 2–I.

A flare is not only an interesting dynamic process but it also has many important consequences resulting from the manner in which the energy is released. Although a flare's energy release rate is only about 10^{-5} that of the total sun, in just the short-wavelength range of the spectrum ($\lambda \simeq 10$ Å) the rate can be increased

TABLE 2-I.—Dual Importance Classification of Flares in Hα

Importance			Area, ten-thousandths of the solar disk	Area, heliographic square degrees	Characteristic angular size, arcmin	Mean duration, hours
Faint	Normal	Brilliant				
Sf	Sn	Sb	<2	<2.1	<0.4	<0.3
1f	1n	1b	2– 5	2.1– 5.1	0.4–0.6	0.3–0.5
2f	2n	2b	5–12	5.1–12.4	0.6–1.0	1
3f	3n	3b	12–24	12.4–24.7	1.0–1.4	3
4f	4n	4b	>24	>24.7	>1.4	3

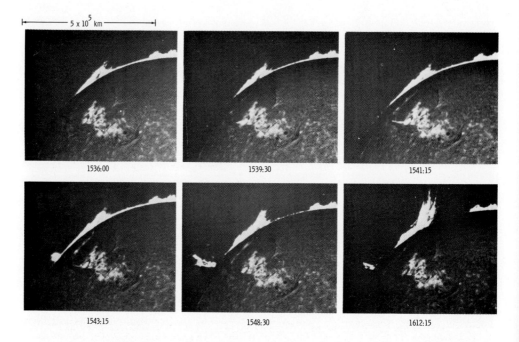

FIGURE 2–48.—A flare surge and filament disruption on May 21, 1967. This is a composite of two filtergrams; the disk is seen in Hα with a ½-Å bandpass and the limb in Hα with a 10-Å bandpass. At 1539:30 a flare is seen in the active region on the disk. At 1543:15 a surge of solar material appears above the limb and by 1548:30 it reaches a height of $\frac{1}{3}R_\odot$ to $\frac{1}{2}R_\odot$, depending upon its angle relative to our line of sight. It is also seen that at 1548:30 and 1612:15 the flare has greatly disrupted the existing prominence. (Courtesy of S. Smith and B. Nolan, Lockheed Solar Observatory.)

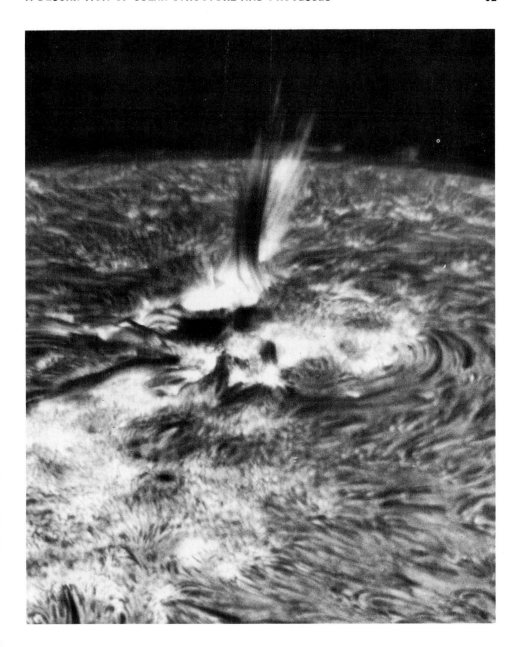

FIGURE 2–49.—Material ejection from an active region. This ejection, shown here in Hα close to the limb, was photographed at 1914:12 on May 22, 1970. (Courtesy of H. Zirin, Big Bear Solar Observatory, California Institute of Technology.)

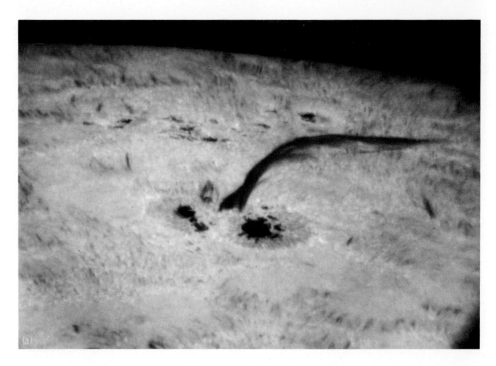

FIGURE 2–50.—Rising material seen in Hα. This sequence of near-limb photographs taken on December 6, 1970, shows that the rising material had a component of motion along the line of sight. That is, the material is evident in absorption at Hα−0.9 Å but not at Hα+0.9 Å. (a) Hα−0.9 Å. (b) Hα line center. (c) Hα+0.9 Å. ((a) and (b) are courtesy of R. Dunn, Sacramento Peak Observatory, Air Force Cambridge Research Laboratories.)

manyfold. In the hard X-ray range ($\lambda < 1$ Å), for example, a factor of enhancement of 10^2 is possible. As the rate of energy release by a flare increases, the radiation shifts toward these shorter wavelengths. Associated with the large enhancement of the short-wavelength radiation, high-energy particle emission sometimes occurs. These particle emissions produce effects which are sometimes observable as geomagnetic storms, ionospheric density fluctuations which affect radio communications, auroras, and biological changes which influence our own evolution and future long-term manned space flight. It is fortunate, however, that the sun is unlike other stars where the total luminosity is observed to change manyfold within a few minutes during a flarelike event.

In addition to flares, the sun exhibits many other rapid transients, most of which are directly related to, and almost as violent as, flares themselves. Puffs, surges, and sprays result from solar plasma which erupts from the surface at the scene of a flare. Surges occur at one or more times during the lifetime of a flare when material rises from the surface and slides along magnetic-field lines (figs. 2–48 to 2–50), then falls back down, either along the same path it came or along a loop

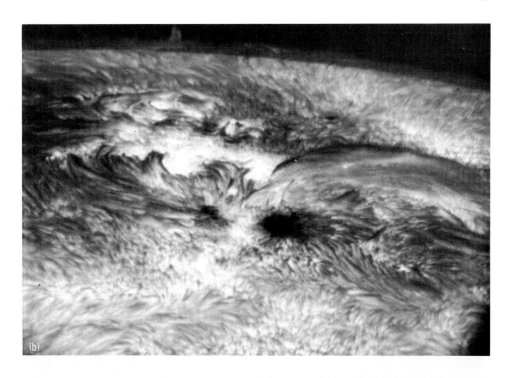

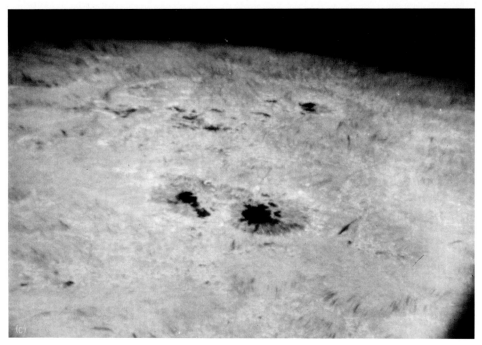

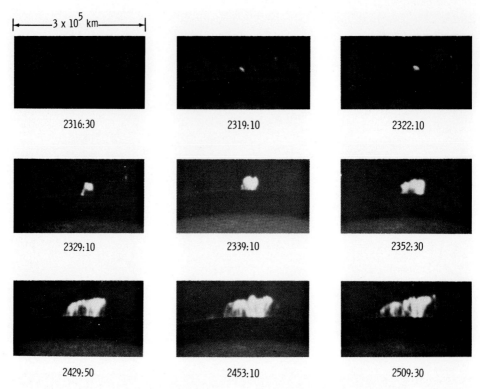

FIGURE 2-51.—Formation of postflare loop prominences on May 26, 1963. This sequence is a
composite of the same type as figure 2-48. The surge of material which appears at 2319:10
is most likely the result of a flare occurring beyond the limb. As material condensed from the
corona, the loop structure is formed. Progressively higher tops are observed as additional
material rains down from above. (Courtesy of S. Smith and B. Nolan, Lockheed Solar Observatory.)

trajectory (figs. 2-37 and 2-51). This material may break up and disappear,
however, before reaching the surface. A definite precursor to a surge often occurs in
the form of a puff, a rapid expansion in a flare region which then fades and becomes
transparent, just as the surge emerges from it. A spray is essentially a more energetic
version of a surge, the spray material having sufficient velocity to completely escape
the sun. In addition to ejecting material, flares also emit MHD waves. These waves
can clearly be seen in accelerated Hα motion pictures where they usually appear
to move into only about one quadrant of the region surrounding the flare (fig. 2-52).
Sometimes filaments impacted by these waves are observed to undergo three or
four vertical oscillations. In other cases, filaments may even disappear, either before
or during a flare, with no MHD wave visible. In the majority of cases, after a
period of several hours to several days, another filament will reform in nearly the
same shape and location as the one which disappeared. Prominences also have been

|←————— 16 x 10⁵ km —————→|

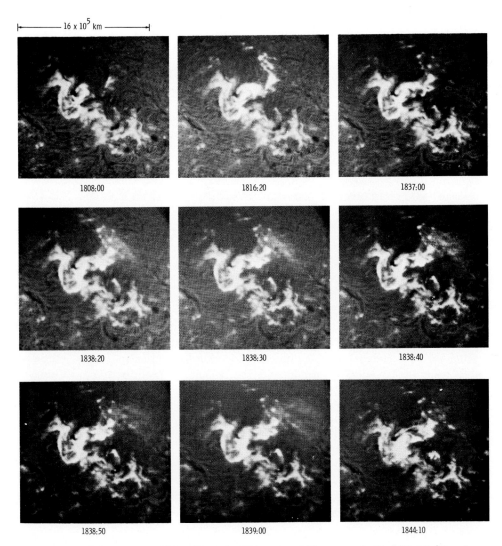

FIGURE 2-52.—Wave event of May 23, 1967. This series of filtergrams in Hα with 0.5-Å bandpass show a diffuse wavefront moving outward from the flare. This front is interpreted by S. Smith and K. Harvey of Lockheed Solar Observatory as a depression and relaxation of the chromospheric fine structure and is best seen in the winds of Hα. A fast, bright diffuse front of emission propagating away from a flare is sometimes seen at Hα line center. These waves are best observed by viewing accelerated Hα patrol films of a flare. (Courtesy of S. Smith and B. Nolan, Lockheed Solar Observatory.)

observed to erupt; figure 2-53 shows the largest eruption ever photographed. The disk of the sun was occulted and the prominence observed in Hα. Before eruption, this large prominence was quiescent and visible for months. The usual form, which

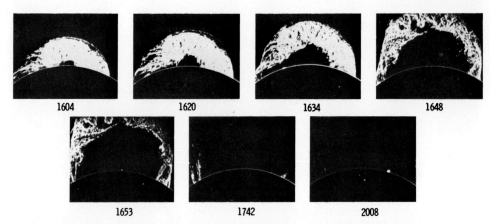

FIGURE 2–53.—Grandpa—the largest eruptive prominence ever photographed, June 4, 1946.
(Universal time is given below each frame.) (Courtesy of G. Newkirk, Jr., High Altitude
Observatory.)

is exhibited here, is a growing arch where the center expands outward and becomes invisible with the ends remaining fixed.

Some structures seen in the corona also undergo rapid changes, the most rapid being a coronal whip. This occurs when one end of a diffuse coronal loop structure, resting above a sunspot region, undergoes a violent release and whips outward. In contrast to an eruptive prominence, the velocity of the disturbance observed here is believed to be that of a wavefront rather than material ejection.

REFERENCES

BABCOCK, H. W.: 1961, Topology of Sun's Magnetic Field and the 22-Year Cycle. Astrophys. J. *133*, 572–587.

DICKE, R. H.: 1970, Internal Rotation of the Sun. Ann. Rev. Astron. Astrophys. *8*, 297–328.

DONNELLY, R. F.: 1968, Early Detection of a Solar Flare: A Study of X-Ray, Extreme Ultra-violet, H-Alpha, and Solar Radio Emission From Flares. ESSA Tech. Rep. ERL 81–SDL2, 34. (Also available as NASA CR–105729, 1968.)

HOWARD, R.; AND HARVEY, J.: 1970, Spectroscopic Determinations of Solar Rotation. Solar Phys. *12*, 23–51.

VAN DE HULST, H. C.: 1953, The Chromosphere and the Corona. The Sun, G. P. Kuiper (ed.), Chicago: Univ. of Chicago Press, 207.

HYNEK, J. A.: 1951, Astrophysics. New York: McGraw-Hill, 272.

KIEPENHEUR, K.: 1959, The Sun. Ann Arbor: Univ. of Michigan Press.

LEIGHTON, R. B.: 1964, Transport of Magnetic Fields on the Sun. Astrophys. J. *140*, 1547–1562.

LEIGHTON, R. B.: 1969, A Magneto-Kinematic Model of the Solar Cycle. Astrophys. J. *156*, 1–26.

LIVINGSTON, W. C.: 1966, Magnetic Fields on the Quiet Sun. Sci. Amer. *215* (5), 107–116.

NEWKIRK, G., JR.: 1967, Structure of the Solar Corona. Ann. Rev. Astron. Astrophys. *5*, 213–266.

In addition to the previous references, most of which contain good discussions of certain topics, the following books are useful for a general background:

ALLER, L. H.: 1963, Astrophysics—The Atmosphere of the Sun and Stars. New York: Ronald Press.

BILLINGS, D. E.: 1966, A Guide to the Solar Corona. New York: Academic Press.

BRANDT, J. C.; AND HODGE, P. W.: 1964, Solar System Astrophysics. New York: McGraw-Hill.

KUIPER, G. P., ed.: 1953, The Sun. Chicago: Univ. of Chicago Press.

SMITH, H. J.; AND SMITH, E. v. P.: 1963, Solar Flares. New York: Macmillan.

TANDBERG-HANSSEN, E.: 1967, Solar Activity. Waltham, Mass.: Blaisdell.

ZIRIN, H.: 1966, The Solar Atmosphere. Waltham, Mass.: Blaisdell.

3

The Interior

Our study of the quiescent sun begins with the solar interior, that portion of the sun which is inaccessible by direct observation of radiation. Thus, it includes all of the material inside the visible atmospheric layer of the sun called the photosphere. It extends from the core, the central region of the sun, outward to the convection zone, which lies immediately below the photosphere. The interior is a natural starting point for our study, since the energy which provides the sun's luminosity is generated in the core and the nonradiative energy flux which largely determines the structure of the outer solar atmosphere is generated in the convection zone. An understanding of the energy generation mechanisms and the nature of solar convection will provide a basis for the investigations of the photosphere, chromosphere, and corona. The term "quiescent" is used here to imply that solar activity, rotation, and general magnetic field are neglected so that the sun has no preferred direction and is spherically symmetric.

Looking at the sun as a star, we see that it is in no way peculiar but is an average member of the main sequence, which refers to a region of near stability in the star luminosity versus the effective surface temperature diagram. It is in this region that a star spends the major portion of its life (fig. 3–1). The techniques and theories employed in the field of stellar evolution are directly applicable to the sun and, in fact, the sun has provided a valuable proving ground for this field of study. These techniques, which have been developed using principles of atomic and nuclear physics, will be discussed in the following sections and a model for the solar interior presented.

3.1 SOLAR COMPOSITION

The "big bang" theory of the origin of the universe, which is backed by nearly all current observations (Iben, 1970), asserts that all matter was at one time in the form of hydrogen and contracted into an extremely high-density, high-temperature primordial fireball. During the early moments of this universe, helium was formed by fusion reactions in addition to much smaller amounts of the higher atomic-number elements. The resulting abundance of helium would have been approximately the same as the solar value, but the abundances of the heavier elements would have been many orders of magnitude less than those observed in the sun. After the initial expansion and cooling of the fireball during the big bang, localized

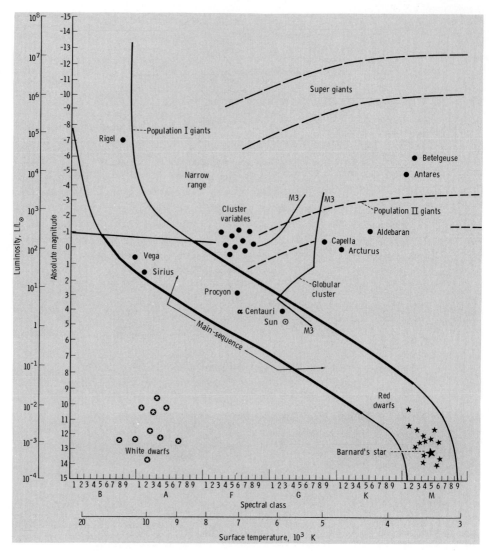

Figure 3-1.—The Hertzsprung-Russel diagram. The S-shaped band running across the center of the figure contains most of the observed stars and is termed the "main sequence." Luminosity and surface temperature have been added. (From Motz and Duveen, 1966; copyright 1966, Wadsworth.)

gravitational contractions took place and stars formed. More nuclear fusion occurred within these stars, the abundance of helium increased slightly, but the abundances of the heavier elements increased substantially. After various violent and non-violent ejection mechanisms returned some of the stellar matter to the interstellar medium, contractions again occurred and second-generation stars formed. From the observed solar abundances, it is inferred that the sun contracted from material which has at one or more times previously experienced nuclear fusion reactions inside of stars (Clayton, 1969). Within our galaxy, there are stars which are older and some which are younger than our sun, and it is exciting to realize that stellar formation is still in progress.

Once the initial composition and total mass are known, the properties of the sun, or most other stars, are, in principle, determined for any later time. The mass loss resulting from the solar wind has been negligible over the lifetime of the sun, so that the present solar mass is essentially the same as its initial value. The initial composition is assumed to have been uniform throughout the sun. The observed spectra (therefore the initial composition) of most nearby stars and of the sun are nearly the same. This strongly suggests that the relatively small region of the interstellar gas which contracted to form the sun was certainly of uniform composition. It is also assumed to be the same as that of its present atmosphere which has been determined by spectroscopic analysis. This is equivalent to assuming that negligible mixing has taken place by turbulence or diffusion between the sun's atmosphere and its core, where the composition has changed by nuclear transmutations. The existence at some time in the sun's past of either a rapidly rotating core promoting turbulent mixing, a flow of meridional currents, or an interior that is convectively turbulent throughout would invalidate this assumption.

It is customary to describe the composition of a star in terms of the fraction of the total mass which is hydrogen X, the fraction which is helium Y, and the remaining fraction which is composed of the heavier elements Z. Thus, $X + Y + Z = 1$. Representative values for the solar composition are given in table 3–I and the results of the general survey are shown in figure 3–2.

Once the mass, composition, and age are specified, physical laws which take two forms are used to determine the structure of a star. The first form is that of differential equations which define the radial variation of properties. The second form explicitly defines some of the properties in terms of the local values of temperature, density, and composition. In principle, the problem of determining the structure is fully specified when boundary conditions are applied at both the solar surface and at zero radius. In practice, however, our inability to properly describe turbulent convection and to calculate its effects introduces a degree of uncertainty into the results.

3.2 THE RADIAL VARIATION OF PROPERTIES

The appropriate differential equations are derived from the radial variation of the physical properties of the solar material. The most straightforward relation is a mass balance involving all of the mass inside a sphere of radius r.

$$M(r) = \int_0^r \rho(r') 4\pi r'^2 \, dr' \tag{3-1}$$

TABLE 3-I.—Solar Composition[a]

[$X = 0.784$, $Y = 0.198$, $Z = 0.018$]

Element	Atomic no.	Log (relative abundance)	$\dfrac{N_{\text{Element}}}{N_{\text{Hydrogen}}}$	Mass fraction
H	1	12.0	1.0×10^{-0}	7.84×10^{-1}
He	2	10.8	6.3×10^{-2}	1.98×10^{-1}
C	6	8.5	3×10^{-4}	3×10^{-3}
N	7	8.3	2×10^{-4}	2×10^{-3}
O	8	8.8	6×10^{-4}	8×10^{-3}
Ne	10	8.1	1.3×10^{-4}	2×10^{-3}
Na	11	6.2	1.6×10^{-6}	3×10^{-5}
Mg	12	7.9	8×10^{-5}	1.5×10^{-4}
Al	13	6.4	3×10^{-6}	6×10^{-5}
Si	14	7.4	3×10^{-5}	6×10^{-4}
S	16	7.2	1.6×10^{-5}	4×10^{-4}
Ar	18	6.3	2×10^{-6}	6×10^{-5}
Ca	20	6.4	3×10^{-6}	9×10^{-5}
Fe	26	6.9	8×10^{-6}	4×10^{-4}
Ni	28	5.6	4×10^{-5}	2×10^{-3}

[a] The relative abundances are from fig. 3-2. X, Y, and Z are calculated neglecting the less abundant elements that are not specified; N refers to the density by number.

where $\rho(r)$ is the mass per unit volume at r. For the present sun, $M(R_\odot) = M_\odot$. Thus, the change of M with r is given by

$$\frac{dM}{dr} = \rho 4 \pi r^2 \qquad (3\text{-}2)$$

The balance of forces on a small element of gas is identical to that used in the study of the earth's atmosphere. That is, the weight of a volume of gas is balanced by the pressure gradient across it. Thus,

$$\frac{dp}{dr} = -\frac{MG}{r^2} \rho \qquad (3\text{-}3)$$

where p is the gas pressure, G is the gravitational constant, and the quantity (MG/r^2) is the local value of gravity $g(r)$. Because the sun is spherically symmetric, only the material internal to r contributes to $g(r)$.

A relation similar to the mass balance exists for the energy balance.

$$L(r) = \int_0^r \epsilon(r') \rho(r') 4 \pi r'^2 \, dr' \qquad (3\text{-}4)$$

Here $L(r)$ is the luminosity at r, or the rate of energy emission from the sphere of

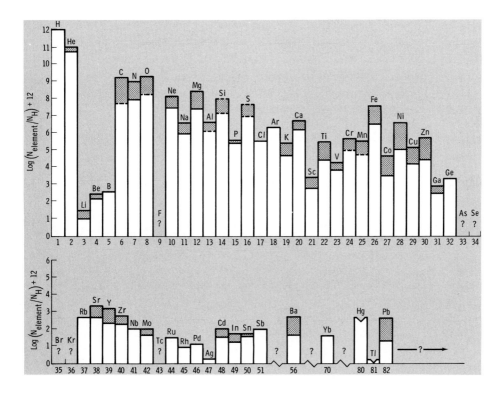

FIGURE 3–2.—Solar abundances. The log (abundance) for hydrogen is taken to be 12 and all other abundances are relative to it. The ranges of reasonable reported values are shown. If only one reported value has been used, no range is indicated. (Data from Brandt, 1966; Clayton, 1969; Danziger, 1970; Goldberg, Kopp, and Dupree, 1964; de Jager and Neven, 1967; Lambert, 1968; Lambert and Warner, 1968a, b, and c; Lambert, Mallia, and Warner, 1969; Ross and Aller, 1968; Warner, 1968; Withbroe, 1969; and Zirin, 1966.)

radius r, and ϵ is the rate of energy production per unit mass from nuclear reactions. In the stages of a star's life when gravitational energy changes proceed at a significant rate, another term must be added to this relation which will not be considered here. Thus, the rate of change of L with r is

$$\frac{dL}{dr} = \epsilon \rho 4 \pi r^2 \qquad (3\text{–}5)$$

The rate of change of temperature in the radial direction is determined in one of two possible ways, depending upon whether radiation or convection is the dominant mode of outward energy transport. Energy transfer by conduction is negligible in the interior of the present sun, but does play the major role in very high density stars. When radiation transfer is dominant, the temperature gradient can be deduced by treating the radiation in the same manner as a gas which has momentum, pressure, and internal energy. When any material absorbs radiant energy, momentum is also absorbed if the radiation has a net flux in any one direction. The rate at which momentum is absorbed by an element of gas of unit area and thickness dr, caused by the net radiant flux $L(r)$, is

$$\text{(Rate of momentum absorption by gas)} = \frac{1}{c} \frac{L}{4\pi r^2} \kappa\rho \, dr \qquad (3\text{--}6)$$

where c is the speed of light (photon speed), $\kappa\rho$ is the absorption coefficient, or the fraction of radiation absorbed per unit length ($1/\kappa\rho = $ photon mean free path), and κ is the opacity, or the mass absorption coefficient. The rate at which the radiation field gives up momentum to the gas is balanced by the pressure change in the radial direction of the radiation across the volume

$$\{\text{Pressure change of radiation}\} = -d\left(\frac{4}{3c} \sigma T^4\right) \qquad (3\text{--}7)$$

where σ is the Stefan-Boltzmann constant and σT^4 is the rate of radiant energy emission by a blackbody surface in equilibrium at temperature T. Equating these two expressions yields

$$\left(\frac{dT}{dr}\right)_{\text{rad}} = -\frac{3}{16\sigma T^3} \frac{L}{4\pi r^2} \kappa\rho \qquad (3\text{--}8)$$

Because the radiant energy released by the gas is emitted isotropically (with equal intensity in all directions), it does not enter into this force balance on the radiation field. Also, the force on the gas resulting from the radiation pressure gradient is negligible with respect to that produced by the gas pressure gradient. Hence, our force balance on the gas (eq. (3–3)) does not require an extra radiation term.

Convection will be the dominant mode of energy transfer when conditions are such that the temperature of a rising blob of gas decreases more slowly than that of its gaseous environment, thereby giving the blob a relatively lower density and making it buoyant (fig. 2–4). This blob of gas carries its excess heat upward and deposits it in its surroundings by radiation and, when it eventually breaks up and dissolves, by direct mixing. When an element of gas undergoes an adiabatic change (no heat is transferred across its boundaries), the temperature and pressure changes are related by

$$\frac{dT}{T} = \frac{\gamma-1}{\gamma} \frac{dp}{p} \qquad (3\text{--}9)$$

where γ is the ratio of the specific heat at constant pressure C_p to the specific heat at constant volume C_v. When only those molecular degrees of freedom which absorb energy as a quadratic function of some variable are considered (translational, vibrational, and rotational, but not electronic), γ is equal to $1+2/\xi$, where ξ is the number of degrees of freedom that are active. Thus, γ is always greater than 1.0 but less than 5/3, the value corresponding to the three translational degrees of freedom which are always active. The adiabatic temperature gradient is

$$\left(\frac{dT}{dr}\right)_{ad} = \frac{\gamma - 1}{\gamma} \frac{T}{p} \frac{dp}{dr}$$

(3-10)

If the absolute value of the adiabatic temperature gradient $|dT/dr|_{ad}$ is less than the absolute value of the temperature gradient in the absence of convection $|dT/dr|_{rad}$, the gas will be unstable to small perturbations in the vertical direction and convection will occur. Thus, the criterion for the existence of convective instability, called the Schwarzschild condition, is

$$\left|\frac{dT}{dr}\right|_{ad} < \left|\frac{dT}{dr}\right|_{rad}$$

(3-11)

To the accuracy with which our incomplete knowledge of turbulent convection allows, this condition is met in the interior at about $0.86 R_{\odot}$, where the temperature has dropped to the relatively low value of 1×10^6 K. The instability results primarily from the recombination of electrons with bare nuclei and ions to form ions of the heavier nuclei which readily absorb radiation. This greatly increases the opacity κ and causes $|dT/dr|_{rad}$ to become large.

Close to the surface of the convection zone, a second effect promotes instability. The ratio of specific heats γ is driven closer to unity because the degrees of freedom by which the atoms and ions absorb energy now include ionization and excitation in addition to translation. This effect, which is primarily caused by hydrogen and to a lesser degree helium, in turn reduces $|dT/dr|_{ad}$. The depth dependence of the ionization of H and He is shown in figure 3-3. It is seen that the helium ionization occurs considerably deeper than that of the hydrogen. Hence, helium ionization would produce a larger scale convection pattern than hydrogen ionization. This has been used to support the speculation that the ionization of the less abundant helium is responsible for supergranulation (Simon and Leighton, 1964). Supergranulation has a larger scale but is not visible in emission as is the normal granulation, which has been attributed to the ionization of the more abundant hydrogen.

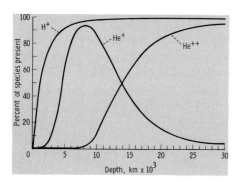

FIGURE 3-3.—Hydrogen and helium recombination below the photosphere. (From Simon and Leighton, 1964; copyright 1964, the University of Chicago Press.)

Because convection is an efficient means of transporting energy, the temperature gradient is usually close to the adiabatic value $(dT/dr)_{ad}$ once it is operative. However, an error does enter because dT/dr is not exactly specified, and to be precise we must resort to a more detailed but not yet well-developed theory of convection. Also, other complexities are encountered very close to the surface. First, convection is no longer an efficient means of energy transport, since a blob of gas can neither contain nor transport a significant amount of thermal energy because of its low density and temperature. Second, once radiation starts to escape the sun directly, $\kappa\rho$ and $|dT/dr|_{rad}$ become small and the atmosphere again becomes stable. This transition to stability occurs in the low photosphere, and the atmosphere remains stable against convection from there outward, except for an effect caused by thermal instability in the chromosphere that we discuss in chapter 5.

3.3 LOCALLY DETERMINED PROPERTIES

To complete our description of the laws which govern the physical nature of the solar interior, the pressure p, the rate of energy generation per unit mass ϵ, and the opacity κ must be defined. These three properties can be specified purely in terms of the local values of the density, temperature, and composition.

Pressure

For an ideal gas, the pressure is given by

$$p = NkT \qquad (3\text{--}12)$$

where N is the total number of particles per unit volume and k is the Boltzmann constant. The density can be specified in terms of a mean atomic weight μ which essentially is the average mass per particle in units of a proton mass m_H.

$$\rho = \mu m_H N \qquad (3\text{--}13)$$

hence

$$p = \frac{k}{\mu m_H} \rho T \qquad (3\text{--}14)$$

The explicit dependence of the pressure on the composition can be explained by examining the factors which determine the mean atomic weight μ.

There are two factors which cause μ to change with radius in the sun. The composition of the core differs from that of the remainder of the sun because of the effect of nuclear transmutations over the past $4\frac{1}{2}$ billion years. Also, because the density and temperature are not uniform, the degree of ionization of each element also varies with the radius. If one electron were removed from every atom in a gas where there was initially no ionization, μ would be reduced by a factor of 2 because there would be twice as many particles, but the mass would be unchanged. The degree of ionization of each element does change considerably, especially close to the surface (fig. 3-3), and in equilibrium conditions is described by the Saha equation

$$\frac{N_{s+1}N_e}{N_s} = \frac{u_{s+1}}{u_s} \frac{2\,(2\pi m_e kT)^{3/2}}{h^3} \exp\left(-\chi_s/kT\right) \tag{3-15}$$

where N_s is the number density of ions formed by removing s electrons from the atom, N_e is the electron number density, m_e is the electron mass, h is Planck's constant, χ_s is the ionization potential or the energy required to remove one electron from the ion which has s electrons already removed, and u_s is the partition function for the sth stage of ionization. u_s is a measure of the total of the number of states of an ion, each multiplied by its probability of occupancy. The degrees of ionization for several elements at conditions representative of the solar core are shown in table 3–II.

When the degree of ionization of each element has been specified, the mean atomic weight can be precisely calculated. For a gas composed only of fully ionized hydrogen, there are two particles for every proton and $\mu_x = \frac{1}{2}$. For fully ionized helium, $\mu_y = \frac{4}{3}$. For the heavier elements with a nuclear charge z, full ionization would yield $z+1$ particles. A good generalization for the heavy elements as a group is that their atomic weights are twice their charge or $2z$ and that z is very much larger than 1. Hence, under fully ionized conditions, $\mu_z = 2$. In terms of X, Y, and Z (the mass fractions of hydrogen, helium, and the heavy elements, respectively), the mean atomic weight for the fully ionized condition is

$$\mu = \frac{1}{2X + \frac{3}{4}Y + \frac{1}{2}Z} \tag{3-16}$$

Throughout the interior, μ is very close to 0.6, except close to the surface, where H and He are not fully ionized, and in the core, where the composition has been altered. The small range of variation of μ is attributed to the small value of Z. That is, even though the ionization of the heavy elements changes considerably, their combined ability to alter the total number of particles is small.

TABLE 3–II.—Ionization in the Solar Core[a]

$[T = 10^7 \text{ K}, N_e = 10^{24} \text{ cm}^{-3}]$

Element	Atomic weight	Nuclear charge	Bound electrons	Free electrons	Free particles per nucleus
H	1.0	1	0.0	1.0	2.0
He	4.0	2	.0	2.0	3.0
O	16.0	8	.24	7.76	8.76
Mg	24.3	12	.3	11.7	12.7
Si	28.1	14	.5	13.5	14.6
Ca	40.1	20	1.9	18.1	19.1
Fe	55.9	26	3.0	23.0	24.0

[a] The information on the heavy elements is from Strömgren (Chandrasekhar, 1957).

Energy Generation

The second locally determined property we are to consider, the energy production per unit mass ϵ, is attributed to the energy released in nuclear fusion reactions. Nuclear fusion can occur when two heavy particles, one usually being a proton, collide with one another with sufficient energy to overcome the electrostatic repulsive forces normally keeping them apart and come close enough to interact on a nuclear scale. The total mass of the particles leaving the collision is smaller than the mass of the particles before collision. This mass deficit shows up in the form of energy, both the kinetic energy of the particles leaving the collision and the radiation energy of the emitted photons, which is in the gamma-ray range. The higher the nuclear charges, the more energy the particles must have to react. Hence, nuclear reactions are limited to very high temperature regions of stars ($> 10^7$ K) and usually to nuclear charges of 7 or less (nitrogen nucleus). Also, for the collision rate to be appreciable, the density must be high. Initially, the sun achieved a high central temperature from the potential energy given up through gravitational contraction. However, once conditions for nuclear reactions became favorable, gravitational contraction became negligible with respect to nuclear reactions as the sun's prime energy source.

Because of high availability and low nuclear charge, the most likely candidates for nuclear reaction are hydrogen nuclei (protons) which combine to form helium in the following series of steps.

$$\left.\begin{array}{l} {}^1\text{H} + {}^1\text{H} \longrightarrow {}^2\text{D} + e^+ + \nu \quad + \ 1.44 \text{ MeV} \\[2ex] {}^2\text{D} + {}^1\text{H} \longrightarrow {}^3\text{He} + \gamma \quad\quad + \ 5.49 \text{ MeV} \\[2ex] {}^3\text{He} + {}^3\text{He} \longrightarrow {}^4\text{He} + {}^1\text{H} + {}^1\text{H} + 12.85 \text{ MeV} \end{array}\right\} \quad (3\text{–}17)$$

The superscripts denote the number of protons plus neutrons in the nucleus. Two protons first collide to form a deuteron (a proton-neutron system), a positron (the antiparticle of an electron that is like an electron in all respects except that it has a positive rather than a negative charge), and a neutrino (a particle of zero charge and mass and an extremely small cross section or interaction probability with other matter). The positron soon reacts with an electron and the pair disappears with the emission of two gamma rays. The neutrino, although formed in the core, does not interact significantly with the solar matter on its path outward, and it leaves the sun. The energy it carries away is not deposited in the interior and must be subtracted from the total energy produced in the reaction when calculating the luminosity. In the second step, the deuteron combines with a proton to form ^{3}He and a gamma ray is emitted. The formation of ^{4}He in the third step can be completed in a variety of ways, the one shown being by far the most frequent. Two ^{3}He particles combine to form one helium nucleus and two protons. Since the last step uses two ^{3}He particles, steps one and two must occur twice as frequently as step three. The net result of this proton-proton cycle is

$$4{}^1\text{H} + 2e^- \longrightarrow {}^4\text{He} + 2\nu + 26.7 \text{ MeV} \qquad (3\text{–}18)$$

However, each neutrino carries away 0.26 MeV (on the average) so that the actual energy liberated for every ^{4}He formed is 26.7 MeV. The first step is the slowest and therefore determines the rate at which the whole chain reaction proceeds. Based on this first step, the rate at which mass is converted to energy by the proton-proton cycle is

$$\epsilon_{pp} = 2.5 \times 10^6 \, \rho X^2 \left(\frac{10^6}{T}\right)^{2/3} \exp\left[-33.8 \, (10^6/T)^{1/3}\right] \quad \text{ergs/gram-sec} \quad (3\text{--}19)$$

A second possible mechanism for producing helium from hydrogen is the carbon cycle, first proposed simultaneously and independently by Hans Bethe and Carl von Weizsäcker. It proceeds by the following steps in which carbon acts as a catalyst:

$$\left.\begin{array}{ll} ^{12}\text{C} + {^1\text{H}} \longrightarrow {^{13}\text{N}} + \gamma & +1.95 \text{ MeV} \\[1em] ^{13}\text{N} \longrightarrow {^{13}\text{C}} + e^+ + \nu & +2.22 \text{ MeV} \\[1em] ^{13}\text{C} + {^1\text{H}} \longrightarrow {^{14}\text{N}} + \gamma & +7.54 \text{ MeV} \\[1em] ^{14}\text{N} + {^1\text{H}} \longrightarrow {^{15}\text{O}} + \gamma & +7.35 \text{ MeV} \\[1em] ^{15}\text{O} \longrightarrow {^{15}\text{N}} + e^+ + \nu & +2.71 \text{ MeV} \\[1em] ^{15}\text{N} + {^1\text{H}} \longrightarrow {^{12}\text{C}} + {^4\text{He}} + \gamma + 4.96 \text{ MeV} \end{array}\right\} \quad (3\text{--}20)$$

The net effect is just the same as that shown by equation (3–18). However, in this case, each neutrino carries away 1.7 MeV on the average, so that 25.0 MeV is liberated for every ^{4}He nucleus formed. The rate of energy generation per unit mass by the carbon cycle is given by

$$\epsilon_{cc} = 9.5 \times 10^{28} \, \rho X X_{CN} \left(\frac{10^6}{T}\right)^{2/3} \exp\left[-152.3 \, (10^6/T)^{1/3}\right] \quad \text{ergs/gram-sec} \quad (3\text{--}21)$$

which is set by the rate at which the fourth step in the chain proceeds. The mass fraction ^{14}N, a product of the third step, has been set equal to the combined mass fractions of carbon and nitrogen X_{CN}. This is a good approximation and simplifies the calculations.

The total rate of energy generation is the sum of the two production processes

$$\epsilon = \epsilon_{pp} + \epsilon_{cc} \quad (3\text{--}22)$$

Thus, like the pressure, ϵ is a function of ρ, T, and the composition. Except for one small range of temperatures, ϵ is determined almost entirely by either ϵ_{pp} or ϵ_{cc} as illustrated in figure 3–4. Because a proton requires much more energy to overcome the potential barrier of ^{14}N than of another proton, the carbon cycle requires relatively higher temperatures to be operative. This is illustrated by the much larger negative exponent in equation (3–21) than in equation (3–19). However,

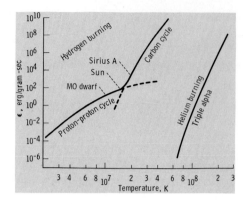

FIGURE 3–4.—Nuclear energy generation as a function of temperature. (From Schwarzschild, 1958; reprinted through permission of the publisher, Dover.)

given sufficient energy, a proton will react with ^{14}N much more readily than with another proton. Hence, the coefficient in equation (3–21) is much larger than that in equation (3–19). In figure 3–4 it is seen that the proton-proton cycle is dominant in the sun. The measurement of the neutrino flux from the sun, an exceedingly difficult measurement to make because the neutrino's mean free path is many light years in ordinary matter, has demonstrated that less than 9 percent of solar energy is generated by the carbon cycle (Davis et al., 1968). In more massive ($>1.5M_\odot$), hotter stars, such as Sirius A, the carbon cycle is the primary energy generation mechanism in the core. The strong dependence of ϵ_{cc} on temperature means that a small region at the center of a star hotter than the sun will generate a large fraction of the total luminosity, both $L/4\pi r^2$ and $|dT/dr|_{rad}$ will be large, and the core will be convectively unstable.

Opacity

Lastly, we must consider the opacity κ which impedes the radiative flow of this generated energy toward the surface. The tendency of the solar gases to inhibit the flow of radiant energy is primarily dependent upon four processes which operate simultaneously:

(1) In bound-bound transitions, an incoming photon is absorbed by an atom (or ion) and one or more photons are emitted which have frequencies characteristic of the atomic energy states (lines) when the atom relaxes to its initial state.

(2) In bound-free transitions (photoionization), an incoming photon of energy is absorbed by an atom (or ion) and an electron is liberated from a bound energy state to become a free electron. This electron will eventually recombine with an ion and one or more photons will be produced which have frequencies characteristic of the electron energy and the atomic energy states (continuum) or just the atomic energy states (line).

(3) In free-free transitions, a part or all of the energy of a photon is absorbed by a free electron and increases the electron's kinetic energy.

(4) In scattering, a photon's direction of travel (but usually not its energy) is altered by interaction with an electron or ion.

The first three mechanisms are functions of the photon frequency, and some type of average over frequency is usually made which is characteristic of the temperature of the radiation field. In the solar core, the scattering by free electrons and bound-free transitions, principally of H and He nuclei, are the major contributors to κ. As the convection zone is approached, bound-free transitions (principally of the heavier elements) become dominant, and κ increases by a factor of approximately 20 over the value at the sun's center. Because of the complexities of the calculations, uncertainties still exist in the value $\kappa(r)$; these in turn introduce some uncertainty in the location of the base of the convection zone.

3.4 A MODEL OF THE PRESENT SUN

In summary, the following relations are used to describe the radial rates of change for solar properties:

$$\frac{dM}{dr} = \rho 4\pi r^2 \tag{3-2}$$

$$\frac{dp}{dr} = -\frac{MG}{r^2}\rho \tag{3-3}$$

$$\frac{dL}{dr} = \epsilon\rho 4\pi r^2 \tag{3-5}$$

$$\left(\frac{dT}{dr}\right)_{\text{rad}} = -\frac{3}{16\sigma T^3}\frac{L}{4\pi r^2}\kappa\rho \tag{3-8}$$

$$\left(\frac{dT}{dr}\right)_{\text{ad}} = \frac{\gamma-1}{\gamma}\frac{T}{p}\frac{dp}{dr} \tag{3-10}$$

where the smallest value of $|dT/dr|$ is used. The quantities p, ϵ, and κ are defined in terms of the local values of ρ, T, and the composition. The description of the interior will be complete when the appropriate boundary conditions for the above equations are specified. Clearly, at $r=0$

$$M=0 \qquad L=0 \tag{3-23}$$

and, on the surface at $r=R$

$$M=M_{\odot} \tag{3-24}$$

For an age of 4.5×10^9 years

$$R=R_{\odot} \tag{3-25}$$

and

$$L(R_\odot) = L_\odot \tag{3-26}$$

The ability to meet this boundary condition is strongly dependent upon the choice of Z, the heavy-element abundance, through its effect on the opacity. Also, at $r = R$,

$$p = \Gamma T^{\gamma/\gamma-1} \tag{3-27}$$

This defines the way in which the pressure and temperature approach zero, and is obtained from the adiabatic relation shown in equation (3–9). The constant Γ is a function of the details of the convective turbulence which, from an empirical point of view, are summarized by the ratio of a "mixing length" to the local atmospheric scale height. A mixing length is essentially the mean free path of a turbulent eddy or distance it travels before losing its identity by breaking up. In

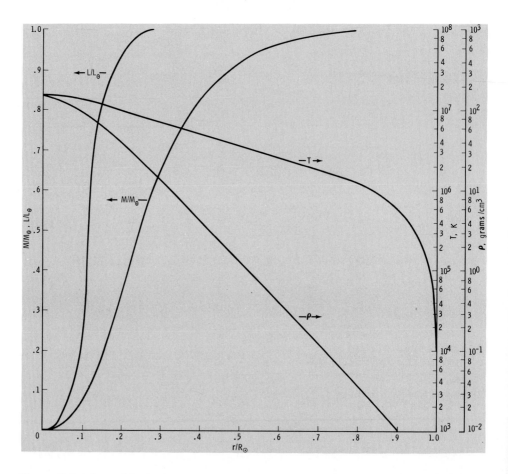

FIGURE 3–5.—A model of the present solar interior. $X = 0.708$, $Y = 0.272$, $Z = 0.020$, $\rho_c = 158$ grams/cm³, and $T_c = 1.57 \times 10^7$ K. (Data from Sears, 1964.)

the convection zone, the ratio of this length to the local atmospheric scale height is of the order of unity. To obtain the correct solar radius, values between approximately 1/15 to 2 have been used in most solar models.

Assuming an initially uniform composition, the solar structure at time zero (the point when nuclear burning replaces gravitational contraction as the primary energy source) is obtained as well as the time rates of change of the composition. The structure, composition, and rates of change are then computed at successively later points in time until an age of 4.5×10^9 years is reached. At that point, equations (3–25) and (3–26) will be satisfied if the initial composition and the ratio of mixing length to atmospheric scale height were properly chosen.

A model of the present sun is shown in figures 3–5 and 3–6. A notable feature is the presence of the dense, high-temperature, energy-generating core. That is, at a radius of only $1/4 R_\odot$, M is $0.5 M_\odot$ and L is $0.99 L_\odot$. The reason for the central mass concentration is, of course, the sun's self-gravitation and the resulting sharp radial decrease of ρ (a factor of $1/7$ out to $1/4 R_\odot$). The sharp decreases of ρ and ϵ are both

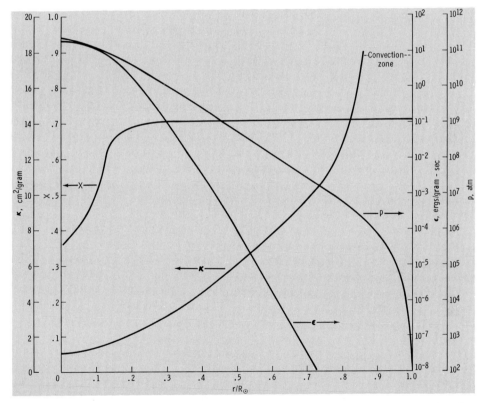

FIGURE 3–6.—Solar locally determined properties and hydrogen mass fraction. (X and p data from Sears, 1964; κ data from Weymann, 1957; and ϵ calculated from eqs. (3–19), (3–21), and (3–22).)

responsible for the central concentration of the energy generation. Although T is reduced only by a factor of $1/2$ out to $1/4R_\odot$, ϵ drops by a factor of $1/40$; $\rho\epsilon$, the rate of energy generation per unit volume, decreases by approximately $1/300$. The central depletion of the nuclear fuel, hydrogen, also outlines the core. Although X is essentially uniform outside $1/4R_\odot$, inside it drops by a factor of $1/2$. Moving outward from the core, another notable feature is a sharp increase in κ which occurs at a radius slightly greater than $0.8R_\odot$. This results in a sharp increase in $|dT/dr|_{\mathrm{rad}}$ which, together with the decrease in γ, promotes the onset of convective instability at $0.86R_\odot$ in this model. Finally, the sharp drop in p close to the surface is also very apparent. The scale height for pressure change, $p \sim e^{-(r/H)}$, from equations (3–3) and (3–14), is proportional to the temperature.

$$H = \frac{kT}{\mu m_{\mathrm{H}} g} \tag{3–28}$$

Hence, as T becomes small when the surface in the convection zone is approached, p begins to decrease more rapidly. Both ρ and T are adiabatically related to p (eq. (3–9)) and display the same characteristics. By the time the base of the photosphere is reached, the values of the gas properties have dropped to $T = 6.4 \times 10^3$ K, $\rho = 3 \times 10^{-7}$ gram/cm^3, and $p = 0.14$ atm. The properties of the convection zone will be investigated further when granulation, supergranulation, and atmospheric heating are considered.

A check on our knowledge of the internal solar structure, processes, and composition is provided by the exceedingly difficult observation of neutrinos from the sun (Davis et al., 1968, and Davis, 1970). Most interestingly, the result of the observations indicate that a fundamental error in our understanding of stellar interiors may exist. The experimental upper limit on the observable neutrino flux is a factor of at least $1/2$ to $1/3$ lower than what current theoretical models predict. The known uncertainties in theoretical and observational parameters cannot account for this discrepancy (Bahcall, 1971). Some of the possible sources of error that have been explored (Iben, 1969) include the following:

(1) The initial helium abundance Y was less than 0.16–0.20.
(2) Unexpected large errors exist in one or more of the relevant nuclear cross sections.
(3) One or more of the neutrino absorption cross sections has been significantly overestimated.
(4) The sun was initially nonhomogeneous and remained so.
(5) Significant mixing in the solar interior has occurred during the nuclear burning phase.
(6) The sun is much younger than $4\frac{1}{2}$ billion years.
(7) Strong large-scale magnetic fields exist in the solar interior of up to 10^9 gauss near the center.
(8) The gravitational constant increases with time.

So far, these possibilities appear to be unlikely and the intriguing discrepancy between theory and observation remains.

3.5 SOLAR EVOLUTION

A general evolutionary characteristic of the sun and most other stars is a progressive contraction of mass by self-gravitation which is periodically interrupted by nuclear burning. Some of the gravitational potential energy of an interstellar gas cloud first is converted into thermal energy as the gas particles fall toward the center of mass and then have their motions randomized by mutual collisions. When the density and temperature are sufficiently high, nuclear fusion occurs and the contraction is temporarily halted. After the nuclear fuel is exhausted, the contraction-burning cycle will be repeated, but at higher temperatures and with higher mass nuclei. The phases of the sun's life from gas-cloud contraction to white-dwarf phase are shown in figure 3-7. The path traced by the sun in the Hertzsprung-Russel (H-R) diagram from contraction to red-giant phase is shown in figure 3-8. In general, there is a rapid movement of the sun toward the main sequence, a lingering in the neighborhood of the sequence, and then a rapid movement toward the approximate direction from which it came. For stars of higher mass, the number of contraction-burning cycles and the rate of energy release will tend to increase, and

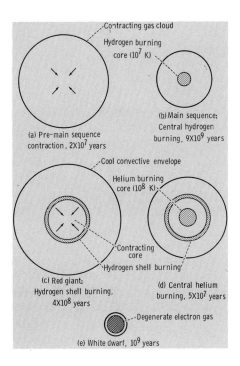

FIGURE 3-7.—Solar evolution.

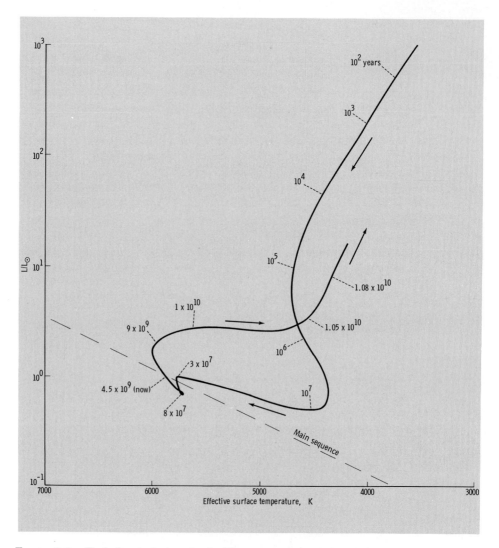

FIGURE 3–8.—Evolution trajectory in the Hertzsprung-Russel diagram for the sun. (Data from Ezer and Cameron, 1965; and Iben, 1965 and 1967.)

the lifetime of each cycle will decrease. One of the major challenges facing astrophysicists is to explain the star distribution in the H-R diagram (fig. 3–1). This is attempted by calculating the many possible evolutionary paths starting with values that fall within acceptable ranges for the gas-cloud mass, composition, angular momentum, and time of contraction. The sun, both unique and valuable because of its proximity to us, is a useful testing ground for many techniques and theories employed in the calculations.

Contraction

The details of the sun's evolution up to the red-giant phase are shown in figures 3–9 and 3–10.[1] In the very early stages of gas-cloud contraction, the motion toward the center of mass is very rapid, and most of the gravitational energy given up goes into heating the gas. Increases in density and temperature result in an increase in the gas pressure gradient. When the gradient is sufficient to balance the gravitational forces, the gas cloud becomes stable enough to prevent a continued collapse. Assuming the gas cloud has negligible angular momentum, this point is reached in approximately 3 years, when the radius has decreased to $64R_\odot$ and the luminosity is $700L_\odot$. All of the radiant energy emitted throughout the contraction phase is derived from the decrease in the gravitational potential energy. Because the luminosity is proportional to the surface area and the fourth power of the effective surface temperature $(L \sim R^2 T_e^4)$, and T_e remains within rather narrow limits (4000 to 6000 K), L varies approximately as R^2 (fig. 3–9).

After 2×10^4 years, the contraction is momentarily slowed by deuterium burning. The central temperature has reached 8×10^5 K and is sufficient to ignite

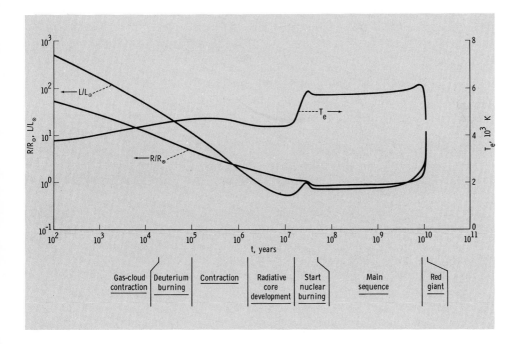

FIGURE 3–9.—Evolution of surface observables for the sun. (Data from Ezer and Cameron, 1965; and Iben, 1965 and 1967.)

---

[1] The following discussion is based primarily on the work of Ezer and Cameron, 1965; and Iben, 1965 and 1967.

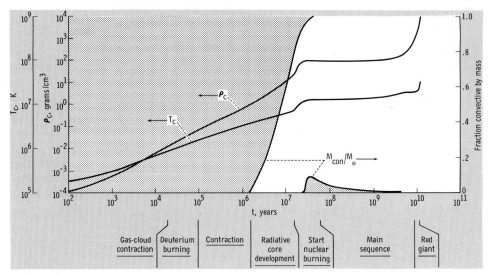

FIGURE 3–10.—Evolution of central gas variables for the sun. Also shown is M_{con}/M, the fraction of the solar mass which is convectively unstable. The shading indicates whether it is the mass internal or external to that specified which is unstable. (Data from Ezer and Cameron, 1965; and Iben, 1965 and 1967.)

the deuterium which burns to form ^{3}He (eq. (3–17)). If it is assumed that the ratio of deuterium to hydrogen was initially the same as the terrestrial value, the deuterium burning will be sufficient to supply much of the sun's energy loss for 1×10^5 years. When all of the deuterium in the sun is exhausted, the contraction proceeds as before.

The sun is fully convective in the contraction phase (fig. 3–10). The temperature is relatively low, which causes the opacity, hence, the radiative temperature gradient, to be large (eq. (3–8)) and the Schwarzschild condition (eq. (3–11)) is satisfied. When the sun is fully convective, the composition is always uniform. This allows nearly all of the deuterium in the sun to be burned, not just that initially in the core. As the sun continues to contract, the central temperature increases and the radiative temperature gradient decreases relative to the convective gradient. At approximately 1.4×10^6 years ($L \simeq 1.5 L_\odot$ and $R \simeq 2 R_\odot$), the core is no longer convectively unstable and energy is transferred outward by radiation (fig. 3–10). The radiative core grows outward and solar energy release is controlled by the interior opacity, which decreases with increasing temperature. Thus, the luminosity reaches a minimum ($\frac{1}{2} L_\odot$ at approximately 1.4×10^7 years), and then starts to increase along with the surface temperature (fig. 3–9).

Nuclear Burning

After 1.4×10^7 years, the central temperature and density are high enough that the sun begins to draw from its primary energy sources. Hydrogen reacts to form

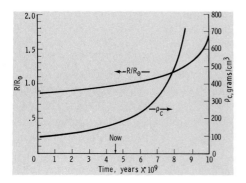

FIGURE 3–11.—Main sequence variation of solar size and central density with time. (Data from Iben, 1967.)

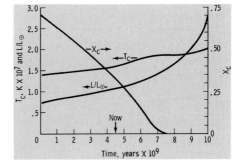

FIGURE 3–12.—Main sequence variation of solar luminosity, central temperature, and central hydrogen mass fraction with time. (Data from Iben, 1967.)

^{3}He (eq. (3–17)) when the central temperature and density reach 7×10^6 K and 20 grams/cm^3, respectively. Then, when the central temperature becomes greater than 1.2×10^7 K, the small amount of ^{12}C present burns to form ^{14}N. This causes a sudden halt in the contraction, the core actually begins to expand and return energy to the gravitational field, nuclear energy rapidly becomes the sole source of the luminosity, and a temperature gradient is established in the core that is large enough to again cause convective instability (fig. 3–10). The convective core grows rapidly to cover a maximum of approximately 10 percent of the solar mass. Then, as the proton-proton cycle becomes dominant and ^{12}C burning fades out, it gradually decreases to zero. Following this relatively dynamic entrance into the nuclear burning phase, the sun settles down to a long quiet life on the main sequence. The sun can be considered, somewhat arbitrarily, to reach the main sequence when 99 percent of the luminosity is supplied by nuclear processes, a state which is reached at approximately 5×10^7 years. From here on R, L, T_c, and ρ_c increase slowly, and X_c, the central mass fraction of hydrogen, decreases steadily toward zero (figs. 3–11 and 3–12). The hydrogen burning, being a very strong function of temperature, acts as a thermostat and creates a very stable energy release. Extremely small changes in the temperature distribution will cause large changes in the energy release, which tends to return the temperature distribution to its original state. At 8×10^9 years, the central hydrogen is nearly exhausted and the sun proceeds rapidly into its next phase of life.

Post-Main Sequence

The hydrogen now burns in a shell around the core, which increases in radius with time. The temperature of the gas above the shell is raised, increasing the scale height of pressure change H, and causing the sun to expand. The increase in L is not as great as the increase in R^2, so T_e decreases and much of the radiation is emitted in red wavelengths. Hence, our sun becomes a red giant. The increase in the temperature at the outer edge of the shell causes an increase in the radiative temperature gradient. The convection zone thickens to cover an increasing amount of the solar mass. Inside the shell the hydrogen has been transformed into the higher atomic-weight helium, increasing the mean atomic weight of the gas, and thereby allowing the core to contract. As it contracts, its temperature is raised and its density is increased to the point where electrons start to become degenerate. That is, the average distance between electrons decreases to the same magnitude as the electron de Broglie wavelength (the characteristic quantum mechanical interaction distance or wave packet dimension). In this state, the pressure becomes independent of temperature and varies as $\rho^{5/3}$ or $\rho^{4/3}$ in the relativistic case. Another important property of the degenerate electron core is that the electrons are extremely mobile and can readily transport heat. Hence, the core is nearly uniform in temperature, which increases as the gas contracts.

When the central temperature reaches approximately 10^8 K, helium, the ashes of the previous burning, undergoes fusion to form carbon and nitrogen (fig. 3–4). The hydrogen burning shell has meanwhile decreased in thickness and continued outward. This phase of burning proceeds quite rapidly. It is followed by a helium-shell-burning phase, through several more steps which are not known with certainty, and finally arrives at the white dwarf phase. At this point in the sun's life, nuclear burning has ceased, almost all of the mass is at very high density and is electron degenerate, and the radius is approximately $10^{-2} R_\odot$. In a time on the order of 10^9 years, the sun's internal heat is conducted to the surface and radiated away with a luminosity of $10^{-2} L_\odot$ to $10^{-3} L_\odot$. The cold, burned-out, deceased mass of solar material which remains is essentially a black dwarf.

REFERENCES

BAHCALL, J. N.: 1971, Some Unsolved Problems in Astrophysics. Astron. J. *76*, 283–290.

BRANDT, J. C.: 1966, The Sun and Stars. New York: McGraw-Hill.

CHANDRASEKHAR, S.: 1957, An Introduction to the Study of Stellar Structure. New York: Dover.

CLAYTON, D. D.: 1969, The Origin of the Elements. Phys. Today *22*(5), 28–37.

DANZIGER, I. J.: 1970, The Cosmic Abundance of Helium. Ann. Rev. Astron. Astrophys. *8*, 161–178.

DAVIS, R., JR.: 1970, A Progress Report on the Brookline Solar Neutrino Experiment. Report to Meeting "Astrophysical Neutrinos," Cortona, Italy: Brookhaven National Laboratory Preprint, 371–374.

DAVIS, R., JR.; HARMER, D. S.; AND HOFFMAN, K. C.: 1968, Search for Neutrinos From the Sun. Phys. Rev. Lett. *20*, 1205–1209.

EZER, D.; AND CAMERON, A. G. W.: 1965, A Study of Solar Evolution. Can. J. Phys. *43*, 1497–1517.

GOLDBERG, L.; KOPP, R. A.; AND DUPREE, A. K.: 1964, The Abundance of Iron in the Solar Photosphere. Astrophys. J. *140*, 707–712.

IBEN, I., JR.: 1965, Stellar Evolution. I. The Approach to the Main Sequence. Astrophys. J. *141*, 993–1018.

IBEN, I., JR.: 1967, Stellar Evolution. VI. Evolution From the Main Sequence to the Red-Giant Branch for Stars of Mass $1M_\odot$, $1.25M_\odot$, $1.5M_\odot$. Astrophys. J. *147*, 624–650.

IBEN, I., JR.: 1969, The Cl^{37} Solar Neutrino Experiment and the Solar Helium Abundance. Ann. Phys. *54*, 164–203.

IBEN, I., JR.: 1970, Globular-Cluster Stars. Sci. Amer. *223*(1), 27–39.

DE JAGER, C.; AND NEVEN, L.: 1967, A Systematic Method for the Analysis of High-Resolution Fraunhofer Line Profiles. Solar Phys. *1*, 27–59.

LAMBERT, D. L.: 1968, The Abundances of the Elements in the Solar Photosphere. I. Mon. Notic. Roy. Astron. Soc. *138*, 143–179.

LAMBERT, D. L.; AND WARNER, B.: 1968, The Abundances of the Elements in the Solar Photosphere. II. Sodium, Aluminium, Phosphorous, Sulphur, and Potassium. Mon. Notic. Roy. Astron. Soc. *138*, 181–212.

LAMBERT, D. L.; AND WARNER, B.: 1968, The Abundances of the Elements in the Solar Photosphere. III. Silicon. Mon. Notic. Roy. Astron. Soc. *138*, 213–227.

LAMBERT, D. L.; AND WARNER, B.: 1968, The Abundances of the Elements in the Solar Photosphere. V. The Alkaline Earths Mg, Ca, Sr, Ba. Mon. Notic. Roy. Astron. Soc. *140*, 197–221.

LAMBERT, D. L.; MALLIA, E. A.; AND WARNER, B.: 1969, The Abundances of the Elements in the Solar Photosphere. VII. Zn, Ga, Ge, Cd, In, Sn, Hg, Tl, and Pb. Mon. Notic. Roy. Astron. Soc. *142*, 71–95.

MOTZ, L.; AND DUVEEN, A.: 1966, Essentials of Astronomy. New York: Wadsworth.

ROSS, J.; AND ALLER, L.: 1968, Determination of Solar Abundances by a Method of Spectrum Synthesis. Astrophys. J. *153*, 235–244.

SCHWARZSCHILD, M.: 1958, The Structure and Evolution of the Stars. New York: Dover.

SEARS, R. L.: 1964, Helium Content and Neutrino Fluxes in Solar Models. Astrophys. J. *140*, 477–484.

SIMON, G. W.; AND LEIGHTON, R. B.: 1964, Velocity Fields in Solar Atmosphere. III. Large-Scale Motions, the Chromospheric Network, and Magnetic Fields. Astrophys. J. *140*, 1120–1147.

WARNER, B.: 1968, The Abundances of the Elements in the Solar Photosphere. IV. The Iron Group. Mon. Notic. Roy. Astron. Soc. *138*, 229–243.

WEYMANN, R.: 1957, Inhomogeneous Stellar Models. VI. An Improved Solar Model With the Carbon Cycle Included. Astrophys. J. *126*, 208–212.

WITHBROE, G. L.: 1969, The Photospheric Abundance of Iron. Solar Phys. *9*, 19–30.

ZIRIN, H.: 1966, The Solar Atmosphere. Waltham, Mass.: Blaisdell.

4

The Photosphere

Moving outward through the quiescent sun, we next encounter the photosphere, the relatively thin but physically important layer immediately above the convection zone. The energy that is generated in the core is emitted directly to space from this layer without further appreciable absorption or scattering. The absorption coefficient κ continues to increase as we move out toward the photosphere. However, the gas density decreases sharply and $1/\rho\kappa$, which is the average distance a photon travels before being scattered or reabsorbed (called the photon mean free path), increases rapidly and becomes the same magnitude as the atmospheric scale height H. If $1/\rho\kappa \ll H$, the emitted photons are scattered or reabsorbed many times before traveling one scale height. If $1/\rho\kappa \gg H$, the emitted photons readily travel outward through one scale height and the remaining atmosphere, which steadily decreases in density. It is from the layer where $1/\rho\kappa \approx H$ that most of the radiation is emitted directly to space. This layer is called the photosphere. Using the definition of H (eq. (3–28)), this condition is defined equivalently by $p \approx g/\kappa$.

In essence, the observations of the solar atmosphere are directed toward determining the intensity of the emitted radiation as a function of surface location, depth in the atmosphere, wavelength, and time of emission. From these observations one seeks to determine the physical state at each point in the atmosphere as a function of time. This includes the determination of the temperature, density, pressure, degree of excitation and ionization of each component element, macroscopic velocity, and magnitudes and directions of the electric and magnetic fields. This is an overly ambitious objective and, in most cases, we have been forced to neglect effects which are relatively small and to work only with integrated properties. Much is yet to be learned by increasing the resolution of the observations in space, wavelength, and time.

Initially, it is assumed that the solar surface is uniform and that the emitted radiation is constant in time. Hence, granulation and all manifestations of solar activity are neglected and the intensity of radiation, as seen from the earth, is a function only of the wavelength and the angle from the center of the sun. The presence of limb darkening or brightening at a wide range of wavelengths in the continuum (ranges where the intensity is a smooth or continuous function of wavelength) is first investigated. Next, the formation of Fraunhofer lines and line broadening are considered. Lastly, a discussion of the effects of not having thermodynamic equilibrium is presented.

4.1 GENERAL DESCRIPTION OF RADIATIVE TRANSFER

The phenomenon of limb darkening is illustrated in figure 4–1. As we shift our observation in white light from the sun's center to the limb, the intensity of radiation decreases and the limb appears darker than the center. This results directly from the temperature gradient in the photosphere. As we shift our sight toward the limb, the number of atoms between us and a given height in the atmosphere increases. Hence, we do not see as far into the atmosphere as at sun center. Conversely, the radiation that escapes the sun directly and travels in our direction comes from higher layers closer to the limb than at the center. Because the temperature decreases as we move higher in the photosphere, the intensity of the emitted radiation will be correspondingly lower. The opposite case, limb brightening, occurs at those wavelengths where the major portion of emitted radiation comes directly from the chromosphere or corona in which the temperature increases rather than decreases with height.

Because the intensity of radiation can be measured as a function of both the distance from sun center and the wavelength, much can be learned about the distribution of physical properties with radius if we understand the processes of radiation emission, absorption, and scattering within the atmosphere. These processes will be described briefly and the solar physical properties will be related to the observations.

The primary variable of interest is $I_\lambda(\mathbf{r}, \boldsymbol{\omega}, t)$, the specific intensity at wavelength λ, which is defined as follows (fig. 4–2). An infinitesimal area dA is specified at an arbitrary location in the solar atmosphere. It is defined by the position vector in spherical coordinates $\mathbf{r}(r, \theta, \Phi)$ and is parallel to the surface. Through this area a certain amount of radiant energy in the frequency range of λ to $(\lambda + d\lambda)$ passes

FIGURE 4–1.—The full sun in white light. This photograph, taken on July 4, 1968, shows the sun to be exceptionally free of activity. (Courtesy of E. Mayfield, San Fernando Observatory of the Aerospace Corp.)

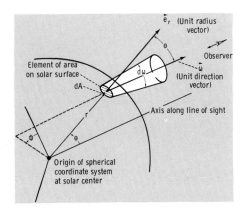

FIGURE 4–2.—Geometric variables of specific intensity.

per unit of time, traveling in the range of directions $\boldsymbol{\omega}$ to $(\boldsymbol{\omega}+d\boldsymbol{\omega})$. This energy flow is given by

$$\frac{d\ (\text{energy})}{dt} = I_\lambda \cos\theta\ dA\ d\lambda\ d\omega \qquad (4\text{--}1)$$

where $\cos\theta\ dA$ is the effective area for the direction $\boldsymbol{\omega}$. Hence, I_λ is the rate of radiant energy flow of wavelength λ at position $\mathbf{r}$ in direction $\boldsymbol{\omega}$ per unit area, solid angle, and wavelength interval. In essence, we have broken the radiation down into as many of its component variables as possible, except for polarization. That is, I_λ specifies a number of photons per unit time, area, wavelength, and solid angle which all have the same energy, emerge from the same point on the surface, and travel in the same direction. Sometimes it is useful to work with the specific intensity integrated over all wavelengths

$$\bar{I} \equiv \int_0^\infty I_\lambda\ d\lambda \qquad (4\text{--}2)$$

or, the specific intensity averaged over all directions

$$J_\lambda \equiv \frac{1}{4\pi} \int_{4\pi} \mathbf{I}_\lambda \cdot d\boldsymbol{\omega} \qquad (4\text{--}3)$$

If the radiation is isotropic, that is, uniform in all directions, $J_\lambda = I_\lambda$. Also useful is

$$\bar{J} \equiv \int_0^\infty J_\lambda\ d\lambda \qquad (4\text{--}4)$$

We refer to $\bar{I}$ as the integrated intensity and I_λ as the monochromatic intensity. With the assumptions of spherical symmetry and steady state, the specific intensity becomes a function only of solar radius and the direction relative to the outward normal. Thus, the specific intensity is $I_\lambda(r, \theta)$, as illustrated in figure 4–3. Observations at the limb correspond to $\cos\theta = 0$.

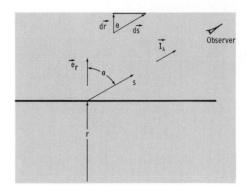

FIGURE 4–3.—Simplified variables of specific
intensity.

As radiation emerges from the atmosphere, the specific intensity is altered by
the processes of absorption, emission, and scattering. Absorption directly reduces
the intensity of a beam of radiation, emission adds directly to it, and scattering can
produce both effects by altering only the direction of travel of a photon (coherent
scattering) or altering both the direction and wavelength (noncoherent scattering).
It is to be noted that coherence here applies to the photon frequency or wavelength
rather than its phase. For the case of removal of photons from a beam of radiation

$$dI_\lambda = - \rho \kappa_\lambda I_\lambda \, ds \qquad\qquad (4\text{--}5)$$

where κ_λ is the opacity at wavelength λ and includes the effects of both absorption
and scattering and s is a measure of distance along the direction of the radiation
flow (fig. 4–3). Thus, the photon mean free path at λ is $1/\rho \kappa_\lambda$. For the case of
addition of photons to the beam

$$dI_\lambda = \rho j_\lambda \, ds \qquad\qquad (4\text{--}6)$$

The emission coefficient j_λ is the rate of energy addition to the beam per unit mass,
solid angle, and wavelength interval. In addition to the effects of spontaneous and
induced emission, it also includes the effects of scattering. Hence, the total change
in specific intensity is

$$dI_\lambda = (j_\lambda - \kappa_\lambda I_\lambda) \rho \, ds \qquad\qquad (4\text{--}7)$$

Defining a "source function" as

$$S_\lambda \equiv \frac{j_\lambda}{\kappa_\lambda} \qquad\qquad (4\text{--}8)$$

Then

$$dI_\lambda = (S_\lambda - I_\lambda) \rho \kappa_\lambda \, ds \qquad\qquad (4\text{--}9)$$

For the case of thermodynamic equilibrium (TE), the gradient of the radiation
is zero and the specific intensity is given by Planck's law, which is a function of
temperature only. Thus, if TE prevails

$$I_\lambda = B_\lambda (T) \qquad\qquad (4\text{--}10)$$

where

$$B_\lambda(T) = \frac{2hc^2}{\lambda^5} \left[\exp\left(hc/\lambda kT\right) - 1\right]^{-1} \qquad (4\text{--}11)$$

and

$$S_\lambda = \frac{j_\lambda}{\kappa_\lambda} = B_\lambda(T) \qquad (4\text{--}12)$$

Specifically, equation (4–12) states that the ratio of the emission to the absorption coefficients for a substance in TE is dependent only on the local temperature and is equal to the Planck function $B_\lambda(T)$. This is a statement of Kirchhoff's law, which is sometimes shortened to "a good absorber is a good emitter."

The shape of $B_\lambda(T)$, the specific intensity for blackbody radiation, is shown in figure 4–4. The peak intensity of the curve is given by

$$B_{\lambda_{\mathrm{max}}}(T) = T^5 \underbrace{\frac{hc^2 \left(\dfrac{1}{\lambda T}\right)^5_{\mathrm{max}}}{\exp\left[hc/k\left(\lambda T\right)_{\mathrm{max}}\right] - 1}}_{\text{constant}} \qquad (4\text{--}13)$$

and occurs at

$$\lambda_{\mathrm{max}} = \left(\frac{2899}{T}\right) 10^4 \qquad \text{Å} \qquad (4\text{--}14)$$

where T is measured in K. This last statement, $\lambda_{\mathrm{max}} T = \text{constant}$, is referred to as the Wien displacement law and shows how the peak of the emitted radiation shifts

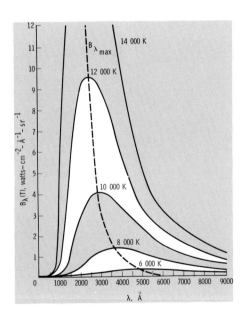

FIGURE 4–4.—Specific intensity of blackbody radiation.

to shorter wavelengths as the temperature is raised. At 5000 K, the approximate temperature of the photosphere, λ_{max} is equal to 5798 Å, which is near the center of the visible spectrum. For temperatures of 10^4 and 10^6 K, the peak will be shifted into the ultraviolet and soft X-ray ranges, respectively. Equation (4–14) is roughly equivalent to the statement that the photon energy at the peak intensity, hc/λ_{max}, is approximately five times the thermal energy kT. The approximations to B_λ at the two ends of the spectrum are also useful. If the product λT is small so that $hc/\lambda kT \gg 1$ or $\lambda T \ll 1.45$ cm-K, then

$$B_\lambda(T) \simeq \frac{2hc}{\lambda^5} \exp\left[-(hc/\lambda kT)\right] \qquad (4\text{–}15)$$

which is the Wien approximation to Planck's law. If $\lambda T \gg 1.45$ cm-K,

$$B_\lambda(T) \simeq \frac{2ckT}{\lambda^4} \qquad (4\text{–}16)$$

which is the Rayleigh-Jeans formula.

Not only are the radiation laws relatively simple when TE prevails, but the distribution of atoms or ions over their possible energy states becomes a function of temperature only and is not dependent upon the detailed microscopic processes taking place. That is,

$$\frac{N_u}{N_l} = \frac{g_u}{g_l} \exp\left[-(E_u - E_l)/kT\right] \qquad (4\text{–}17)$$

where the subscripts u and l denote an upper and a lower energy state, respectively, of the same species, N is the number density, g is a statistical weight, and E is a state's energy. This is termed a Boltzmann distribution and the factor $\exp(-\Delta E/kT)$ is the Boltzmann factor. This distribution is in agreement with our intuition in that states of the higher energy are not as densely populated as those of lower energy. The factor prescribing the population ratio is strongly dependent upon the ratio of the energy difference between two states to the quantity kT, which is nearly the average energy of each type of gas particle or of the photons.

The assumption of TE is not valid in a strict sense in the photosphere because the temperature gradient is not zero and radiation escapes from the gas into space. However, the effects of these two perturbations can usually be considered small and the photospheric gas is assumed to be in thermodynamic equilibrium corresponding to the local value of temperature at each height. That is, local thermodynamic equilibrium (LTE) is assumed. Thus, the local value of temperature is used in the Boltzmann distribution (eq. (4–17)), the Saha ionization relation (eq. (3–15)), and the source function which is set equal to the Planck distribution (eq. (4–12)). One step removed from LTE is the sometimes valid assumption that excitation, ionization, and the resulting source function correspond to LTE at the local particle kinetic temperature, which may differ from the local radiation temperature. This, in essence, assumes that the processes that create and destroy states of excitation and ionization are dominated by particle collisions. Although not correct in a strict sense, this condition is very often termed LTE and one must always be careful to determine what implicit assumptions are made when the concept of LTE is employed. When a single temperature is no longer sufficient to specify particle properties, we enter the complex realm of non-LTE (NLTE). The assumptions made and the relations valid in TE, LTE, and NLTE will be further discussed in section 4.8.

4.2 OPTICAL DEPTH

Optical depth τ_λ is a useful physical concept used to measure the depth which we see into a partially transparent medium such as the solar atmosphere. Optical depth is defined by

$$d\tau_\lambda = -\rho\kappa_\lambda \, dr \tag{4-18}$$

Because optical depth varies as a physical length over the photon mean free path, it can be thought of as the number of "photon collisions." For an observer looking at the sun center

$$\tau_\lambda(r) = \int_r^\infty \rho(r')\kappa_\lambda(r') \, dr' \tag{4-19}$$

Thus, $\tau_\lambda = 0$ at infinity, the location of the observer, and increases as we move in toward the sun.

To illustrate optical depth, we investigate the following case. When a beam of radiation of intensity $I_\lambda{}^\circ$ tries to penetrate a nonemitting layer of solar material in the outward radial direction (fig. 4–5(a)), the following equation applies.

$$dI_\lambda = -I_\lambda\rho\kappa_\lambda \, dr \tag{4-20}$$

$$\frac{I_\lambda}{I_\lambda{}^\circ} = \exp\left(-\int_{r_0}^r \rho\kappa_\lambda \, dr\right) \tag{4-21}$$

or, using equation (4–19)

$$\frac{I_\lambda}{I_\lambda{}^\circ} = \exp\left[-(\tau_0 - \tau)\right] \tag{4-22}$$

Hence, when the optical depth τ_0 increases by 1, the intensity will be attenuated by $1/e$.

Introducing the optical depth (eq. (4–19)) into the situation we are considering (eq. (4–9)), we obtain

$$\cos\theta \, \frac{dI_\lambda(\tau_\lambda, \theta)}{d\tau_\lambda} = I_\lambda(\tau_\lambda, \theta) - S_\lambda(\tau_\lambda) \tag{4-23}$$

where the source function has been assumed to be isotropic. This relationship is valid when the contribution of scattering to j_λ is small so that j_λ and κ_λ can be considered to be material properties independent of direction. This integrates to

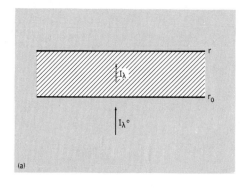

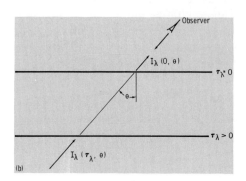

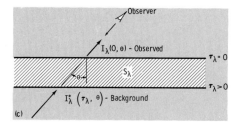

FIGURE 4–5.—Simple models of radiation attenuation.

$$I_\lambda(0, \theta) = I_\lambda(\tau_\lambda, \theta) \exp\left[-(\tau_\lambda/\cos \theta)\right] \int_0^{\tau_\lambda/\cos \theta} S_\lambda(\tau_\lambda') \exp\left[-(\tau_\lambda'/\cos \theta)\right] \frac{d\tau_\lambda'}{\cos \theta}$$

$$(4\text{–}24)$$

which is depicted in figure 4–5 (b). Neglecting the sun's curvature, the maximum value possible for τ_λ will correspond to a semi-infinite medium; that is, τ_λ will approach infinity. Thus, the final relation used to describe solar radiation emission is

$$I_\lambda(0, \theta) = \int_0^\infty S_\lambda(\tau_\lambda') \exp\left[-(\tau_\lambda'/\cos \theta)\right] \frac{d\tau_\lambda'}{\cos \theta} \qquad (4\text{–}25)$$

This is the result we might intuitively expect. The contribution to I_λ made by each element along the ray's trajectory is the source function times the fraction of the energy which escapes $\exp(-\tau_\lambda/\cos \theta)$. In LTE, S_λ is replaced by the Planck function at $T(\tau_\lambda')$. An approximate rule of thumb that should be condensed from equation (4–25) is that when S_λ is a strong function of τ, as in the solar atmosphere, the radiation which we see, $I_\lambda(0, \theta)$, will be most characteristic of the physical region where $\tau_\lambda/\cos \theta$ is approximately unity. Thus, the physical depth that we see into the sun can be varied by changing our viewing angle ($\cos \theta$ or position on the solar disk) or the wavelength at which we observe. (κ_λ changes greatly from one region of the spectrum to another, as well as across an absorption line.)

Returning to equation (4–24) for a moment and assuming that a layer exists of finite thickness with $I_\lambda(\tau_\lambda, \theta) = 0$ and that $S_\lambda(\tau_\lambda)$ is a constant, we have

$$I_\lambda(0, \theta) = S_\lambda[1 - \exp(-\tau_\lambda/\cos\theta)] \qquad (4-26)$$

If $\tau_\lambda/\cos\theta \ll 1$, then $I_\lambda(0, \theta) \simeq S_\lambda\tau_\lambda/\cos\theta$. That is, we sum up all the direct contributions of S_λ without considering reabsorption. However, if $\tau_\lambda/\cos\theta \gg 1$, then $I_\lambda(0, \theta) \simeq S_\lambda$. In this case, no matter how large $\tau_\lambda/\cos\theta$, the effect of reabsorption is to limit I_λ to a maximum value of S_λ. Equation (4–24) can also be used to describe the contrast between a physical structure and the background solar emission (fig. 4–5(c)). A layer assumed to be of uniform source function, which could represent a spicule (to be discussed in the next chapter), a filament, or a surge of solar material, lies above an area of the solar surface which emits a background radiation of intensity $I_\lambda^\circ(\tau_\lambda, \theta)$. Equation (4–24) is easily integrated and the difference between the radiation from the physical structure $I_\lambda(0, \theta)$ and the background $I_\lambda^\circ(\tau_\lambda, \theta)$ is

$$I_\lambda - I_\lambda^\circ = (S_\lambda - I_\lambda^\circ)[1 - \exp(-\tau_\lambda/\cos\theta)] \qquad (4-27)$$

Thus, the structure will appear either light or dark, depending upon whether S_λ is greater than or less than I_λ°, and the contrast will approach the maximum as $\tau_\lambda/\cos\theta$ becomes much larger than unity.

When the sun's curvature is taken into account, the path length for integration in equation (4–25) will be altered according to

$$\Delta s = \frac{\Delta r}{\cos\theta}\left(1 - \frac{\Delta r}{2R_\odot}\tan^2\theta + \cdots\right) \qquad (4-28)$$

Hence, neglect of curvature introduces an error on the order of $\Delta r/2R_\odot \tan^2\theta$. Taking Δr to be 140 km, the height over which τ_{5000} Å decreases from 1.0 to 0.1 in the photosphere, $\Delta r/2R_\odot \simeq 1.0 \times 10^{-4}$. Therefore, the error will be less than 1 percent if θ is less than 84°, which is equivalent to a distance of $0.995R_\odot$ from the center of the sun. The availability of high-speed machine calculations allows the curvature to be considered in the computations if required.

From equation (4–25), it is seen that once $S_\lambda(\tau_\lambda)$ is specified, $I_\lambda(0, \theta)$ is known. However, in reality one measures $I_\lambda(0, \theta)$ and then seeks to determine $S_\lambda(\tau_\lambda)$. This can be done mathematically by inverting equation (4–25) to get an explicit expression for $S_\lambda(\tau_\lambda)$ or by assuming $S_\lambda(\tau_\lambda)$ and trying to fit the data by iteration. In either case, we are limited by the spatial and wavelength resolutions with which we can measure $I_\lambda(0, \theta)$.

4.3 OBSERVATIONS AND RELATION TO PHYSICAL PROPERTIES

Figures 4–6(a) to 4–6(c) show the progression of limb darkening in the visible spectrum to limb brightening in the extreme ultraviolet (XUV) and X-ray ranges. The observed crossover point is about 1600 Å. Figure 4–7 shows the limb darkening

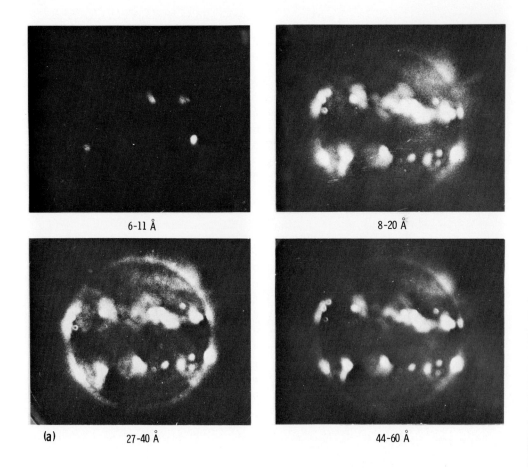

6-11 Å   8-20 Å

(a)   27-40 Å   44-60 Å

in the ultraviolet (UV) range. The range of wavelengths in the visible to infrared (IR) range is shown in figure 4–8. Limb darkening occurs for wavelengths greater than approximately 1600 Å because $\tau_\lambda = 1$ in the photosphere where the temperature gradient is negative. Because the gas is optically thick, we observe radiation from higher, cooler layers as we look toward the limb, and a relative darkening is apparent. For wavelengths less than approximately 1600 Å in the XUV range, the opposite is true. We observe radiation from higher, hotter layers at the limb and a relative brightening occurs. This same effect leads to limb brightening at radio wavelengths and will be considered in chapter 6. At X-ray wavelengths, the solar atmosphere is optically thin in the upper, hot, X-ray emitting layers (upper chromosphere and corona), but optically thick in the lower, cold, non-X-ray emitting layers (lower chromosphere and photosphere). Hence, limb brightening also occurs but is not dependent on the sign of the temperature gradient. In this case, the optical depth of emitting regions increases as we look toward the limb because more X-ray emitters and absorbers exist along our line of sight. The limb radiation

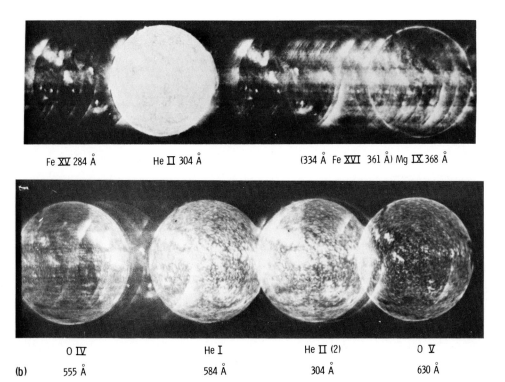

Fe XV 284 Å   He II 304 Å   (334 Å Fe XVI 361 Å) Mg IX 368 Å

O IV   He I   He II (2)   O V

(b)   555 Å   584 Å   304 Å   630 Å

FIGURE 4–6.—The sun at various wavelengths. Limb brightening and darkening can be seen in addition to the bands of solar activity. (a) X-ray photograph of the sun on October 30, 1967. (Courtesy of J. Underwood, NASA Goddard Space Flight Center.) (b) The XUV sun dispersed in wavelength. This series of overlapping solar images (taken on September 22, 1968) results from dispersing the whole solar disk in wavelength by a diffraction grating rather than dispersing just one point or a vertical slice. (Courtesy of R. Tousey, Naval Research Laboratory, U.S. Navy photograph.) (c) The solar photosphere. This photograph was taken on November 14, 1969, with a narrowband filter several angstroms from Hα line center. It closely resembles wideband white-light photographs even though it was taken in the continuum with a narrowband filter. (Courtesy of N. Christie, SPAN Observatory, MSC.)

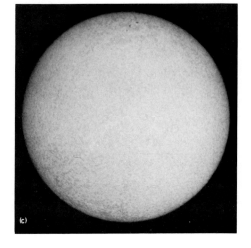

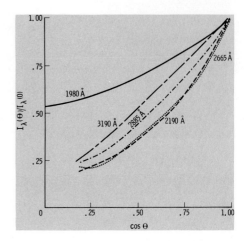

FIGURE 4–7.—Ultraviolet limb darkening.
(From Bonnet and Blamont, 1968; copyright 1968, D. Reidel.)

is therefore more intense. In fact, the number of X-ray emitters will double as we
shift our line of sight from below to above the cold, absorbing, inner atmosphere.

A relation for the temperature distribution in the atmosphere $T(\tau_\lambda)$ can be
obtained by using the source function $S_\lambda(\tau_\lambda)$ found from limb-darkening observations and calculating $S_\lambda(T)$. If LTE is assumed and S_λ is set equal to the Planck
function, $T(\tau_\lambda)$ can be obtained directly. Using these assumptions in the visible
and UV wavelengths, the family of curves of $T(\tau_\lambda)$ shown in figure 4–9(a) were
obtained. It is seen that for all of the wavelengths considered, the slopes of the

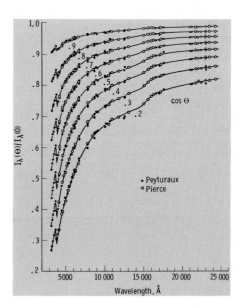

FIGURE 4–8.—Infrared limb darkening.
(From Pierce and Waddell, 1961; copyright
1961, Blackwell Scientific Publications.)

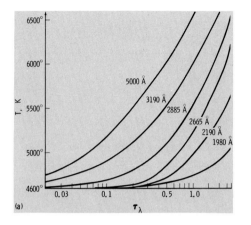
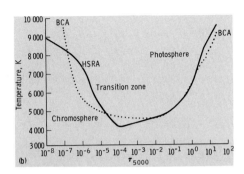

FIGURE 4–9.—Temperature versus optical depth. (*a*) Blackbody temperature versus optical depth
for several wavelengths. (From Bonnet and Blamont, 1968; copyright 1968, D. Reidel.)
(*b*) Temperature versus optical depth at 5000 Å. Relative to the BCA model, the HSRA
model has a sharper and lower temperature minimum (4170 compared to 4600 K), is hotter
in the convection zone, and tends toward a flatter temperature profile in the chromosphere.
Below the region of $\tau_{5000} \simeq 10^{-5}$, the opacity of 5000 Å, κ_{5000}, is determined by H⁻. Above
$\tau_{5000} \simeq 10^{-5}$, it is determined primarily by electron scattering. (From Gingerich et al., 1970;
copyright 1970, D. Reidel.)

curves are positive. Hence, the temperature increases as we move to greater depths,
and the radiation at sun center is more intense than at the limb. As the wavelength
decreases from 5000 to 1980 Å, the slopes of the curves decrease, and $\tau_\lambda = 1$ occurs
closer to the temperature minimum. As we move to wavelengths less than 1600 Å,
the crossover wavelength, the slopes of the curves become negative, the radiation
intensity decreases with increasing depth, and limb brightening occurs.

   In the interest of simplicity, usually only one wavelength is used for τ_λ when
specifying a height in the atmosphere, or a mean value of τ is determined by averaging τ_λ over the flux of emitted radiation. The wavelength of 5000 Å is often used
because the photosphere emission peaks near this value. A plot of T as a function
of a wide range of τ_{5000} is shown in figure 4–9 (*b*) for two different models.

   Once $T(\tau_\lambda)$ has been determined, $p(\tau_\lambda)$ can also be found. As was done in the
case of the solar interior, hydrostatic equilibrium is assumed,

$$dp = -\rho g \, dr \qquad (3–3)$$

In this case g can be assumed constant throughout the photosphere and chromosphere. Using equation (4–18), which relates the optical depth to the geometrical
depth, we obtain

$$\frac{dp}{d\tau_\lambda} = \frac{g}{\kappa_\lambda} \qquad (4–29)$$

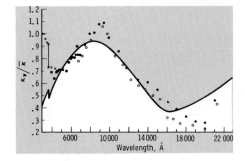

FIGURE 4–10.—Monochromatic continuous absorption coefficient of H⁻ relative to the mean absorption coefficient calculated for 5740 K. (From Chandrasekhar, 1960; copyright 1960, Dover.)

where κ_λ can be specified as a function of p and τ_λ using $T(\tau_\lambda)$. Hence, equation (4–29) can be integrated to obtain $p(\tau_\lambda)$. Returning to equation (3–3), it is seen that now all properties can be related to the geometric depth r.

The results of a recent effort to determine an atmospheric model which is consistent with our observational knowledge, the Harvard-Smithsonian Reference Atmosphere (HSRA), will be discussed shortly. First, however, we shall consider the phenomenon that gives rise to the large increase in κ_{5000} close to the surface, which was mentioned in section 3.4, was illustrated in figure 3–6, and is important in establishing the location of the photosphere.

As the temperature of the solar material is decreased to photospheric values, not only do electrons and hydrogen ions recombine to form neutral hydrogen, but electrons also attach themselves to neutral hydrogen through relatively weak bonding to form negative hydrogen ions, H⁻. This ion has a relatively large interaction probability with photons in and near the visible range as shown in figure 4–10, where $\bar{\kappa}$ is the monochromatic opacity averaged over flux. Because $p \approx g/\bar{\kappa}$ in the photosphere, the effect of a species that contributes substantially to $\bar{\kappa}$, such as H⁻, is to decrease the pressure; hence, the temperature where the photosphere occurs. The Fraunhofer lines also make a substantial contribution to $\bar{\kappa}$. It is estimated that the total line absorption is approximately 15 percent of the solar flux (Labs and Neckel, 1968). This enhanced impedance to the flow of radiation and the resulting decrease of photospheric temperature is termed the "line blanketing effect." Other contributions to $\bar{\kappa}$ in the photosphere include the bound-free absorption of neutral hydrogen, absorption by metal atoms in the UV range, and, to a lesser extent, bound-free absorption by H_2^+ molecules, also in the UV range. Rayleigh scattering (the scattering of photons by atoms and molecules which is proportional to $1/\lambda^4$) and electron scattering become important contributors to $\bar{\kappa}$ in the lower chromosphere.

4.4 THE HARVARD-SMITHSONIAN REFERENCE ATMOSPHERE

As observations throughout the spectrum become more plentiful and theoretical and computational techniques become more advanced, efforts are periodically made to compute new models of the solar atmosphere. The simplest and most widely used of these models made to date are single-stream models. These assume, as we have up to this point, that the atmosphere is static, varies only with height, and is uniform over any one horizontal plane. Although these models serve as very useful references, they are hypothetical since the real solar atmosphere contains a significant amount of nonuniform dynamic structure. The construction of an accurate multistream model is a more valid approach but has proved to be quite difficult. A recent single-stream model generated is the Harvard-Smithsonian Reference Atmosphere (HSRA) (Gingerich et al., 1971) which followed and is similar to the Bilderberg Continuum Atmosphere (BCA) (Gingerich and de Jager, 1968). The BCA model utilized accurate absolute intensity measurements made over a wide range of wavelengths in the continuum. The HSRA altered this model by using the results of more recent space observations in the UV and airborne observations in the IR as well as including NLTE hydrogen ionization. It will be seen that direct emission ($\tau_\lambda = 1$) from the region of the temperature minimum occurs in the UV at approximately 1600 Å and again in the IR at approximately 100 to 300 μm (fig. 4–15). Measurements in the UV around 1600 Å determine a blackbody temperature of less than 4000 K (Parkinson and Reeves, 1969), while observations in the IR at about 300 μm indicate a blackbody temperature of approximately 4370 K (Eddy et al., 1969). Thus, a minimum temperature considerably below the value of 4600 K of the BCA model was used in the HSRA model. The HSRA model is presented in figures 4–11 to 4–16. The ratio of helium to hydrogen by number is 0.10. The remaining composition is given by Gingerich et al. (1971), and is consistent with that specified in table 3–I. Although the HSRA and other models cannot claim to be completely accurate representations of the solar atmosphere, they do serve as focal points for furthering our understanding.

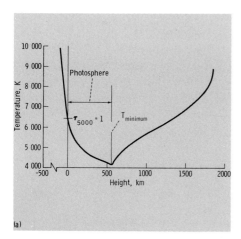
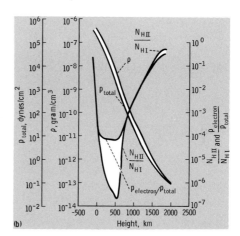

FIGURE 4–11.—Gas properties versus height (HSRA model). (a) Temperature as a function of height. (b) Pressure, density, electron pressure, and hydrogen ionization as functions of height.

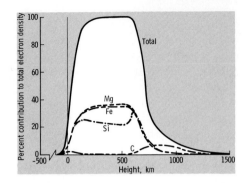

FIGURE 4–12.—Contribution of ionized metals to total electron density (HSRA model).

Figure 4–11 (a) illustrates the steepness of the temperature gradient below the temperature minimum and again above 1800 km. The region from $\tau_{5000} = 1$, where the height scale is set equal to zero, up to the temperature minimum ($h \simeq 550$ km) is defined to be the photosphere. Alternately, the photosphere could be defined as the region where most of the energy is emitted to space, approximately -50 to $+50$ km, and the region between it and the chromosphere termed the transition region. The value of the temperature minimum, 4170 K, is not well determined and must be considered an approximation. Relative to the broad BCA temperature minimum, the HSRA minimum has a pronounced inflection (fig. 4–9 (b)). Figure 4–11 (b) shows that even though the density and total pressure decrease rapidly with height, logarithms of the ratios $P_{electron}/P_{total}$ and $N_{\text{H II}}/N_{\text{H I}}$ both mimic the temperature profile. In the chromosphere and below the photosphere, the temperature is high enough that the hydrogen ionization is the dominant contrib-

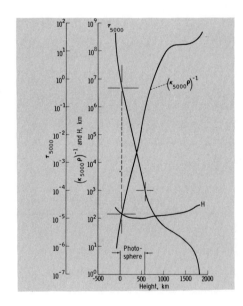

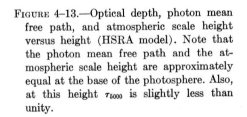

FIGURE 4–13.—Optical depth, photon mean free path, and atmospheric scale height versus height (HSRA model). Note that the photon mean free path and the atmospheric scale height are approximately equal at the base of the photosphere. Also, at this height τ_{5000} is slightly less than unity.

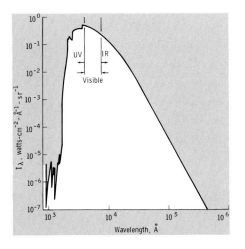

FIGURE 4–14.—Specific intensity of solar emission (HSRA model). Series limits barely detectable on this curve include the following in angstroms: 912 (H), 1100 (C), 1197 (S), 1238 (C), 1527 (Si), 1683 (Si), 1700 (Fe), 1950 (Si), 2078 (Al), 2517 (Mg), and 3646 (H).

utor to the electron density. However, in the photosphere, the relatively low temperature causes most electrons to arise from ionization of metals and $P_{electron}/P_{total} \gg N_{H\,II}/N_{H\,I}$, as illustrated. Figure 4–12, which shows the contribution to the electron density made by ionized metals, also illustrates this. It is seen that Mg, Fe, and Si are the primary contributors.

Figure 4–13 shows that the photon mean free path at 5000 Å, $(\kappa_{5000}\,\rho)^{-1}$, equals the atmospheric scale height of 135 km at +43 km where τ_{5000} is approximately unity. As indicated in the discussion at the opening of this chapter, this is to be expected. The extreme thinness of the emitting region, arising physically because of the sharp decrease in the density of H⁻, is evidenced by the drop of τ_{5000} from 2 to 1/2 in only 60 km. Also shown is the large decrease of τ_{5000} from 1 to 10^{-4} in moving up through the photosphere.

The specific intensity of the radiation emitted from sun center is shown in figure 4–14. The peak of 0.2 to 0.4 watt/cm²-Å-sr is emitted in the visible and UV

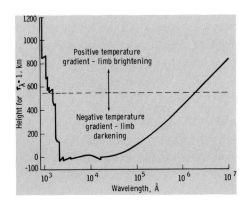

FIGURE 4–15.—Source height of continuum radiation emission (HSRA model).

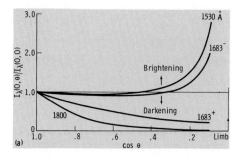

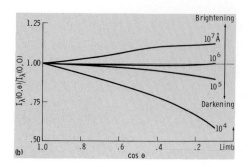

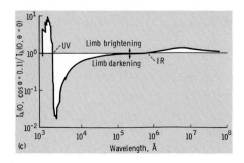

Figure 4–16.—Specific intensity as a function of wavelength and cos θ (HSRA model). (a) UV transition. (b) IR transition. (c) I_λ at cos $\theta = 0.1$.

ranges. However, the UV emission of the model (1800 to 3500 Å) is considerably above the observed emission because of the difficulties of accurately calculating the opacity in this wavelength range. In reality, the solar energy emitted in the UV range is small relative to that emitted in the visible range. The sharp discontinuities barely noticeable in the curve are series limits which will be discussed when the absorption lines are considered. Figure 4–15 is a plot of the height at which the continuum radiation of figure 4–14 is emitted ($\tau_\lambda = 1$), as a function of wavelength. Because the temperature gradient is zero at a height of 550 km, we expect limb darkening in the range of 1683 Å to approximately 2×10^6 Å (200 μm). Immediately outside of this range, we expect limb brightening as long as we are observing in the continuum. However, by observing at wavelengths of absorption or emission lines, this picture can be greatly altered. Also evident is that most of the continuum radiation from 2000 to approximately 20 000 Å is emitted from the lowest observable region of the atmosphere where $h \simeq 0$.

The variation of I_λ with distance from sun center is shown for the darkening/brightening transitions in the UV and IR in figures 4–16 (a) and 4–16 (b), respectively. The pronounced transition at 1683 Å is due to a series cutoff of silicon. Figure 4–16 (c) shows the value of I_λ at cos $\theta = 0.1$ (84.26°), normalized by the value at sun center as a function of wavelength. The ranges of limb darkening and brightening are evident.

4.5 ABSORPTION LINE FORMATION

Up to this point, we have considered only the continuum radiation emitted by the photosphere. The only discontinuities in the intensity-versus-wavelength curve so far mentioned occur at series cutoffs as illustrated in figure 4–14. However, in the observed spectrum there are many absorption lines called Fraunhofer lines that appear as sharp, narrow dips in intensity (figs. 4–17 and 4–18). A list of the strongest of these lines is given in appendix A. From comparison of the theory and the observations of continuum limb darkening, one is able to deduce only the averaged atmospheric structure. That is, the variations with height of the density, the temperature, and the continuous absorption coefficient $\rho \kappa_\lambda$ are determined. On the other hand, the Fraunhofer lines yield a wealth of detailed information on the solar atmosphere including its temperature, pressure, dynamic state, chemical composition, and the local value of the magnetic field. The price of all this extra information is, of course, a greatly complicated problem of interpretation. In most cases, to account accurately for a line profile, the heterogeneous, dynamic, NLTE character of the atmosphere must be taken into account. Also, because of the narrowness of the lines, stringent requirements are usually placed on the spectral resolution of the observations. The art of acquiring and interpreting the immense amount of information available to us in the Fraunhofer line profiles is in a stage of rapid development.

Basic Atomic Concepts

The preference of an atom or ion to absorb and emit radiation at discrete wavelengths is primarily responsible for the formation of Fraunhofer lines. This preference will now be explored by briefly discussing some of the basic concepts of atomic physics from a strictly classical viewpoint. The application to Fraunhofer line formation will follow.

The simplest atom to consider and, conveniently, the one which is the most abundant in the solar atmosphere is hydrogen. The discrete or quantized energy levels which are available to the one electron in motion about a proton can be pictured graphically as those corresponding to particular circular orbits as shown in figure 4–19. In general, the actual trajectories can be elliptical but must have the same energy as one of the circular trajectories. The requirement of quantized energy levels that must be imposed is expressed by the Wilson-Sommerfield quantization rule: The phase integral of any variable over a complete cycle of motion is equal to an integer times h, Planck's constant. For the case at hand, this yields

$$\int P_r \, dr = n_r h \qquad \int P_\theta \, d\theta = n_\theta h \qquad \text{and} \qquad \int P_\phi \, d\phi = n_\phi h \qquad (4\text{–}30)$$

Here r, θ, and ϕ refer to the coordinates of a spherical coordinate system; P_r is the linear momentum corresponding to r; P_θ and P_ϕ are the angular momenta corresponding to θ and ϕ, respectively; and n_r, n_θ, and n_ϕ are integers $(0, 1, 2, \ldots)$ which are called the quantum numbers and specify the energy and geometry of the most

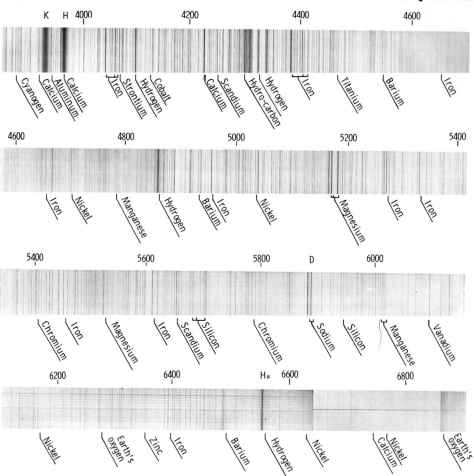

FIGURE 4–17.—The Fraunhofer spectrum. (a) The visible range. (Courtesy of H. Zirin, Mount Wilson and Palomar Observatories.)

probable electron orbits (fig. 4–20). The total energy of an orbit is specified by the total quantum number $n \equiv n_r + n_\theta + n_\phi$, which has the meaning conveyed simply in figure 4–19. That is, n specifies the electron shell. The extent to which the orbit is elliptical is given by the azimuthal quantum number defined by $l + 1 \equiv n_\theta + n_\phi$. Lastly, the extent to which the orbital angular momentum projects onto the arbitrarily chosen z axis is given by the magnetic quantum number $m \equiv n_\phi$. When one specifies the energy level n, it is understood that this level actually contains a number of unique states depending upon the values of l and m. It can be shown that for a given value of n, there are n possible values of l; $2l + 1$ possible values of $\pm m$; and, therefore, a total of n^2 possible states. In addition, an electron itself can have two possible energy states for any given set of n, l, and m by virtue of its

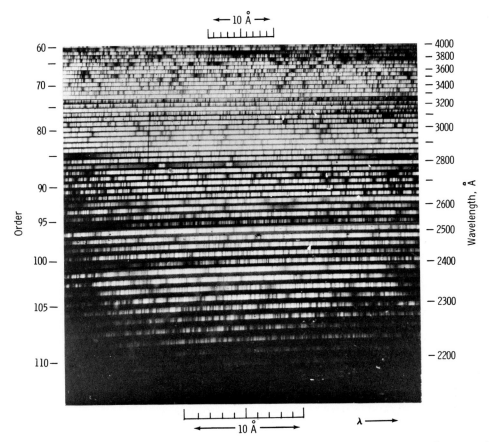

FIGURE 4–17 (concluded).—The Fraunhofer spectrum. (b) The ultraviolet range. (Courtesy of R. Tousey, Naval Research Laboratory, U.S. Navy photograph from an Aerobee-Hi rocket.)

own internal angular momentum or spin (spin plus or spin minus). Thus, there actually are $2n^2$ possible states for each n. This existence of several states with equal energies is termed "degeneracy." A degenerate level splits into observationally different states when an atom is perturbed by internally or by externally produced electromagnetic fields.

The possible energy of electron shells and the transitions that can occur between them are shown for hydrogen in figure 4–21, where the energy levels are given by $E_n = 13.59[1 - (1/n^2)]$ electron volts (eV). Thus, the preference of an atom to absorb energy at discrete wavelengths can be explained in terms of transitions between the quantized energies of different shells. For example, when Hα radiation, 6563 Å, falls on a hydrogen atom with an electron in the second shell ($n=2$), the atom can absorb a photon of energy hc/λ_{6563}, and a transition occurs to the third shell ($n=3$). The probability of a 6563-Å photon being absorbed in this manner is

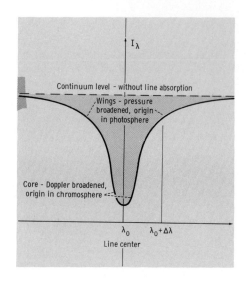

FIGURE 4–18.—Nomenclature for an absorption line profile.

proportional to the absorption "cross section," which is the effective area of an
atom for capturing the free photon, and to the number density of hydrogen atoms
with an electron in the second shell. Thus, when most atoms are in the first shell
($n=1$), absorption by the Lyman series will predominate. As the upper shells
become more populated, the Balmer, Paschen, and Brackett series will become
important, in that order. It is obvious now why Hα has been used so extensively
in earthbound solar observations; it is the strongest line in the visible spectrum of
the most abundant element. The series limit encountered in the continuous spectrum
(fig. 4–14) is also explained in terms of figure 4–21. For example, looking at the
Balmer limit, 3646 Å, it is seen that a hydrogen atom with an electron in the second
shell can absorb radiation of shorter wavelengths by ejecting an electron into the
continuum of shells above $n \to \infty$. Practically, $n \to \infty$ does not correspond to an
infinite orbital radius but to a distance from the nucleus where external electrostatic

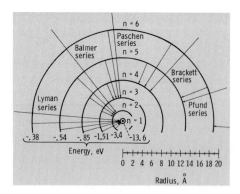

FIGURE 4–19.—Series of radiative transitions
for the hydrogen atom.

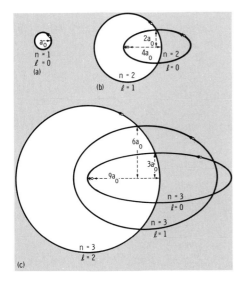

FIGURE 4–20.—Most probable electron orbits for hydrogen. (Pauling and Wilson, 1935; copyright 1935, McGraw-Hill.)

fields produced by other particles are of comparable magnitude to the field of the atom. As the energy corresponding to 3646 Å is approached from above, or the wavelength 3646 Å is approached from below, the probability of photon absorption increases. Then, in moving across the limit to energies less than this limit, the probability of an absorption of this type drops to zero and the discontinuous jump in radiation intensity occurs.

Basic Line Formation Concepts

To understand how the discrete character of the Fraunhofer absorption lines arises, it is essential to understand why these lines do not appear in emission rather than absorption. An atom which has a strong preference for absorbing a photon by changing its state from u to l should have a correspondingly strong preference for emission of the same energy photon by dropping back down from state l to u. The explanation lies in the fact that most Fraunhofer lines in the visible spectrum are formed primarily in the photosphere where the temperature gradient is negative. The cores of the lines are formed higher in the atmosphere than the wings and nearby continuum where the temperature, and thus the emission, is relatively low. Conversely, below 1600 Å lines are formed above the photosphere where the temperature gradient is positive and they are seen in emission rather than in absorption. This simple explanation is adequate as a generalization but, since the atmosphere above the photosphere is in NLTE where the radiation and kinetic temperatures can greatly differ, line formation above the photosphere requires a more thorough analysis. A concept once used to interpret the absorption lines is that of a reversing layer. It was assumed that a continuous spectrum was emitted lower in the photosphere and that preferential absorption at the Fraunhofer lines occurred higher up in a reversing layer where the temperature was lower. In reality, there are not two

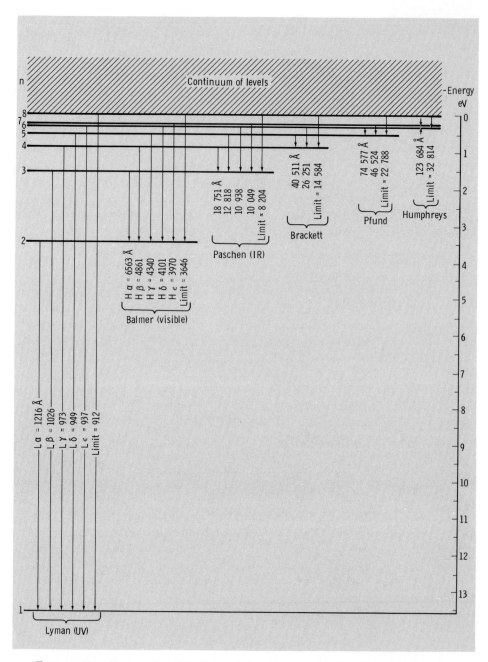

FIGURE 4–21.—Energy of shells and transitions between them for the hydrogen atom.

distinct layers. The absorption coefficient in a line is greater than in the nearby continuum. Thus, an optical depth of unity at line center occurs higher in the photosphere and the resulting radiation is of lower intensity than in the neighboring continuum, which receives the major contribution to its intensity from lower hotter regions.

At present, a major method of extracting information from Fraunhofer lines is to study the variation of the shape of a line while scanning from sun center to the limb. Center-to-limb scans are complicated, however, by the lack of LTE at higher levels and by quiet-sun inhomogeneities such as granulation and the chromosphere network, which introduce nonlinear effects. Also contributing to the complexity are inhomogeneities arising from active-sun features, such as plage remnants, which cannot always be excluded. Another useful method is the observation of actual line profiles and comparison with theoretical predictions.

Our discussion of Fraunhofer lines will now turn to the manner in which their formation can be described using our previously developed equation of radiative transfer. Equation (4–7) can now be written so that the contribution to absorption and emission of both a line and the continuum are explicit

$$\frac{\cos\theta}{\rho}\frac{dI_\lambda}{dr} = -(\kappa_\lambda{}^l+\kappa_\lambda{}^c)I_\lambda + (j_\lambda{}^l+j_\lambda{}^c) \qquad (4\text{–}31)$$

where the superscripts l and c refer to line and the neighboring continuum, respectively. We can quickly arrive at the solution as before

$$I_\lambda(0,\theta) = \int_0^\infty S_\lambda(\tau_\lambda)\exp\left[-(\tau_\lambda/\cos\theta)\right]\frac{d\tau_\lambda}{\cos\theta} \qquad (4\text{–}25)$$

but here,

$$d\tau_\lambda = -(\kappa_\lambda{}^l+\kappa_\lambda{}^c)\rho\,dr \qquad (4\text{–}32)$$

and

$$S_\lambda = \frac{j_\lambda{}^l+j_\lambda{}^c}{\kappa_\lambda{}^l+\kappa_\lambda{}^c} \qquad (4\text{–}33)$$

However, it is more useful to separate the continuum and line contributions and arrive at the following

$$\cos\theta\,\frac{dI_\lambda}{d\tau_\lambda{}^c} = (1+\eta_\lambda)I_\lambda - (S_\lambda{}^c+\eta_\lambda S_\lambda{}^l) \qquad (4\text{–}34)$$

where

$$\eta_\lambda = \frac{\kappa_\lambda{}^l}{\kappa_\lambda{}^c} \qquad (4\text{–}35)$$

$$d\tau_\lambda{}^c = -\kappa_\lambda{}^c\rho\,dr \qquad (4\text{–}36)$$

and

$$S_\lambda{}^c = \frac{j_\lambda{}^c}{\kappa_\lambda{}^c} \qquad S_\lambda{}^l = \frac{j_\lambda{}^l}{\kappa_\lambda{}^l} \qquad (4\text{–}37)$$

The solution is

$$I_\lambda(0, \theta) = \int_0^\infty (S_\lambda{}^c + \eta_\lambda S_\lambda{}^l) \exp\left\{-\int_0^{\tau_\lambda{}^c} [1 + \eta_\lambda(t)] \frac{dt}{\cos\theta}\right\} \frac{d\tau_\lambda{}^c}{\cos\theta} \qquad (4\text{--}38)$$

where t is a dummy variable of integration. From this solution, it is seen that if $S_\lambda{}^c(\tau_\lambda{}^c)$, $S_\lambda{}^l(\tau_\lambda{}^c)$, and $\eta_\lambda(\tau_\lambda{}^c)$ are known over the whole line, center-to-limb variations and line profiles can be predicted. However, here our knowledge is lacking. The relative weighting of all the possible line emission and absorption mechanisms to be used in arriving at the correct expression for $S_\lambda{}^l(\tau_\lambda{}^c)$ is still an unsolved problem. Also, errors encountered in the solution for a continuum model atmosphere like the HSRA directly contribute to errors here because this model or a similar one is usually used as a starting point. The correct chemical composition and the variation with depth of the density, temperature, and continuum absorption and emission coefficients must be known initially. The problem of specifying the line emission and absorption coefficients and, in particular, the line source function $S_\lambda{}^l$, will now be discussed from a physical standpoint.

Line Source Function

To generalize, let us examine an atom in its ground level and try to determine how it gets into an excited level so that it can emit radiation by dropping back down to a level of lower energy. In essence, there are two ways: collisions with other particles and collisions with photons (figs. 4–22(a) and 4–22(b)). In the case of a particle collision, the colliding particle gives up the energy (usually part of its translational kinetic energy) required to raise the atom to an excited level. Electrons

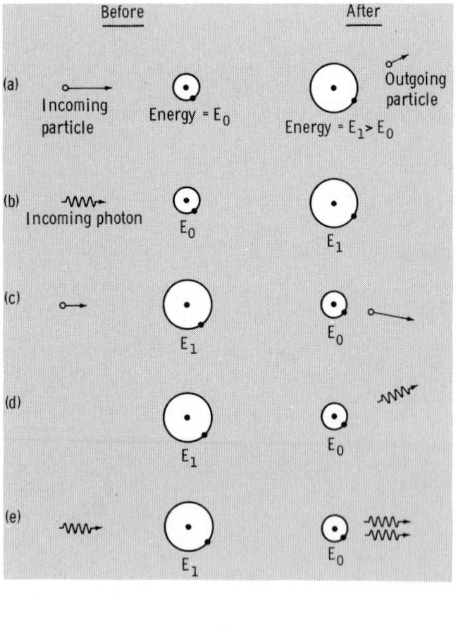

FIGURE 4–22.—Modes of energy level change for bound electrons. (a) Particle excitation. (b) Photon excitation. (c) Particle deexcitation. (d) Spontaneous emission. (e) Induced emission; outgoing photons move in same direction and in phase.

are by far the most efficient particles for exciting an atom by collision and, unless the electron density is relatively low, the random kinetic energy available in the electron gas, specified by T_e, determines the degree of excitation of each atomic species. In the case of a photon collision, the photon energy, unlike the energies of colliding particles, must be the same as the difference between the energies of the upper and lower levels.

The manner in which an excited atom can drop back to a lower level is now easily understood as just the reverse of the above means of excitation (figs. 4–22 (c), 4–22 (d), and 4–22 (e)). A superelastic collision, sometimes called a collision of the second kind, is one in which an atom in an excited level drops to a lower level by releasing the energy difference to another particle through a collision. Thus, the kinetic energy of the colliding particle is higher after the collision than before, and the energy of the excited level is not added to the radiation field but remains in the gas. Just the opposite is true in the second means of deexcitation. The excited atom drops down by the emission of a photon, either spontaneously (not in response to external stimuli) after a small period at the excited level, usually 10^{-8} to 10^{-7} sec, or after being induced or stimulated by radiation at the wavelength corresponding to the transition. The latter process is sometimes called negative absorption. When many atoms are considered, spontaneous emission is isotropic; that is, the photons have an equal probability of being emitted in any given direction. On the other hand, when an incoming photon stimulates emission from an atom in an excited level, the emitted photon will be identical to the incoming one in both phase and direction. In LTE, the ratio of spontaneous to stimulated emission is $[\exp (hc/\lambda kT) - 1]$; if $T = 6000$ K, $hc/\lambda kT = 1$ at $\lambda = 24\,000$ Å. Hence, in the photosphere, stimulated emission will only be important for wavelengths in the intermediate infrared range and longer.

We return now to consideration of the line source function, $S_\lambda{}^l$. When an incoming photon is absorbed by an atom, which then reemits a photon of the same wavelength but in a different direction (figs. 4–22 (b) and 4–22 (d)), the radiation is said to be coherently scattered. The only function the atom performs is to randomly alter the photon's direction but not its wavelength. The same function can also be performed directly by free electrons. However, the presence of continuous absorption (by H^- for example) means that photons at a line wavelength eventually will be absorbed and reemitted at another wavelength while being scattered many times and traveling long distances. This reemission is most likely to occur in the continuum. Hence, radiant energy at the wavelength corresponding to each line is shifted into the continuum as it diffuses radially outward and a dark absorption line is produced. Assuming that the scattering is done isotropically and letting $(1 - \bar\varepsilon)$ represent the fraction of absorbed radiation that is scattered, the line emission coefficient is given by

$$j_\lambda{}^l = \frac{1 - \bar\varepsilon}{4\pi} \int_{4\pi} \kappa_\lambda{}^l \mathbf{I}_\lambda (\boldsymbol{\omega}) \cdot d\boldsymbol{\omega} \qquad (4\text{–}39)$$

and the source function by

$$S_\lambda{}^l = (1-\bar{\epsilon})J_\lambda \tag{4-40}$$

where J_λ is defined by equation (4-3).

In considering coherent absorption, we have neglected the fact that a line is not infinitely thin. This broadening results from a combination of natural broadening caused by the natural uncertainty in atomic-energy levels, Doppler broadening caused by the random thermal motions of the atoms, and pressure broadening caused by the shift of atomic-energy levels by the electric fields of surrounding particles. These mechanisms will be considered in the next section. Radiation which is absorbed at one point in the line profile can now be reemitted at another and a random redistribution of photons over the line profile will occur (fig. 4-23). The rate of radiant energy emission in a line can still be equated to the fraction of the energy absorbed, but only when the total line profile is considered and not just each point within it. Thus, integrating equation (4-39) over a wavelength range that is defined to be much larger than the line width, λ^- to λ^+, the following is obtained:

$$\int_{\lambda^-}^{\lambda^+} j_\lambda{}^l \, d\lambda = \frac{(1-\bar{\epsilon})}{4\pi} \int_{\lambda^-}^{\lambda^+} \kappa_\lambda{}^l \, d\lambda \int_{4\pi} \mathbf{I}_\lambda(\boldsymbol{\omega}) \cdot d\boldsymbol{\omega} \tag{4-41}$$

It can usually be assumed that the reemitted radiation is proportional to that absorbed at any wavelength; that is, $j_\lambda{}^l/\kappa_\lambda{}^l$ is independent of wavelength. The source function resulting from scattering can then be obtained from equation (4-41).

$$S_\lambda{}^l = (1-\bar{\epsilon}) \langle J_\lambda \rangle \tag{4-42}$$

where

$$\langle J_\lambda \rangle = \frac{\displaystyle\int_{\lambda^-}^{\lambda^+} J_\lambda \kappa_\lambda{}^l \, d\lambda}{\displaystyle\int_{\lambda^-}^{\lambda^+} \kappa_\lambda{}^l \, d\lambda} \tag{4-43}$$

After an atom in an initial ground or excited level absorbs a photon and arrives at a higher level of excitation, there are many alternatives to direct return to its initial state by the reemission of a photon, the process we have called scattering. A superelastic collision could occur and the absorbed energy would be given up to the gas. Second, the atom could decrease its energy by spontaneous emission to a level of excitation that could be above or below its initial level. If there are many available levels closely spaced, a cascading downward through these levels could occur. Alternatively, the atom could be excited to higher levels, or even ionized, by further collision with other particles (probably electrons). In this way a mixing or energy exchange takes place between the atomic levels of excitation and the electron gas. The net result of a complete mixing is that the atomic levels are populated according to a Boltzmann distribution (eq. (4-17)) at the electron

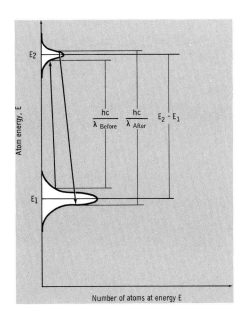

FIGURE 4–23.—Doppler broadening. E_1 and E_2 are two energy levels of an atom as measured directly from the energy of an emitted or absorbed photon by an observer at rest. They are broadened by the random thermal motions of the atoms. Thus, the wavelength corresponding to $E_2 - E_1$ is also broadening and a photon absorbed at one point in the line profile can be reemitted in another as shown.

kinetic temperature T_e, and the absorption and emission of radiation correspond to the Planck function at T_e

$$S_\lambda{}^l = B_\lambda(T_e) \tag{4-44}$$

In contrast to scattering, this type of interaction of photons with particles is termed "absorption."

Returning to our description of radiation transfer (eq. (4–34)), we assume that the scattering is noncoherent and contributes the fraction $(1-\bar\epsilon)$ to the line source function, that absorption contributes the fraction $\bar\epsilon$, and that the source function for the nearby continuum also is governed by LTE at T_e. We thereby obtain

$$\cos\theta\,\frac{dI_\lambda}{d\tau_\lambda{}^c} = (1+\eta_\lambda)I_\lambda - (1-\bar\epsilon)\eta_\lambda\langle J_\lambda\rangle - (1+\bar\epsilon\eta_\lambda)B_\lambda(T_e) \tag{4-45}$$

| Rate of change with the optical depth of the nearby continuum | Absorption by continuum and line | Effective emission from scattered photons | Emission in LTE at T_e from continuum and line absorption and reemission |

Analytical solutions to this equation have been obtained with a variety of further assumptions: $\bar\epsilon=0$, $\bar\epsilon=1$, $\eta_\lambda=$ constant, or $\eta_\lambda=$ constant plus small variation. In most cases, however, numerical methods must be used to arrive at a solution. With regard to the accuracy of these solutions, it should be noted that NLTE effects are only crudely included in the scattering term. This has made possible a great simplification in the analysis and is sufficient in the lower photosphere. However, when the major contribution to I_λ comes from above this region, the procedure is incorrect and NLTE effects must be fully analyzed.

Equivalent Widths

Although a great deal of information is contained in the details of absorption line profiles, measurements of only the overall absorption strength or of the equivalent width have yielded significant results, primarily in the areas of element abundance determinations and of analysis of line-broadening mechanisms. The equivalent width W is defined as the relative amount of radiation subtracted from the continuum by the line in wavelength units (fig. 4–24).

$$W \equiv \int_{\lambda_0^-}^{\lambda_0^+} \left(1 - \frac{I_\lambda}{I_\lambda^c}\right) d\lambda \qquad (4\text{–}46)$$

Because the rate of absorption per unit volume is proportional to $\rho\kappa_\lambda{}^l$ at a line, one would expect W to increase in a continuous way with the number density of species responsible for that line. This effect on the profile of the absorption line 3934 Å (K line of Ca II) is shown in figure 4–25 (a). Here, $\underline{N}$ is the number of absorbing atoms per unit area along the line of sight above the photosphere. Another factor which affects W in the same way as $\underline{N}$ is the atomic oscillator strength f. Essentially, f is the effective number of electrons per atom that can oscillate or absorb radiation energy at the line wavelength by undergoing a transition from one level to another. The quantity f need not be an integer, but when the f's are added together for all possible atomic transitions between all possible atomic states, the total should be equal to the number of optically active electrons in the atom. Thus, the significant

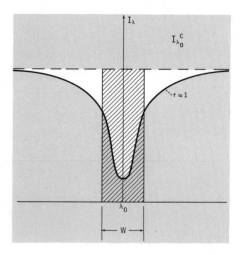

FIGURE 4–24.—Equivalent width. The equivalent width W is defined as that width, in units of wavelength, which takes out the same amount of flux as does the line integrated over its entire profile.

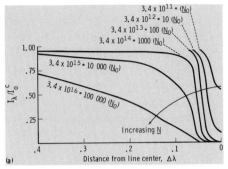

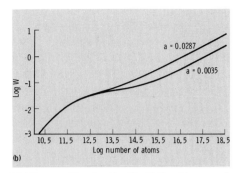

FIGURE 4-25.—Line profiles and curves of growth. (a) Line profiles for the Ca K line for several Ca II number densities per unit area along the line of sight. For $N_0 = 3.4 \times 10^{11}$, $\tau_\lambda = 1$ at the center of the line. These profiles were calculated assuming a uniform absorbing layer, a constant source function, and using Doppler and natural as the only two broadening mechanisms operative. For low optical depths, the profile is determined by Doppler broadening. For large optical depths, the core is saturated and natural broadening controls the profile. (From Aller, 1963; copyright 1963, Ronald Press.) (b) Curve of growth for the Ca K line. This curve, made by integrating the profiles of 4-25 (a), is determined by Doppler broadening at the low end and natural broadening at the high end. The parameter a is proportional to the ratio of the combined natural and impact broadening to the Doppler broadening. (See eqs. (4-65) and (4-73).)

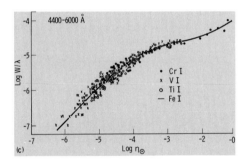

FIGURE 4-25 (concluded).—Line profiles and curves of growth. (c) A curve of growth from normalized observed data for the iron group. (From Warner, 1964; copyright 1964, Blackwell Scientific Publications.)

parameter for determining W is Nf, not simply N. When Nf is small, so that the optical depth at the line center is much less than unity, W will be proportional to Nf. As Nf becomes large, the rate of increase of the optical depth at the line center decreases, the absorption far from the line center becomes appreciable, and pronounced wings begin to appear. Even though the optical depth at the line center becomes as high as 10^4, the optical depth will be approximately unity at those parts of the line producing the major increases in the value of W. At the center of a strong line, we observe the radiation originating high in the atmosphere. Correspondingly, as we observe farther out into the wings, we see farther down and closer to the height at which the continuum originates. Eventually, as Nf becomes very large, W will vary only as $(Nf)^{1/2}$. It is important to note that there is a definite difference between broadening of an observed line by a high abundance, sometimes called abundance broadening, and broadening caused by changing the physical environment of the absorbers. The growth in line strength resulting from increases in the number of absorbers is seen in a plot of W versus $\underline{N}f$, which is termed a curve of growth, in figure 4–25(b). Of course, for each line in the solar spectrum, we obtain only one value of W by observation because we cannot vary $\underline{N}f$. To obtain a curve from observational data, we must look at many lines of one element, or of several similar elements, and divide out the effects of the atomic and atmospheric parameters that differ for each line. A curve resulting from data normalized in this way is shown in figure 4–25(c). The actual details of such a curve of growth are determined by the mechanisms which produce the broadening of the line. These mechanisms will now be considered.

4.6 LINE BROADENING

In contrast to the changes in line profile caused by changes in the number density of the absorbing species, the line-broadening mechanisms we now consider are peculiar to the atom itself. These mechanisms are either an inherent property of the atom (natural broadening), a result of its state of motion (Doppler broadening), or a result of a perturbation of its energy states by surrounding particles (pressure broadening). A knowledge of the details of these line-broadening mechanisms will enable us to determine kinetic temperature, densities, and velocities within the solar atmosphere from observations of the line strengths and profiles. More detailed discussions of line broadening are found in Aller (1963), Griem (1964), and Jefferies (1968).

When discussing broadening on the atomic scale, it is natural to work with an atomic absorption coefficient, a_λ, which is the effective cross-sectional size for absorption of an atom as "seen" by a photon of wavelength λ. It is related to κ_λ by

$$N_{\lambda_0} a_\lambda = \rho \kappa_\lambda \qquad (4\text{--}47)$$

where N_{λ_0} is the number density of atoms capable of absorbing radiation in the line centered at λ_0. We are ultimately interested in both S_λ and τ_λ in order to compute I_λ and compare it with observed values. In the case of LTE, S_λ and N_{λ_0} are determined simply by equilibrium relations (the Planck function, the Saha equation, and the Boltzmann factor), but τ_λ depends upon the details of the line strength and the profile expressed in a_λ. For NLTE, S_λ and N_{λ_0} can be determined easily only in a few limiting cases which will be discussed in section 4.8.

Natural Broadening

When an atom is at rest relative to the observer and experiences no external electromagnetic fields, the atomic absorption coefficient is described by a dispersion profile

$$a_\lambda = \pi r_0 \lambda_0^2 f \; \frac{\Delta\lambda_N}{4\pi^2 (\lambda - \lambda_0)^2 + \left(\dfrac{\Delta\lambda_N}{2}\right)^2} \qquad (4\text{--}48)$$

where r_0 is the classical radius of an electron $(e^2/4\pi\epsilon_0 mc^2 = 2.82 \times 10^{-5}$ Å$)$, λ_0 is the wavelength at line center, $\Delta\lambda_N$ is the natural width of the line, and the assumption has been made that $\Delta\lambda_N/\lambda_0 \ll 1$. The atomic oscillator strength f, termed the absorption f value, is effectively the number of classical oscillators that are required to give the same absorption as the atom-absorbing radiation centered at wavelength λ_0. It is the same quantity introduced when discussing equivalent width. For example, the oscillator strengths for the first six members of the Balmer series are (Griem, 1964) as follows:

$$H\alpha = 0.6408 \qquad H\beta = 0.1193 \qquad H\gamma = 0.0447$$

$$H\delta = 0.0221 \qquad H\epsilon = 0.0127 \qquad H\zeta = 0.0080$$

The rapid decrease of the f values that occurs as we go toward the higher members of all the hydrogenlike series is evident here. The importance of f in specifying line strength is illustrated by the expression for the total amount of absorption by an atom from a beam of radiation of unit intensity.

$$\int_0^\infty a_\lambda \, d\lambda = \pi\lambda_0^2 r_0 f \qquad (4\text{--}49)$$

Thus, the total absorption is directly proportional to λ_0^2 and to the oscillator strength f, but is not dependent on the natural width or on other atomic parameters.

According to the quantum-mechanical picture of a transition, a photon has precise energy, but the energy of the two states involved in the transition are to a small degree indefinite. If the atom has a long lifetime in a given state before transitioning to a lower one by spontaneous emission, we can determine the energy of that state very accurately. Conversely, if the lifetime is short, knowledge of its state is more indefinite. The fundamental constant that fixes the limit to which the energy of a state is defined is Planck's constant, h.

$$\Delta E \, \Delta t \geq h \qquad (4\text{--}50)$$

where ΔE is the uncertainty in the energy of the state and Δt is the state's characteristic lifetime. In a transition, the uncertainty in wavelength or natural width is

$$\Delta\lambda_N = \frac{\lambda_0^2}{hc} \Delta E = \frac{\lambda_0^2}{c}\left(\frac{1}{\Delta t_{\text{upper}}} + \frac{1}{\Delta t_{\text{lower}}}\right) \qquad (4\text{--}51)$$

Thus, long lifetimes lead to small natural widths. At line center, the atomic absorption coefficient is

$$a_{\lambda_0} = 4\pi r_0 \lambda_0^2 f/\Delta\lambda_N \qquad (4\text{--}52)$$

Even though the total absorption over a line profile is a constant, the absorption at line center is inversely proportional to the natural width. At line center, long lifetimes lead to increased probability of absorption per atom. For a wavelength of 5500 Å and a realistic value of 10^{-8} sec for the combined lifetime of the upper and lower states, $\Delta\lambda_N = 10^{-3}$ Å and $a_\lambda = f \times 10^{-9}$ cm^2. As we will see shortly, this width is very small, relative to other widths. In fact, natural broadening is usually overwhelmed by other broadening mechanisms operating in the solar atmosphere even though it is of fundamental importance in understanding atomic structure.

Doppler Broadening

From the standpoint of learning about solar atmospheric dynamics and kinetic temperatures, Doppler broadening is the most useful line-broadening mechanism. Our ability to determine kinetic temperatures is dependent upon our knowledge of the velocity distribution of the absorbing and emitting particles. In the case of LTE, this distribution can be specified in a relatively simple manner. The Boltzmann factor (eq. (4–17)) is applicable to the translational degrees of freedom of the particles. A particle's energy state is specified by the speed v, and is equal in magnitude to $mv^2/2$, where m is the particle's mass. The statistical weight of a state, appearing in equation (4–17), is proportional to the number of velocity states available to a particle of total speed v in a three-dimensional velocity space. That is, the statistical weight is proportional to the volume of a spherical shell of radius v and thickness dv, $4\pi v^2\, dv$. Thus, the fraction of the particles with a speed between v and $v+dv$, $f(v)\, dv$, is

$$f(v)\, dv = \text{constant} \times \exp\,(-mv^2/2kT)4\pi v^2\, dv \tag{4–53}$$

where T is the kinetic temperature. The constant is determined by the condition

$$\int_0^\infty f(v)\, dv = 1 \tag{4–54}$$

Thus, $f(v)$, termed the Maxwellian distribution of velocities, is

$$f(v) = 4\pi v^2 \left(\frac{m}{2\pi kT}\right)^{3/2} \exp\,(-mv^2/2kT) \tag{4–55}$$

The dependence of $f(v)$ on v produces a distribution that is peaked at a speed V_0, the most probable speed. It is determined from the condition $df/dv = 0$.

$$V_0 = \left(\frac{2kT}{m}\right)^{1/2} \tag{4–56}$$

Because particles of equal mass equilibrate their energy readily during only a few collisions, it is almost always safe to assume that the random motions of particles below the solar corona follow the Maxwellian distribution law and can be characterized by a kinetic temperature T.

To determine the amount of line broadening from particle motion, we must consider the distribution of velocities along only one direction, $f_1(v_1)$. For this case, the energy corresponding to one degree of freedom is $1/2mv_1^2$, where v_1 is the velocity along only one axis of a three-dimensional Cartesian coordinate system. The statistical weight or number of velocity states available between v_1 and v_1+dv_1 is independent of v_1. Thus, $f_1(v_1)$, normalized to unity, is

$$f_1(v_1) = \frac{1}{V_0\sqrt{\pi}} \exp\left[-(v/V_0)^2\right] \qquad (4\text{-}57)$$

To relate this distribution to the broadening of a line, we note that if a radiating source is moving toward an observer, the wavelengths will be crowded together or shortened according to

$$\frac{\Delta\lambda}{\lambda_0} = -\frac{v_1}{c} \qquad (4\text{-}58)$$

Thus, the shift is to shorter wavelengths or toward the blue. Correspondingly, if the source and observer are moving away from one another, the shift is toward the red. Combining these last two relations yields $f_1(\Delta\lambda)\, d(\Delta\lambda)$, the probability of a wavelength shift from line center between $\Delta\lambda$ and $\Delta\lambda + d(\Delta\lambda)$

$$f_1(\Delta\lambda)\, d(\Delta\lambda) = \frac{1}{\Delta\lambda_D\sqrt{\pi}} \exp\left[-(\Delta\lambda/\Delta\lambda_D)^2\right] d(\Delta\lambda) \qquad (4\text{-}59)$$

where $\Delta\lambda_D$ is the Doppler width and is characteristic of the width of the broadening

$$\Delta\lambda_D = \lambda_0 V_0/c \qquad (4\text{-}60)$$

This is the line profile we would observe if Doppler were the only broadening mechanism operative. Because $V_0 \sim T^{1/2}$, a measurement of the Doppler width will yield a measure of the kinetic temperature of the emitting or absorbing particles in the region of line formation.

In addition to thermal motions, turbulence in the region of line formation could give a similar broadening. If the scale of the line-forming region is much larger than the scale of the turbulence, each cell of moving gas produces wavelength shifts in the same way as a moving particle. In fact, the broadening caused by turbulence is sometimes assumed to be analogous to that caused by thermal motions. It is crudely taken into account by assuming the distribution of turbulent velocities to be Maxwellian and redefining V_0 so that

$$V_0{}^2 = \frac{2kT}{m} + (V_{\text{turbulent}})^2 \qquad (4\text{-}61)$$

Because V_0 is a function of the mass m of the absorbing or emitting atom, the determination of the Doppler widths of lines from different atomic elements should allow the separation of the thermal and turbulence contributions. In the cases where the velocity is nearly uniform over both the depth of the line-forming region and the smallest spatially resolved area, individual motions can be resolved and a line will be shifted rather than broadened. For example, if mass is ejected toward an observer at 1000 km/sec, as in a fast-moving spray, all wavelengths will be shifted toward the blue by $\Delta\lambda/\lambda = 1/300$ (about 22 Å for Hα). The motion caused by solar rotation will produce shifts of $\Delta\lambda/\lambda = \pm 6.0 \times 10^{-6}$ (± 0.04 Å for Hα) at the solar equatorial limbs. Lastly, the motion of an observer in low-earth orbit would also induce shifts, but of magnitude $\Delta\lambda/\lambda = \pm 2.6 \times 10^{-5}$ (± 0.17 Å for Hα) at the earth's terminators.

Because the natural- and Doppler-broadening mechanisms operate simultaneously, the description of the line profile should include their combined effect. The atomic absorption coefficient for an observer at rest and for only one value of Doppler shift $\Delta\lambda$ is

$$a_\lambda(\lambda+\Delta\lambda) = \pi r_0 \lambda_0^2 f \frac{\Delta\lambda_N}{4\pi^2(\lambda+\Delta\lambda-\lambda_0)^2+(\Delta\lambda_N/2)^2} \tag{4-62}$$

The effect of all possible Doppler shifts is included by multiplying the natural-broadening absorption coefficient $a_\lambda(\lambda+\Delta\lambda)$ by the probability of a shift of $\Delta\lambda$, $f_1(\Delta\lambda)$, and by integrating over all $\Delta\lambda$.

$$a_\lambda^{ND}(\lambda) = \int_{-\infty}^{+\infty} a_\lambda(\lambda+\Delta\lambda) f_1(\Delta\lambda)\, d(\Delta\lambda) \tag{4-63}$$

where $a_\lambda^{ND}(\lambda)$ is the atomic absorption coefficient resulting from the combined effect of natural and Doppler broadening. The lower limit has been extended from $-\lambda$ to $-\infty$ for mathematical convenience and introduces negligible error. Substitution into equation (4-63) yields

$$a_\lambda^{ND}(a, w) = \frac{r_0 \lambda_0 a f}{\sqrt{\pi}\ \Delta\lambda_D} \int_{-\infty}^{+\infty} \frac{e^{-x^2}}{(w-x)^2+a^2}\, dx \tag{4-64}$$

where

$$\left. \begin{aligned} x &= \Delta\lambda/\Delta\lambda_D \\ a &= \Delta\lambda_N/4\pi\Delta\lambda_D \\ w &= (\lambda_0-\lambda)/\Delta\lambda_D \end{aligned} \right\} \tag{4-65}$$

For the case of $a \to 0$, we obtain a pure Doppler profile as found previously (eq. (4-59)).

$$a_\lambda^D(w) = a_{\lambda_0}^D e^{-w^2} \tag{4-66}$$

where the cross section at line center is

$$a_{\lambda_0}^D = \sqrt{\pi}\ V_0 \lambda_0^2 f/\Delta\lambda_D \tag{4-67}$$

Hence, $a_\lambda^{ND}(a, w)$ can be written

$$a_\lambda^{ND}(a, w) = a_{\lambda_0}^D H(a, w) \tag{4-68}$$

where

$$H(a, w) = \frac{a}{\pi} \int_{-\infty}^{+\infty} \frac{e^{-x^2}}{(w-x)^2+a^2}\, dx \tag{4-69}$$

Further evaluation of $a_\lambda^{ND}(a, w)$ must be done numerically. The function $H(a, w)$, the Hjerting function, has been evaluated by Harris (1948) and plotted by Brandt and Hodge (1964) as shown in figure 4–26.

Several characteristics of $a_\lambda^{ND}(w)$, which are evident from equation (4–64) and figure 4–26, are worthy of discussion.

(1) When $a \gg 1$ (that is, $\Delta\lambda_N \gg 4\pi\Delta\lambda_D$)$a_\lambda$ assumes a pure natural broadening or dispersion profile (eq. (4–48)).

(2) When $\Delta\lambda_N \ll 4\pi\Delta\lambda_D$ and is close to line center, $|\Delta\lambda| \lesssim \Delta\lambda_D$, a_λ is determined by Doppler broadening; $a_\lambda \sim \exp[-(\Delta\lambda/\Delta\lambda_D)^2]$.

(3) When $\Delta\lambda_N \ll 4\pi\Delta\lambda_D$ and is far from line center, a_λ varies as $|\Delta\lambda|^{-2}$. The number of particles moving with a velocity that would yield a large Doppler shift decreases exponentially; $f_1(v_1) \sim \exp[-(v_1/V_0)^2]$. On the other hand, natural broadening decreases only as $|\Delta\lambda|^{-2}$ for large $\Delta\lambda$ and it eventually becomes the dominant factor. As $\Delta\lambda_D$ becomes very much larger than $\Delta\lambda_N$ ($a \to 0$), we must go farther from line center for this approximation to be valid.

(4) Because the transition between the Doppler-broadened core and the natural-broadened wings is abrupt for $\Delta\lambda_N \ll 4\pi\Delta\lambda_D$, a reasonable approximation for the atomic absorption coefficient, when $|\Delta\lambda| \gg (\lambda_N\Delta\lambda_D)^{1/2}$, is

$$a_\lambda^{ND} \simeq a_{\lambda_0}^{D}\left\{\exp\left[-\left(\frac{\Delta\lambda}{\Delta\lambda_D}\right)^2\right] + \frac{a}{\sqrt{\pi}}\left(\frac{\Delta\lambda_D}{\Delta\lambda}\right)^2\right\} \qquad (4\text{--}70)$$

The transition occurs at the $\Delta\lambda$ defined by the condition of equality of the two terms on the right-hand side of equation (4–70). Because of the rapid variation of the exponential term and the characteristic values for a, this transition occurs at values of $\Delta\lambda$ between $3\Delta\lambda_D$ and $4\Delta\lambda_D$ for most solar lines.

(5) The atomic absorption cross section of the total line remains unchanged by the combination of natural and Doppler broadening

$$\int_0^\infty a_\lambda^{ND}(\lambda)\, d\lambda = \pi\lambda_0^2 r_0 f \qquad (4\text{--}71)$$

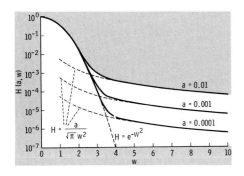

Figure 4–26.—The Hjerting function. The abrupt transition from a Doppler-broadened core to natural-broadened wings is evident. This transition occurs when $w^2 e^{-w^2} = a/\sqrt{\pi}$. Because of the abrupt nature of this transition, a reasonable approximation for $H(a, w)$, when $w^2 \gg a$, is just the sum of the terms representing the two limiting cases; $e^{-w^2} + (a/\sqrt{\pi})(1/w^2)$. (From Brandt and Hodge, 1964; copyright 1964, McGraw-Hill.)

As a numerical example, consider the $H\alpha$ line produced by hydrogen gas at a temperature of 6000 K. The natural width of $H\alpha$, $\Delta\lambda_N$, is 8×10^{-3} Å, $V_0 = 10$ km/sec, $\Delta\lambda_D = 0.2$ Å, and $a = 3\times10^{-3}$. From figure 4-26, it is seen that the line profile would be Doppler broadened out to approximately $3\Delta\lambda_D$ or 0.6 Å from line center and natural broadened farther out in the wings. If the temperature is raised to 2×10^6 K (characteristic of the corona), the Doppler width is increased to 4 Å, $a = 1.5\times10^{-4}$, and the transition from Doppler to natural broadening is increased to approximately 16 Å ($4\Delta\lambda_D$) from line center.

Pressure Broadening

To this point we have considered the broadening mechanism to be either a basic property of the atom (natural broadening) or a property of its state of motion (Doppler broadening). A third type of mechanism important for solar lines involves the effect of neighboring atoms, ions, or electrons on the absorbers and emitters. Because this effect is one which increases with pressure, it is termed "pressure broadening." It is an important mechanism in the photosphere, in the lower chromosphere, and possibly in flares.

Because the discrete energy levels of an atom result from a quantization of the combined kinetic and electrostatic energies of its constituent particles, additional externally applied electrostatic forces will perturb these levels. This is termed the "Stark effect." Thus, when a particle with an electric field passes close to the atom, the atom's energy levels are perturbed and the wavelength of an emitted or absorbed photon is slightly shifted. This instantaneous wavelength shift can be approximated by

$$\Delta\lambda = \frac{C}{r^m} \tag{4-72}$$

where r is the distance between the atom and the perturbing particle, C is a constant that defines the strength of interaction, and m is determined by the type of atom-perturber electrostatic interaction (table 4-I). Because the electric field of a charged particle varies as $1/r^2$, a wavelength shift that is proportional to $1/r^2$ is linearly proportional to the electric field. Thus, the interaction when m is 2 is

TABLE 4-I.—Types of Particle Interactions

m	Description	Name
2	Electrons or ions perturbing hydrogen	Linear Stark effect
3	Neutral atoms perturbing atoms of the same kind	Resonance broadening
4	Electrons or ions acting upon nonhydrogenlike atoms	Quadratic Stark effect
6	Neutral atoms perturbing atoms of a different kind	van der Waals' forces

termed the "linear Stark effect." The linear Stark effect is dominant when ions broaden the lines of hydrogen, and the quadratic effect is dominant when ions broaden the lines of metal atoms or ions. When the atom and perturbing atom are of the same kind, as for hydrogen-hydrogen in the sun, m is 3 and the broadening is called "resonance broadening." When the atom and perturber are different, m is 6 and the broadening is termed "van der Waals' broadening." This is an important mechanism in the broadening of many solar lines by hydrogen.

Approximations that are made in analyzing the details of these types of broadening mechanisms are that the position and momentum of a perturbing particle can be specified simultaneously with no uncertainty and that this trajectory is not sensitive to the energy levels or changes of the energy levels of the perturbed atom. That is, a perturbing particle will remain on its classical path, which is a straight line if either one of the colliding particles is electrically neutral or a hyperbola if both particles are charged.

In general, the method of describing pressure broadening is relatively simple in two extreme cases. First, if the lifetime of a radiating atom is long, compared with the time between collisions, the successive pieces of the emitted photon do not form a single coherent wave train. The line width more closely corresponds to the time between collisions rather than to the natural lifetime of the state, because each piece of the photon tends to be independent of all others. Although the collision frequency is high, the duration of each collision is relatively short and the atom is unperturbed most of the time. The broadening can be simply described in this case because the natural uncertainty in the energy of the photon and the uncertainty in energy corresponding to the mean time between collisions, Δt_{coll}, is cumulative. Thus, the natural width $\Delta\lambda_N$, used in equation (4–64), can be replaced by $\Delta\lambda_{NC}$, which includes collisions.

$$\Delta\lambda_{NC} = \frac{\lambda_0^2}{c}\left(\frac{1}{\Delta t_N} + \frac{1}{\Delta t_{coll}}\right) \tag{4–73}$$

The line profile, as previously described, varies as $(1/\Delta\lambda)^2$ in the wings, but the transition from a Doppler to a dispersion profile occurs closer to the line center. This description of pressure broadening, in which the collisions are considered as discrete encounters, is called the impact or collision approximation and is applicable when the perturbing particles are fast-moving electrons.

In the second method of describing pressure broadening, the opposite assumption to the impact approximation is made. That is, during the emission the atom experiences a steady electric field from the surrounding particle configuration instead of a succession of rapid impacts. The wavelength of an emitted photon will be shifted by the Stark effect and the line profile will be obtained by summing over all possible shifts according to their statistical probability. This is called the quasi-static or the statistical approximation and is usually valid when the perturbing particles are relatively slow moving ions. In considering a gas composed of both electrons and ions, such as the plasma of the photosphere, the impact and quasi-static approximations can be combined. The impact approximation is first applied to electron-collision broadening of lines resulting from transitions between states perturbed by an electric field of the static ions. This result is then statistically averaged over all possible electric fields or ion configurations.

As an example of the quasi-static approximation, consider the important case of broadening of lines from hydrogen or hydrogenlike ions by other ions (the linear Stark effect). Let $W(r)\,dr$ be the probability of a perturbing particle being a distance r to $r+dr$ from the hydrogenlike ion. Assuming a uniform distribution of particles, $W(r)$ will be proportional to r^2. In order to relate $W(r)$ to $W(\Delta\lambda)$, the probability of a wavelength shift of magnitude $\Delta\lambda$ per unit $\Delta\lambda$, we note that the wavelength shift is proportional to the electric field of the perturbing particles or the inverse square of the distance between the two particles: $\Delta\lambda\sim E\sim r^{-2}$. Because $W(\Delta\lambda)$ is related to $W(r)$ by

$$W(\Delta\lambda)=W(r)\,\frac{dr}{d(\Delta\lambda)} \tag{4-74}$$

it is evident that

$$W(\Delta\lambda)\sim\left|\frac{1}{\Delta\lambda}\right|^{5/2} \tag{4-75}$$

Thus, the wings of lines from hydrogen or hydrogenlike ions will vary as $|\Delta\lambda|^{-5/2}$ under the quasi-static approximation, rather than as $|\Delta\lambda|^{-2}$ determined by the impact approximation. A crude but informative estimate of the magnitude of the broadening can be obtained by equating $hc\Delta\lambda/\lambda^2$, the broadening in energy units, to $\Delta(\text{energy})_p$, the approximate magnitude of the energy perturbation of the electronic states involved in the transition (diameter of electron orbit$\times$electron charge$\times$electric field of perturbing particle). This latter quantity is

$$\Delta(\text{energy})_p=\left(\frac{2a_0n^2}{z}\right)\left(\frac{e^2}{4\pi\epsilon_0r^2}\right) \tag{4-76}$$

where the first term in parentheses is the diameter of a circular electron orbit in a hydrogenlike ion of nuclear charge z, the second term is the electron charge times the electric field of a perturbing particle which is assumed here to be a proton at a distance r, a_0 is the Bohr radius ($\epsilon_0h^2/\pi m_ee^2=0.529$ Å), n is the principal quantum number of the shell, and ϵ_0 is the capacitivity of vacuum. Thus,

$$\Delta\lambda=\left(\frac{n_u{}^2+n_l{}^2}{2\pi^2z}\right)\left(\frac{\lambda_c\lambda^2}{r^2}\right) \tag{4-77}$$

where n_u and n_l are the principal quantum numbers of the upper and lower states, respectively, and λ_c is the Compton wavelength of an electron ($h/m_ec=2.43\times10^{-2}$ Å). A representative value of r can be obtained from $\bar{r}^3=1/N_{\text{proton}}$. As a numerical example, consider the linear Stark broadening of the Hα wings formed in the photosphere at $\tau_{5000}=1$: $T\simeq6000$ K, $N_{\text{proton}}\simeq7\times10^{13}$ cm^{-3}, $\bar{r}=2.4\times10^3$ Å, and $\Delta\lambda=0.11$ Å. The Doppler width previously calculated under these same conditions was 0.2 Å, which is of the same magnitude as calculated here. Thus, the Stark effect will have a noticeable influence on the $H\alpha$ wing profile.

The broadening of atomic states not only leads to line broadening but it also changes the wavelength at which the series limits or continuum cutoffs are observed. For a hydrogenlike ion, the energy of the nth shell is

$$E_n = \frac{z^2 e^2}{8\pi\epsilon_0 a_0}\left(1 - \frac{1}{n^2}\right) \tag{4-78}$$

Thus, when n is large, the energies of the shells are close together and the change in E_n when n changes by $+1$ is approximately

$$\Delta E_n = \frac{dE_n}{dn} = \frac{z^2 e^2}{4\pi\epsilon_0 a_0 n^3} \tag{4-79}$$

Equating one-half of this energy between shells to the shift in energy, $\Delta(\text{energy})_p$ (eq. (4-76)), and letting N_e determine the mean ion-proton distance $(\bar{r}^3 = 1/N_e)$, we obtain the principal quantum number of the effective shell for the start of the continuum:

$$n_c = \left(\frac{1}{2}\right)^{2/5}\frac{z^{3/5}}{(a_0^3 N_e)^{2/15}} \tag{4-80}$$

Using more detailed reasoning, it has been shown that the factor $(1/2)^{2/5}$ should be $\frac{1}{2}$ (Griem, 1964). Lines which involve transitions to or from shells above n_c will be so broadened that they merge with their neighboring lines (fig. 4-21). The series limits (fig. 4-14) will not correspond to $n \rightarrow \infty$ but will be slightly altered because they correspond to n_c. For the height in the solar atmosphere at which $\tau_{5000} = 1$, $(N_e = 7 \times 10^{13}$ cm$^{-3})$, the energy shells of hydrogen merge at $n_c \simeq 15$.

We will now briefly discuss the effects of magnetic fields on line formation before NLTE is considered.

4.7 LINE SPLITTING

In addition to the Stark effect, the energy levels of an atom can be altered by the application of a magnetic field, called the Zeeman effect. In contrast to the electric fields of pressure broadening, however, the magnetic fields will almost always be uniform over microscopic distances. Hence, all atoms at a given location will be perturbed to the same extent and a splitting of lines rather than a broadening will result. Because the Zeeman effect fits in well with our discussion of broadening and atomic-energy levels, it will be considered at this time. The observations of this splitting provide the major method of measuring the strength and direction of solar magnetic fields.

The splitting of energy levels arises from the fact that when a system with a net magnetic moment is placed in a magnetic field, an interaction energy $\Delta\epsilon_M$ exists which depends upon the orientation of the magnetic moment $\mathbf{\mu}$ with respect to the magnetic field **B**

$$\Delta\epsilon_M = -\,\mathbf{\mu}\cdot\mathbf{B} \qquad\qquad (4\text{--}81)$$

Because the system tends to configure itself in the state of lower potential energy, $\mathbf{\mu}$ will tend to aline itself with **B**. If a closed loop of current I flows in a plane and encloses an area A (fig. 4–27), the magnetic moment is defined by

$$\mathbf{\mu} = IA\mathbf{n} \qquad\qquad (4\text{--}82)$$

where $\mathbf{n}$ is the unit vector normal to area A. This equation is valid regardless of the shape of the loop. Magnetic moments exist within atoms because of both the motion of electrons in closed orbits and the spin of the electrons themselves. It is the interaction of these magnetic moments with an applied magnetic field which causes the splitting of the energy levels.

In our previous discussion of the discrete nature of the energy levels of the hydrogen atom (sec. 4.5), it was pointed out that for each value of n, the principal quantum number, there can be n different values of the quantized orbital angular momentum ($l=0,\ 1,\ 2,\ \dots\ n$) and ($2l+1$) possible projections of each angular momentum on an arbitrarily chosen axis ($m=0,\ \pm1,\ \pm2,\ \dots\ \pm l$). Prescribing that this axis be along the magnetic-field direction and considering only the magnetic moment arising from the orbital motion of the electrons, it is seen that there are $2l+1$ possible values of magnetic interaction energy since $\mathbf{\mu}\cdot\mathbf{B}$ assumes the possible values for the projection of $\mathbf{\mu}$ on **B** (fig. 4–28). Numerically, the splitting of an energy level is given by

$$\Delta\epsilon_M = \frac{1}{2}\left(\frac{ehB}{2\pi m_e}\right)M_J g \qquad\qquad (4\text{--}83)$$

where M_J represents the contributions to $\mathbf{\mu}$ made by electron spin as well as by orbital motion. In the general case, the total angular momentum of a multielectron atom is the vector sum of the electron spin vector and the electron orbital angular momentum vector, and is represented by the quantum number J. Then, M_J becomes the possible quantized projection of this total angular momentum on an arbitrarily

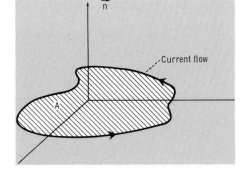

FIGURE 4–27.—Magnetic moment of closed loop of current flowing within a plane; $\mathbf{n}$ is the unit vector perpendicular to plane A.

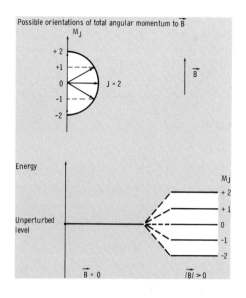

FIGURE 4–28.—Energy level splitting by a nonzero magnetic field.

chosen axis. Thus, the quantum numbers J and M_J are analogous to the previously used quantum numbers l and m. The quantity g is called the Landé g factor. This factor is a dimensionless quantity of the order of unity which accounts for the proportionality factor between the magnetic moment and the orbital and spin angular moments. The combined factor of proportionality between $\Delta\epsilon_M$ and B in equation (4–83) can be both theoretically calculated and experimentally determined in many instances.

The direction of the magnetic field can be determined from the polarization of lines which originate from split energy levels. A simple case, similar to that considered by Zirin (1966), is shown in figure 4–29. If we look perpendicular to $\mathbf{B}$, we see the unperturbed line, called the π component, which is linearly polarized in a direction parallel to $\mathbf{B}$. By this, we mean that the electric field in the electromagnetic wave propagated to the observer oscillates sinusoidally with time in a direction parallel to $\mathbf{B}$ (fig. 4–29). In figure 4–29(b), σ_1 and σ_2 are the two lines that are split off the unperturbed line and are linearly polarized in the direction perpendicular to $\mathbf{B}$. The sum of all the radiation emitted by the transitions from the upper to the lower state must be unpolarized, as in the case of no perturbation. Hence, the intensity of the π component is twice that of either σ component. If we now observe the radiation that is emitted in the direction parallel to the magnetic field, we do not see the π component at all, and the two σ components are circularly polarized in opposite directions (fig. 4–29). Circular polarization means that the observer sees an electric-field vector of the electromagnetic wave which is constant in magnitude but rotates with time, either clockwise or counterclockwise. Because photon energy is hc/λ, its change (because of the Zeeman effect) is $(hc/\lambda^2)\Delta\lambda_M$.

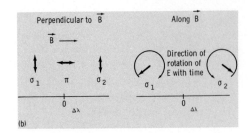

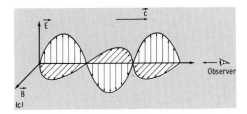

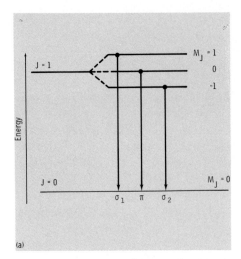

FIGURE 4–29.—Polarization of split lines. (*a*) A simple case. (*b*) Electric-field vector polarization for looking two ways at **B**. (*c*) Electric and magnetic fields of a linearly polarized electromagnetic wave. The **E** and **B** field configuration moves toward observer with velocity **c**.

Using this and equation (4–83),

$$\Delta\lambda_M = \frac{1}{2}\left(\frac{eB}{2\pi m_e c}\right)\lambda^2 M_J g$$

$$= 4.67 \times 10^{-13}\, \lambda^2 M_J g B \qquad \text{Å} \tag{4–84}$$

where λ is in Å and B is in gauss. When $M_J g = 1$, $\lambda = 7000$ Å, and $\Delta\lambda_M = 0.1$ Å, B must be 4370 gauss. Thus, Zeeman splitting can only be directly observed by normal means in very strong sunspots because it is normally below our wavelength resolution. However, magnetographs which use the Zeeman effect and which map solar magnetic fields have cleverly circumvented this problem and can measure fields as small as 1 gauss.

4.8 NONLOCAL THERMODYNAMIC EQUILIBRIUM

A major objective of our discussion of the photosphere is to relate the characteristics of the observed radiation to the physical properties of the atmosphere. It has been seen that there is an immense quantity of information contained in the strengths and detailed profiles of the absorption lines. We have generally assumed that our task of specifying the atmospheric properties is complete once the temperature, density, composition, and turbulent velocity at each height have been determined. However, the physical realities are more complex. In particular, our use of the concept of temperature must be revised if we are to account for obvious discrepancies. Consider the cores of strong lines which originate in the chromosphere, where the temperature gradient is positive, and which should display limb brightening. In Hα and Ca K (figs. 2–14, 2–15, and 2–17), just the opposite, limb darkening, is observed. Also, the radiation temperature at the cores of these strong lines is much below the gas temperature where these lines are formed. Thus, the source function in a line, $S_\lambda{}^l$, is not adequately represented by the Planck function at the kinetic temperature of the gas. In general, line formation above the photosphere is not properly described as an LTE process. To properly represent the source function in terms of the gas properties, we must investigate each individual physical mechanism leading to radiation emission and absorption. We shall see that variables which define the source functions are themselves functions of the ambient radiation intensity and that coupled nonlinear equations result. In these ways, our task of description and data interpretation is greatly complicated. However, analyzing the detailed but real physical processes taking place often produces fundamental understanding.

TE, LTE, and NLTE

When we assume thermodynamic equilibrium (TE), we make the supposition that the distributions of each of the different types of gas particles and photons over the various energy states available to them (kinetic, excitation, ionization, etc., and photon energy) are statistically the most probable ones. Once the total gas composition and the total energy are specified, the most probable distributions are uniquely determined. These distributions are all functions of temperature which is proportional to the average photon and particle energies, is the same for the radiation field and gas, and is spatially uniform. When the temperature is no longer spatially uniform, we first attempt to retain the TE assumption, but only on a local scale (LTE). That is, the particles and photons at each point in space interact completely with those at neighboring points having only slightly different average properties. All particle and photon mean free paths are assumed to be much smaller than the corresponding characteristic distances for change. We see that even in the solar core, LTE is not a correct assumption in a strict sense, because the neutrinos that are generated do not interact with the surrounding matter but directly leave the sun. In the photosphere, where the photon mean free paths become the same magnitude as the pressure scale height, we certainly would not expect LTE to exist. Nevertheless, the assumption of LTE does greatly simplify the calculations and provides a baseline for reference. For weak lines that are formed low in the photosphere, the agreement between calculations and observations is fairly good.

In LTE theory, the Boltzmann factor and the Saha equation are used to determine the density of excited and ionized states, and the source function is set equal to the Planck function $B_\lambda(T)$, where T is the local equilibrium temperature. A relatively simple departure from LTE is obtained by setting the temperature in these calculations equal to T_e, the electron kinetic temperature which does not have to be the same as the radiation temperature. In essence, this assumes that all rate processes which determine the density of excited and ionized states are controlled by heavy-particle collisions with electrons. The relatively high electron thermal velocity and interaction cross sections yield high collision frequencies so that this assumption is frequently valid. If the gas is not highly ionized but the relevant rate processes are dominated by collisions involving heavy particles, the heavy-particle kinetic temperature should be used in place of T_e. As mentioned previously, this simple departure from strict LTE is often used itself as a definition of LTE. When rate processes are no longer collision dominated, we must resort to a complete non-LTE (NLTE) analysis. The large radiation leak from the photosphere greatly perturbs the LTE balance of the rate processes, and the best that we can do is to assume a statistical steady state. That is, at each point in the gas the rate of production of a state is equal to the rate of its removal. Because we must now specify the rate of each individual process, rather than just the parameter T_e, we become very dependent on our knowledge of rate constants, a significant fraction of which are not well known.

Because of the complexity of NLTE calculations, it is important that our objectives and methods of pursuit be clearly defined. We seek to determine the intensity of radiation emitted by the solar atmosphere, $I_\lambda(0, \theta)$, as a function of atomic parameters and radially varying gas properties. From equation (4–38), it is seen that this is equivalent to determining η_λ, $S_\lambda{}^c$, and $S_\lambda{}^l$ as functions of $\tau_\lambda{}^c$ and relating $\tau_\lambda{}^c$ to r through $\kappa_\lambda{}^c$. Low in the photosphere where LTE is a valid assumption, the major contributor to the continuum source function, $S_\lambda{}^c$, comes from the negative hydrogen ion, H⁻. Here, $S_\lambda{}^c$ is set equal to $B_\lambda(T_e)$; N_H/N_{H^-} is calculated by the Saha equation at T_e which determines $\kappa_\lambda{}^c$.

Most of the information on the properties of the lower solar atmosphere comes from absorption lines. For strong lines in which $\eta_\lambda S_\lambda{}^l \gg S_\lambda{}^c$ and $\eta_\lambda \gg 1$, equation (4–38) is approximated by

$$I_\lambda(0, \theta) \simeq \int_0^\infty S_\lambda{}^l \exp(-\tau_\lambda{}^l/\cos\theta)\, d\tau_\lambda{}^l/\cos\theta \qquad (4\text{–}85)$$

Therefore, we focus our attention on the line source function $S_\lambda{}^l(\tau_\lambda{}^l)$ for the remainder of our discussion, realizing that $\kappa_\lambda{}^l$ must also be determined to relate $S_\lambda{}^l$ to physical height in the atmosphere. The emphasis will be placed on describing the physical mechanisms which determine the value of $S_\lambda{}^l$, and the formidable algebraic complexities of the calculation will be suppressed.

The Line Source Function

A general relation for $S_\lambda{}^l$ can be derived from expressions for the line absorption and emission coefficients, since $S_\lambda{}^l$ is equal to $j_\lambda{}^l/\kappa_\lambda{}^l$. The energy absorbed in a line is the net result of photoexcitations minus stimulated emissions. That is,

$$\kappa_\lambda{}^l = (N_l B_{lu} - N_u B_{ul})\phi(\lambda)hc/\lambda \qquad (4\text{–}86)$$

N_l and N_u are the densities of atoms in the lower and upper levels, respectively; $\phi(\lambda)$ is the absorption line profile normalized to unity

$$\int_{\lambda^-}^{\lambda^+} \phi(\lambda)\, d\lambda = 1$$

hc/λ is the energy difference between the two levels involved in the transition; B_{lu} is the Einstein coefficient for absorption, which gives the rate of transitions from the lower to the upper levels ($l \to u$) per unit N_l and I_λ; B_{ul} is the Einstein coefficient of negative absorption or stimulated emission, which gives the corresponding rate for $u \to l$ transitions. Energy is added to the radiation field by spontaneous emissions,

$$j_\lambda{}^l = N_u A_{ul} \chi (\lambda) hc/4\pi\lambda \qquad (4\text{-}87)$$

where A_{ul} is the Einstein coefficient for spontaneous emission per unit N_l, $\chi(\lambda)$ is the emission line profile also normalized to unity, and the factor $hc/4\pi\lambda$ gives the energy radiated in each emission per steradian. These absorption and emission coefficients are assumed to be isotropic. Using these expressions, the line source function is

$$S_\lambda{}^l = \frac{N_u A_{ul} \Psi (\lambda)}{4\pi (N_l B_{lu} - N_u B_{ul})} \qquad (4\text{-}88)$$

where $\Psi(\lambda)$ is the ratio of the emission to absorption line profiles.

The above general relation for $S_\lambda{}^l$ can be expressed in more useful form by using the relations between the Einstein coefficients. Because these coefficients are atomic parameters which are independent of the radiation and particle distributions over available energy states, we can determine their values from the relatively simple case of TE. In TE the rate of absorption balances the sum of the rates of spontaneous and stimulated emissions, I_λ is given by $B_\lambda(T)$, and the Boltzmann factor determines the ratio N_u/N_l. That is,

$$N_l B_{lu} B_\lambda (T) = N_u [A_{ul}/4\pi + B_{ul} B_\lambda (T)] \qquad (4\text{-}89)$$

where

$$\frac{N_u}{N_l} = \frac{g_u}{g_l} \exp (-hc/\lambda kT)$$

and

$$B_\lambda (T) = \frac{\lambda hc^2}{\lambda^5} [\exp (hc/\lambda kT) - 1]^{-1}$$

Using these relations and the fact that the Einstein coefficients must be independent of T, it is easily shown that

$$g_l B_{lu} = g_u B_{ul} \qquad (4\text{-}90)$$

and

$$B_{ul} = \frac{\lambda^5}{8\pi hc^2} A_{ul} \qquad (4\text{-}91)$$

Thus, the line source function is

$$S_\lambda{}^l = \frac{2hc^2/\lambda^5}{\left[\dfrac{g_u N_l}{g_l N_u} - 1 \right]} \Psi (\lambda) \qquad (4\text{-}92)$$

Because the only way that NLTE can enter this equation is through N_l/N_u and $\Psi(\lambda)$, equation (4–92) provides an exceptionally useful expression for understanding NLTE line formation.

An excitation temperature T_{ex} can be defined by

$$\frac{N_u}{N_l} = \frac{g_u}{g_l} \exp\ (-hc/\lambda k T_{ex}) \qquad (4\text{--}93)$$

which is the same as T_e only in the case of LTE. When $\Psi(\lambda)$ is equal to unity, $S_\lambda{}^l$ is formally given by

$$S_\lambda{}^l = \frac{2hc^2/\lambda^5}{\left[\dfrac{g_u N_l}{g_l N_u} - 1\right]} \qquad (4\text{--}94)$$

and

$$S_\lambda{}^l = B_\lambda(T_{ex}) \qquad (4\text{--}95)$$

This has the property of isolating all our ignorance into one parameter, T_{ex}. Although this tends to conceal the physics, it is useful for simplified treatments of line formation. In practice, the deviations of $\Psi(\lambda)$ from unity are rarely significant. That is, the natural-, Doppler-, and pressure-broadened absorption and emission profiles are not greatly different.

An important feature of this source function (eq. (4–94)) is its independence of pronounced variation with wavelength across a line. The observed line shapes exist primarily because $\kappa_\lambda{}^l$, hence $\tau_\lambda{}^l$, are functions of $\Delta\lambda$. Even though $S_\lambda{}^l$ is nearly a constant at a given height, each part of the line profile is formed at a different height where $S_\lambda{}^l$ is generally not the same.

Equation (4–94) allows us to pursue further the previously mentioned discrepancy of limb darkening for lines produced in the chromosphere where the temperature gradient is positive. Limb darkening implies that $S_\lambda{}^l$, hence N_u/N_l, decrease with height. If the populations of excited levels were controlled by collisions only, this could not occur, because T_e is increasing. However, the rate of $l \rightarrow u$ transitions by radiation absorption is important in determining N_u/N_l and decrease with height because an increasing fraction of photons directly escape the atmosphere. On the other hand, the rate of $u \rightarrow l$ transitions depends primarily upon spontaneous emission that is not diminished by the escape of radiation. Thus, T_{ex} may become appreciably less than T_e because of an underpopulation of excited levels. As $S_\lambda{}^l$ decreases with height, limb darkening is produced. We shall see, however, that T_{ex} can increase with height over limited ranges and that self-reversed emission cores result, like those of Ca H and K and $L\alpha$.

Before considering what determines N_l and N_u, it is useful to relate the Einstein coefficients just introduced to the absorption f number previously discussed. This is done by equating two expressions for the rate of energy absorption per unit volume.

$$\left(\frac{hc}{\lambda}\right) I_\lambda N_l B_{lu} = I_\lambda N_l \int_0^\infty a_\lambda\, d\lambda \qquad (4\text{--}96)$$

Use of equations (4–49), (4–90), (4–91), and (4–96) yields

$$A_{ul} = 8\pi^2 \frac{g_l}{g_u} \frac{r_0 c}{\lambda_0^2} f \tag{4–97}$$

Numerically, for Hα, $f = 0.6408$ and $A_{32} = 4.3 \times 10^7$ sec, which gives a characteristic lifetime of approximately 2×10^{-8} sec.

Excited-State Production and Removal

The determination of the density of each excited state is accomplished by a steady-state balance of the production and removal mechanisms. These mechanisms are both collisional and radiative. For example, the relatively simple case of a two-level atom is considered. The rate of $l \rightarrow u$ transitions is balanced by the rate of $u \rightarrow l$ transitions.

$$[4\pi B_{lu}\langle J_\lambda\rangle + N_e C_{lu}]N_l = [A_{ul} + 4\pi B_{ul}\langle J_\lambda\rangle + N_e C_{ul}]N_u \tag{4–98}$$

| Absorption | Collisional excitation | Spontaneous emission | Induced emission | Collisional deexcitation |

Here, $\langle J_\lambda\rangle$ is the value of $\mathbf{I}_\lambda$ averaged over all directions and over the absorption coefficient profile,

$$\langle J_\lambda\rangle = \frac{1}{4\pi} \int_{\lambda^-}^{\lambda^+} \phi(\lambda)\, d\lambda \int_{4\pi} \mathbf{I}_\lambda \cdot d\boldsymbol{\omega} \tag{4–99}$$

which is the same as that defined by equation (4–43). The collision rate constants, C_{lu} and C_{ul}, are independent of particle and radiation densities. Lastly, electrons are assumed to dominate the collisional excitation and deexcitation processes. In addition to this balance of transition rates, the total number of particles of a species is unchanged for arbitrary degrees of excitation and ionization. For this two-level atom, the conservation of species simply requires $N_l + N_u$ to be constant. Equation (4–98) illustrates the coupling that exists between radiative and collisional processes. The degree to which one type of process dominates the other is evident by a comparison of the relative magnitudes of the terms. Before proceeding further with this comparison, however, the nature of the collision terms must be investigated.

The rate at which an electron excites atoms from $u \rightarrow l$ is equal to the relative speed of the electron and atom, essentially v_e, divided by the electron's mean free path for excitation collisions, $1/N_l Q_{lu}$. Here, Q_{lu} is the electron-atom collision cross section for the $l \rightarrow u$ transition and is a function of v_e. Averaging over electron speed yields

$$C_{lu} = \int_{v_e\text{min}}^\infty v_e Q_{lu}(v_e) f(v_e)\, dv_e \tag{4–100}$$

where $f(v_e)$ is the electron Maxwellian velocity distribution normalized to unity (eq. (4–55)). The speed v_e^{min} corresponds to the minimum electron kinetic energy required to cause the $l \to u$ transition;

$$\frac{m_e}{2} (v_e^{\mathrm{min}})^2 = \frac{hc}{\lambda} \qquad (4\text{-}101)$$

Thus, C_{lu} becomes

$$C_{lu} = \frac{2}{\sqrt{\pi}} V_0 e^{-\zeta_m} \int_0^\infty (\zeta + \zeta_m) Q_{lu}(\zeta) e^{-\zeta} d\zeta \qquad (4\text{-}102)$$

where V_0 is $(2kT_e/m_e)^{1/2}$, the nondimensional energy variable ζ is $(m_e v_e^2/2 - hc/\lambda)/kT_e$, and ζ_m is $hc/\lambda kT_e$. When $hc/\lambda kT \gg 1$, the variation of C_{lu} is dominated by the factor $\exp(-hc/\lambda kT_e)$. As the temperature is increased, the number of electrons having sufficient energy to cause excitation increases exponentially, which explains the mechanism leading to the Boltzmann factor (eq. (4-17)) in collision-dominated LTE. Also, close-lying energy levels like those near the continuum (fig. 4-21) or those having the same principal quantum number, can have large C_{lu} (large λ). Two levels which are close together in energy can have a relative population in accord with the Boltzmann factor because of the relatively high rate of collisional transitions, even though the ground and continuum levels are far from LTE.

In the same way in which the Einstein coefficients are related to one another by the unique case of TE, so are the collision rate constants, C_{lu} and C_{ul}, related. In TE, not only do the overall rates balance, but there is a balancing of each detailed process at the microscopic level. That is, the rate by which an atom undergoes transitions from one energy level to another by a given mechanism is balanced by the rate at which this same mechanism occurs in reverse. This is the principle of detailed balancing and allows us to evaluate the rate constant for a process as a function of initial particle energies, if the constant for the reverse process is already known. An overall balance of the collision terms of equation (4-98) in TE yields

$$\frac{C_{lu}}{C_{ul}} = \frac{g_u}{g_l} \exp(-hc/\lambda kT_e) \qquad (4\text{-}103)$$

which will also be true in NLTE if the electron velocity distribution is Maxwellian. A detailed balance on the microscopic scale yields

$$g_l E Q_{lu}(E) = g_u [E - E_m] Q_{ul}(E - E_m) \qquad (4\text{-}104)$$

where $E = (m_e/2)v_e^2$, $E_m = m_e/2 (v_e^{\mathrm{min}})^2$, and $Q_{lu} = 0$ for $E < E_m$. The rate at which electrons of energy E excite atoms in energy level l is balanced by the rate at which electrons of energy $(E - E_m)$ deexcite atoms in level u. Because the electron energy is increased by E_m in the $u \to l$ collisions, these collisions are "superelastic." A significant result of equations (4-103) and (4-104) is that C_{ul}, unlike C_{lu}, does not contain the factor $\exp(-hc/\lambda kT_e)$ and is only slightly temperature dependent. All electrons are able to deexcite an atom, because there is no energy barrier to overcome.

The steady-state balance (eq. (4–98)) and conservation of species allows us to solve for N_l/N_u and obtain an expression for the line source function from equation (4–94).[2] For the idealized case of an atom with two or more discrete energy levels (excitation) and a continuum (ionization), the line source function can be algebraically reduced to

$$S_\lambda{}^l = \frac{\langle J_\lambda \rangle + \eta B_\lambda(T^*) + \epsilon B_\lambda(T_e)}{1 + \eta + \epsilon} . \qquad (4\text{–}105)$$

This will prove to be a most useful expression for analyzing the physical mechanisms leading to NLTE line formation. The denominator, $1+\eta+\epsilon$, accounts for the three different mechanisms which return an atom from an upper to a lower energy level. The first term represents the rate of spontaneous emission and has been normalized to unity. The second term accounts for further excitation and for ionization from the upper level followed by return to the lower level. That is, the first term represents the direct radiative $u \rightarrow l$ transition, while the second represents all of the roundabout $u \rightarrow l$ transitions. The third term, ϵ, accounts for direct collisional deexcitation.

$$\epsilon \simeq N_e C_{ul}/A_{lu} \qquad (4\text{–}106)$$

Unlike the first term (unity), η and ϵ account for processes which do not return photons to the radiation field at the line wavelength. Therefore, the fraction $1/(1+\eta+\epsilon)$ is the fraction of transitions out of the upper level which actually result in line photons.

The three contributions to $S_\lambda{}^l$ (eq. (4–105)) arise from three distinct physical mechanisms. The first term, $\langle J_\lambda \rangle/(1+\eta+\epsilon)$, is the scattering term which accounts for photons returned immediately to the radiation field by spontaneous emission after causing a $l \rightarrow u$ transition. The second term, $\eta B_\lambda(T^*)/(1+\eta+\epsilon)$, is the photoelectric term which accounts for photons spontaneously emitted from atoms in the upper level that were created by the fluorescence mechanism. That is, the atom is ionized from the lower level by continuum radiation (effective because absorption is not limited to a line width), recombines back into the upper level, and then spontaneously emits a line photon in returning to the lower level. The quantity T^* is a radiation temperature. The last term, $\epsilon B_\lambda(T_e)/(1+\eta+\epsilon)$, is the collision term which accounts for spontaneous emission from the upper level created by direct collisional excitation.

Photon Scattering

The scattering term in equation (4–105), $\langle J_\lambda \rangle/(1+\eta+\epsilon)$, accounts for photons which cause the atom to undergo the transitions $l \rightarrow u \rightarrow l$. If the scattering is coherent, $\langle J_\lambda \rangle$ should be replaced simply by J_λ. In this case, a wavelength dependence is

---

[2] Much of the following discussion of the steady state of a gas and the resulting NLTE line formation mechanisms are extensively treated by Jefferies (1968) and Thomas and Athay (1961).

introduced into $S_\lambda{}^l$. A line, which is only naturally broadened and whose lower level is the atom's ground level, scatters coherently in its own reference frame. The atom, excited by the incoming photon, must return to a lower level which has an infinite lifetime and no corresponding uncertainty in energy. Hence, the incoming and scattered photons are of the same energy. On the other hand, Doppler broadening causes noncoherent scattering because a photon absorbed by a moving atom has an equal probability of being scattered in any direction. The Doppler shifts of the incoming and scattered photons are not the same and a redistribution of photons over the Doppler profile will occur. In the case of complete redistribution, $S_\lambda{}^l = \langle J_\lambda \rangle$. Pressure broadening, in which the time between collisions is much less than the lifetime of the excited level, also produces noncoherent scattering; the wavelengths of the incoming and scattered photons are uncorrelated. In general, scattering in the solar atmosphere is noncoherent and leads to a complete redistribution of photons over the line profile, except for the natural-broadened wings of resonant lines.

An important result of this redistribution is that a photon will tend to diffuse, not only in space but also in wavelength in a direction away from line center where resistance to escape from the atmosphere is lower. Thus, if noncoherent scattering were the only mechanism contributing to the line source function in the solar atmosphere, dark absorption lines would still result.

Photoelectrically Controlled Lines

A line profile may tend to have either of two distinct characteristics, depending upon whether its source function is photoelectrically or collisionally controlled. If $\eta B_\lambda(T^*) \gg \epsilon B_\lambda(T_e)$, $S_\lambda{}^l$ is controlled by photoelectric rather than collisional processes. The production of new line photons is dependent on the fluorescence mechanism. Also, because $B_\lambda(T_e)$ is usually the same magnitude as, or significantly greater than, $B_\lambda(T^*)$, ϵ/η must also be very much less than unity. The removal of the upper levels is dominated by spontaneous emissions and photoelectric absorptions, with collisional deexcitation playing a negligible role. The important distinction is that for photoelectrically controlled lines, the source function is associated not with the local electron temperature, but with the electron temperature at significantly greater depths where the continuum radiation responsible for the fluorescence is produced. The ratio N_u/N_l is more characteristic of the low-temperature photosphere continuum radiation rather than the high-temperature chromospheric electron temperature. This effect plus the photon leak results in a source function that decreases monotonically outward in the atmosphere and in an emergent line intensity that decreases monotonically toward line center. The classification of source functions into those which are collisionally controlled and those which are photoelectrically controlled does not mean that there is a sharp and absolute division between the two types. Instead, the classification defines tendencies only. Source functions which are classified as having a tendency to be photoelectrically controlled can also be significantly influenced by collisions. The reverse holds true for collisionally controlled lines. The classification for resonance lines of idealized two-level

TABLE 4-II.—Classification of S_λ^l for Resonance Lines of Atoms and Ions for an Idealized Two-Level Atom

[From Thomas, 1957]

Class	Excitation (E_{12}) and ionization (E_∞) energies	Examples	ϵ/η	$\dfrac{\epsilon B_\lambda(T_e)}{\eta B_\lambda(T^*)}$	Upper state removal	Control of S_λ^l
1	E_{12} and E_∞ large ($\gtrsim 10$ eV)	H I, He I, He II, other nonmetals	$\ll 1$	$\gg 1$	Spontaneous emission +photoelectric absorption	Collision
2	E_{12} small (~ 3 eV) and E_∞ large	Ca II, Mg II	$\gg 1$	$\gg 1$	Spontaneous emission +collisional de-excitation	Collision
3	E_{12} and E_∞ small ($\lesssim 7$ eV)	Na I, Mg I, Al I, K I, neutral metals, H I Balmer series	$\ll 1$	$\ll 1$	Spontaneous emission +photoelectric absorption	Photoelectric

atoms and ions in the solar atmosphere is shown in table 4–II. In general, it is seen that only when the excitation and ionization energies are small can the relatively low-temperature continuum radiation flux from the photosphere dominate the production and removal of upper levels. Although the excitation and ionization energies of H I (10.2 and 13.6 eV, respectively) clearly place it in class 1, the Balmer series is placed in class 3. This is done because the Hα, Hβ, Hγ, etc., transitions effectively use the first excited level of hydrogen as a ground level (excitation and ionization energies of 1.9 and 3.4 eV, respectively) and detailed balance exists between the hydrogen ground level and first excited level in the region where the Balmer lines are formed.

As an example of a photoelectrically controlled source function (class 3), the Hα line will be considered. The observed profile is shown in figure 4–30 where the transition from a Doppler-broadened core to pressure-broadened wings is displayed. The kinetic temperature and excitation temperatures for Hα, Hβ, and Hγ as functions of $\tau_{\lambda_0}(\text{H}\alpha)$ are shown in figure 4–31. The continuum source function is $B_\lambda(T_e)$, while the line source functions are $B_\lambda(T_{ex})$. The location of $\tau_{\lambda_0}(\text{H}\alpha)=1$ is approximately 2500 ± 700 km (White and Wilson, 1966). The monotonic decrease of T_{ex} and increasing difference between T_{ex} and T_e with increasing height, which are characteristic of photoelectrically controlled lines, are well illustrated in figure 4–31. According to White (1964), $T_{ex} < T_e$ down to an optical depth of 30 at Hα line center. As we move outward through the photosphere into the chromosphere, the photon leak to free space becomes large, the effect of photoelectric excitations and ionizations is diminished, and N_u becomes underpopulated with respect to the value of N_u in LTE. In fact, N_u/N_l actually decreases with height. Thus, $S_\lambda{}^l$ also decreases with height, and we find both limb darkening and a monotonic decrease of $I_\lambda(0, \theta)$ as the displacement from line center goes to zero.

As we observe farther out in the wings of Hα, the origin of the radiation shifts from the chromosphere down into the photosphere. Altitudes are finally reached where T_{ex} and T_e are equal. According to Gompertz and Hindmarsh (1969), $T_{ex}(\text{H}\alpha)$ and $T_{ex}(L\alpha)$ are the same as T_e in the range $0.2 \leq \tau_\lambda{}^c \leq 1.0$. This corresponds to wavelengths at least 1.3 Å from Hα line center (six Doppler widths at ~6000 K).

Collisionally Controlled Lines

If $\epsilon B_\lambda(T_e) \gg \eta B_\lambda(T^*)$, $S_\lambda{}^l$ is controlled by collisional processes rather than by photoelectric absorption and can acquire completely different characteristics. When the rate of production of upper states by direct collisional excitations ($N_l C_{lu}$) is no longer negligible, the ratio N_u/N_l, hence $S_\lambda{}^l$, tends to be driven toward LTE values at the local value of T_e. Because T_e increases rapidly with height in the chromosphere, $S_\lambda{}^l$ can also increase for a range of heights above the temperature minimum. This appears formally through the term $\epsilon B_\lambda(T_e)$. However, the effect of this term eventually becomes comparable to and then less than $\eta B_\lambda(T^*)$ because of the decrease of $N_e (\epsilon = N_e C_{21}[T_e]/A_{21})$. Approximately at this point $S_\lambda{}^l$ again

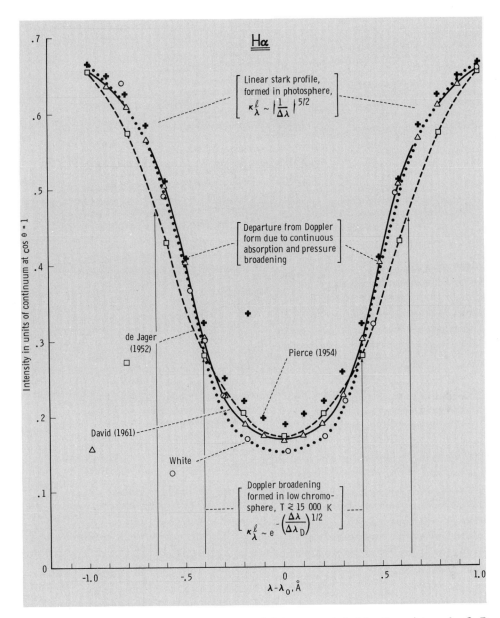

FIGURE 4-30.—Hα line profile. The four sources of data are as plotted for the quiet sun by O. R. White (1962). The average height of formation of the Hα line center is 2500 ± 700 km (White and Wilson, 1966). This height will be larger on the chromospheric network and smaller in the supergranular cells off the network. At $|\Delta\lambda| > 0.8$ Å, the radiation originates primarily in the photosphere.

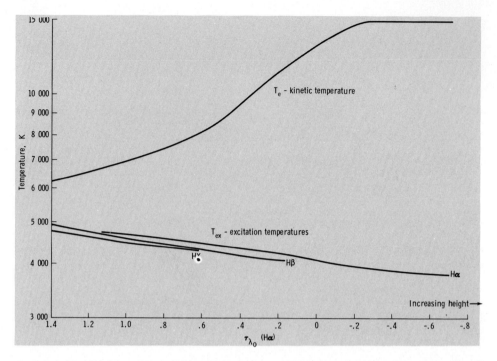

F<small>IGURE</small> 4–31.—Kinetic and excitation temperatures of the Balmer series. The increasing divergence with increasing height between the kinetic temperature $[S_\lambda{}^l = B_\lambda(T_e)]$ and the excitation temperature $[S_\lambda{}^l = B_\lambda(T_{ex})]$ for photoelectrically controlled lines is evident. Also evident is the monotonic decrease of $T_{ex}[S_\lambda{}^l]$ with height which leads to limb darkening and a monotonic decrease observed in $I_\lambda(H\alpha)$ as we move toward line center. A third point to observe is that over this limited range in the atmosphere, the line source functions $B_\lambda(T_{ex})$ differ only slightly from line to line for the three Balmer lines investigated. (Data from White, 1964.)

decreases with height because of the presence of the large photon leak and the resulting decrease of $\eta B_\lambda(T^*)$. We shall see that the maximum in $S_\lambda{}^l(h)$ leads to self-reversed line profiles in the cores of strong lines. For weak lines, this is not observed because they are formed primarily in the photosphere and low chromosphere where T_e does not experience a large and rapid rise.

The H and K lines of ionized calcium are the two strongest absorption lines in the solar spectrum (equivalent widths of 15 and 20 Å, respectively). The profiles of their cores at several distances from the limb are shown in figure 4–32. The slight emission peaks in the H line and pronounced peaks in the K line at approximately ± 0.2 Å from line center are evident. The strength and self-reversed emission core of Ca K makes it a most useful wavelength for observing chromospheric structure with high contrast (see fig. 2–15 and discussion in ch. 5). The center of the line, $K3$, is formed at approximately 1800 km; the emission peaks, $K2$, are formed at

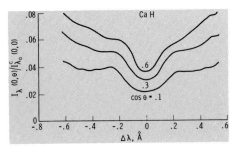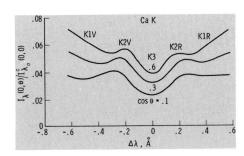

FIGURE 4–32.—Self-reversed emission cores of Ca H and K. The line intensity at several distances
from the limb, $I_\lambda(0, \theta)$, normalized by the continuum intensity at disk center and line center,
$I_{\lambda_0}{}^c(0, 0)$ is plotted versus the distance from line center. Note the very low central intensities,
0.02 to 0.04, and the emission peaks at ± 0.2 Å from line center. (From Zirker, 1967; copyright 1967, D. Reidel.)

approximately 700 km where $T_e \simeq 7000$ K; and the sides of the line outside of the
peaks, $K1$, are formed in and below the region of the temperature minimum (Athay,
1970).

The low excitation potential (≈ 3 eV) and high ionization potential (~ 12 eV)
for Ca II place the source function for the H and K lines in class 2 (table 4–II).
Thus, the production of new line photons is dominated by collisions. The calculated
line source function, shown for Ca K in figure 4–33, displays the characteristic
maximum in the chromosphere. Mg II has an outer electron configuration like Ca II
and has H and K resonance lines which also fall into class 2. The line source function
and computed line profiles of Mg H, Mg K, and $B_\lambda(T_e)$ are shown in figure 4–34.
The emission peaks observed in the H and K lines of Mg II are more pronounced
than those of Ca II. The correspondence between the line source functions and the
line profiles is as follows. Low in the photosphere, LTE prevails and $S_\lambda{}^l = B_\lambda(T_e)$.
As we move through the temperature minimum, where the photon leak is appre-
ciable, but $S_\lambda{}^l$ remains closely coupled to and parallel to $B_\lambda(T_e)$. The strength of
this coupling is measured by ϵ, which is directly proportional to N_e and is only
slightly dependent on T_e. As we move into the sharp temperature rise in the chromo-

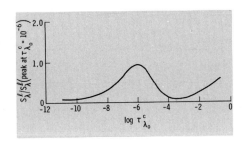

FIGURE 4–33.—The Ca K line source func-
tion. The peak at $\tau_{\lambda_0}{}^c \simeq 10^{-6}$ corresponds to
the $K2$ emission peaks formed at approxi-
mately 700 km and 7000 K. For $\tau_{\lambda_0}{}^c > 10^{-6}$,
$S_\lambda{}^l$ approaches $B_\lambda(T_e)$ and reflects the
variation of the temperature minimum.
(From Athay and Skumanich, 1968b; copyright 1968, D. Reidel.)

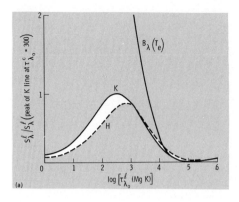 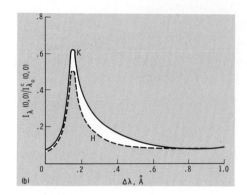

FIGURE 4–34.—Mg II H and K line formation. (a) Mg II H and K line source functions. (b) Mg II H and K computed line profiles. (From Athay and Skumanich, 1968a; copyright 1968, D. Reidel.)

sphere, $S_\lambda{}^l$ reaches a maximum which corresponds to $K2$. The coupling becomes weak as we move higher, because of the decrease of N_e, and the photon leak allows N_u/N_l and $S_\lambda{}^l$ to relax to low NLTE values. The magnitude of the emission peaks is dependent upon the rate of temperature rise, the height variation of the coupling (ϵ), the optical depth of the chromosphere, and the height variation of the absorption coefficient profile (Athay and Skumanich, 1968a).

The models of the solar atmosphere, which are found to yield calculated H and K profiles and center-to-limb variations matching the observations, are characterized by a low-temperature minimum ($\approx$4200 K), a very rapid temperature rise in the chromosphere, and a chromosphere which is optically thick in H and K (Athay and Skumanich, 1968a and b; and Dumont, 1967 and 1969). The fact that we have been able to produce these atmospheric models and an NLTE theory which result in fair agreement with observations is a significant step forward. However, inspection of the details of the real solar atmosphere reveals that our model is still greatly simplified. Figure 2–15, the Ca K photographs to which we previously referred, and the Hα photographs of figure 2–17 reveal that there is much structure to the quiet sun. Clearly, significant nonhomogeneities exist across the surface which must be included in our models. In addition, we shall see that the atmosphere is not static but has several organized velocity patterns within it which cause local Doppler shifts of the total absorption coefficient. Thus, the real description of emission from the atmosphere of the quiet sun should include not only NLTE effects, but must adequately treat spatial nonhomogeneities and time-dependent dynamic phenomena.

We now turn to a discussion of these organized velocity patterns and the nonhomogeneous atmospheric structure. We explore what role they play in the flow of solar energy from the interior to free space.

REFERENCES

ALLER, L. H.: 1963, The Atmosphere of the Sun and Stars. New York: Ronald Press.

ATHAY, R. G.: 1970, Emission Cores in H and K Lines. V. Asymmetries in K_2 and K_3. Solar Phys. *11*, 347–354.

ATHAY, R. G.; AND SKUMANICH, A.: 1968*a*, Emission Cores in H and K Lines. I. The Optically Thick Chromosphere. Solar Phys. *3*, 181–203.

ATHAY, R. G.; AND SKUMANICH, A.: 1968*b*, Emission Cores in H and K Lines. IV. Center-to-Limb Variation. Solar Phys. *4*, 176–184.

BONNET, R. M.; AND BLAMONT, J. E.: 1968, Limb-Darkening Observations Between 1800 and 2900 Å. Solar Phys. *3*, 64–81.

BRANDT, J. C.; AND HODGE, P. W.: 1964, Solar System Astrophysics. New York: McGraw-Hill.

CHANDRASEKHAR, S.: 1960, Radiation Transfer. New York: Dover.

DUMONT, S.: 1967, Contribution to the Study of the Transition Zone Between the Photosphere and Chromosphere From the Resonance Lines of Ca II and Mg II. Ann. Astrophys. *30*, 861–866.

DUMONT, S.: 1969, On the Interpretation of the Center-Limb Observations of Ca II Emission Cores. Astron. Astrophys. *2*, 45–51.

EDDY, J. A.; LÉNA, P. J.; AND MacQUEEN, R. M.: 1969, Far Infrared Measurement of the Solar Minimum Temperature. Solar Phys. *10*, 330–341.

GINGERICH, O.; AND DE JAGER, C.: 1968, The Bilderberg Model of the Photosphere and Low Chromosphere. Solar Phys. *3*, 5–25.

GINGERICH, O.; NOYES, R. W.; KALKOFEN, W.; AND CUNY, Y.: 1971, The Harvard-Smithsonian Reference Atmosphere. Solar Phys. *18*, 347–365.

GOMPERTZ, G.; AND HINDMARSH, W. R.: 1969, The Interpretation of the Wing of the Solar Line Hα. Mon. Notic. Roy. Astron. Soc. *142*, 97–112.

GRIEM, H. R.: 1964, Plasma Spectroscopy. New York: McGraw-Hill.

HARRIS, D. L.: 1948, On the Line-Absorption Coefficient Due to Doppler Effect and Damping. Astrophys. J. *108*, 112–115.

JEFFERIES, J. T.: 1968, Spectral Line Formation. Waltham, Mass.: Blaisdell.

LABS, D.; AND NECKEL, H.: 1968, The Radiation of the Solar Photosphere From 2000 Å to 100 μ. Z. Astrophys. *69*, 1–73.

PARKINSON, W. H.; AND REEVES, E. M.: 1969, Measurements in the Solar Spectrum Between 1400 and 1875 Å With a Rocket-Borne Spectrometer. Solar Phys. *10*, 342–347.

PAULING, L.; AND WILSON, E., JR.: 1935, Introduction to Quantum Mechanics. New York: McGraw-Hill.

PIERCE, A. K.; AND WADDELL, J.: 1961, Analysis of Limb Darkening Observations. Mem. Roy. Astron. Soc. *68*, 89–112.

THOMAS, R. N.: 1957, The Source Function in a Non-Equilibrium Atmosphere. I. The Resonance Lines. Astrophys. J. *125*, 260–274.

THOMAS, R. N.; AND ATHAY, R. G.: 1961, The Physics of the Solar Chromosphere. New York: Interscience.

WARNER, B.: 1964, Solar Curves of Growth for Neutral Iron. Mon. Notic. Roy. Astron. Soc. *127*, 413–427.

WHITE, O. R.: 1962, The Center to Limb Variation of Hα, Hβ, and Hγ in the Solar Spectrum. Ph.D. dissertation, Univ. of Colorado.

WHITE, O. R.: 1964, On the Empirical Temperature Structure of the Solar Chromosphere. Astrophys. J. *140*, 1164–1169.

WHITE, O. R.; AND WILSON, P. R.: 1966, On the Height of Formation of H-Alpha in the Solar Chromosphere. Astrophys. J. *146*, 250–255.

ZIRIN, H.: 1966, The Solar Atmosphere. Waltham, Mass.: Blaisdell.

ZIRKER, J. B.: 1967, The Solar H and K Lines of Ionized Calcium. Solar Phys. *3*, 164–180.

5

The Chromosphere

Our model of the quiet sun began in the radially symmetric core where energy is generated through nuclear fusion reactions. This energy is carried outward by radiation diffusion and convection and is liberated to space by the very thin photosphere. We have considered the sun to be uniform over any given layer; that is, none of the physical properties vary over an area of fixed solar radius. However, even in the case of the quiet sun, this is not physically correct. Fluid motions that originate in the convection zone produce observable nonuniformities in the overlying atmospheric velocity, radiation emission, and magnetic field. The principal velocity patterns identified to date are those of granulation, supergranulation, and vertical oscillations. These are of fundamental importance in determining the characteristics of the solar atmosphere by establishing an organized magnetic-field structure and by aiding the outward propagation of nonradiative energy. Although these velocity patterns are basically quiet-sun characteristics and are not dependent upon solar activity for their existence, limited interaction between quiet- and active-sun processes occurs. For example, the formation of granules is altered by the very strong magnetic fields within sunspots, and the progression of the solar cycle is related to the poleward diffusion of magnetic fields via supergranulation (sec. 2.8). Our concept of uniformity is altered so that we now consider the properties of the organized velocity patterns to be uniform but not the local physical properties of the solar material. Model atmospheres, such as the HSRA, can be considered as giving only gross mean values, which must suffice until the details of the nonuniformities are better understood and can be included in the calculations. The processes that produce the nonuniformities are nonlinear in nature; the fluctuations of physical properties about average values must be considered in determining mean values of the source function in the real solar atmosphere.

In the layer above the photosphere, the velocity and structural nonuniformities change in character and become very much more pronounced. Even though different features become dominant, they are still directly related to the velocity fields below. The magnetic fields in the photosphere are easily shuffled about by the gas motions. However, as we move up into the less dense chromosphere, these fields do not differ greatly in strength, but they now control the gas motions and the resulting atmospheric structure. Thus, the chromosphere resembles a light froth on top of the turbulent photosphere, a froth that is magnetically coupled to the dynamics below. The flamelike structures called spicules, which leap high into the corona, and the network pattern visible in the chromosphere offer evidence of this magnetic-field coupling.

The convective turbulence not only leads to observed nonuniformities in atmospheric structure above but also is responsible for the somewhat surprising rapid rise in temperature in the chromosphere. On the average, the temperature decreases at a rate of 23 K/km from the core to the photosphere. Yet in a range of only 2000 km in the chromosphere, the temperature jumps back up to approximately 10^6 K at an average rate of 500 K/km. As has been previously noted, this puzzling occurrence may be explained by consideration of the mechanical energy generated in the convective motions. Rather than being dissipated where it is generated, some of this mechanical energy propagates outward and is dissipated in the tenuous chromosphere and corona which results in an abrupt temperature rise. The high temperature above the photosphere causes the radiation emission to be concentrated in the UV and XUV. This emission can be observed directly during an eclipse when the moon covers the photosphere and only a crescent-shaped slice of the chromosphere is seen. Fraunhofer lines normally seen in absorption are then seen in emission along with many UV and XUV lines.

We have delayed discussion of the atmospheric velocity fields to this point so that cause and effect can be considered together. The macroscopic gas motions in the convection zone produce the observed velocity fields. These, in turn, produce the pronounced chromospheric structures and the sharp temperature rise. In attempting to explain the observations, we should be careful not to allow the attraction of currently plausible and esthetically pleasing physical models to underplay the real difficulties of interpretation. In most cases, the detailed structure of the velocity fields and chromospheric structures have not been observed with sufficient spatial, temporal, and spectral resolution to validate current theories. Thus, even though it is useful to have physical models in mind when discussing the observations, these models must be regarded as being tentative and will be refined or replaced as better observations become available.

5.1 ORGANIZED VELOCITY PATTERNS

Granulation

Granulation is easily observed in white light if a resolution of a few arcseconds can be obtained, as shown in figure 5–1. Granulation was the first and most apparent quiet-sun nonuniformity observed, and consequently, the one which has received the most study. The characteristics of granulation are summarized in table 5–I.

Granules are seen to be relatively bright cells of irregular polygonal shape separated by narrow dark lanes. The average distance between cells is approximately 1800 km. However, there is a wide range in possible cell sizes, as shown in figure 5–2; brighter cells tending to be larger (Namba and Diemel, 1969). Occasionally, there are relatively large intercell dark areas which appear to result from the absence of a granule. These areas are characteristic of granulation. They should not be confused with pores, which are small sunspot umbra that have no penumbra and have diameters of less than approximately 1500 km (Simon and Weiss, 1970). Pores are also darker and longer lived (Bray and Loughhead, 1967). Because of the convective motion present, relatively hotter gases surge up from below, form a bright granule, cool by radiating away their excess energy, and then flow downward in the relatively thin, dark channels between cells. What we actually see are the tops of the convective cells that have penetrated into the photosphere. This velocity pattern is not stable, and a granule will last an average of only 10 min. By that time it will have faded away, broken up, or coalesced with another granule.

The average variation in temperature from cell center to edge is a difficult quantity to determine. Estimates range from somewhat greater than 100 K (Bray and Loughhead, 1967) to as high as 2000 K (Wilson, 1969a and b) because the calculations of the mean temperature variation depend upon the accuracy of measured intensity variations. A large uncertainty exists here because the observations do not have sufficient resolution to clearly resolve the dark narrow lanes between granules so that a lower limit on intensity can be determined. In fact, the smearing of white-light detail by the effect of atmospheric "seeing" can produce features on a photograph like those normally attributed to granulation (Musman, 1969). Because of the limits imposed on resolution by atmospheric turbulence and diffraction-limited optics, finer details of granulation cannot be observed unless large telescopes are flown above the atmosphere or large earthbound vacuum telescopes are utilized. Some of the highest resolution white-light photographs so far obtained are from the 80 000-foot balloon flights of a 12-inch telescope made during Project Stratoscope (1957 to 1959).

Estimates of the vertical velocity of the convective motion range from approximately 0.3 to 3.0 km/sec. The downward velocity at the edges of the cells is relatively high and is confined to the narrow dark channels. Thus, like the temperature variations, the lack of high resolution (0.1 arcsec) restricts the accuracy of velocity determinations. High-resolution spectrograms, such as the one shown in figure 5–3, exhibit Doppler displacement of the absorption lines caused by granule motion. There is some correlation between a line shift to the blue (upward velocity) and the bright areas in the continuum. However, the correlation is not good quantitatively because the granule velocities are partially masked by a superimposed pattern of vertical oscillations, which will be discussed shortly. Assuming a value of 0.5 km/sec for the upward velocity at the center of a cell and a thickness of 400 km, a transit time of 13 min is obtained. This time is comparable with the mean cell lifetime of 10 min. Thus, a rising blob of relatively hot expanding gas at cell center breaks up into disordered motion and dissipates in a time comparable with its turnover time. This breakup and dissipation is characteristic of nonstationary convection and is in direct contrast to stationary convection in which an element of gas makes many round trips through the same fixed velocity structure.

The existence of granulation is independent of solar activity. Its properties have not been observed to vary with the phase of the solar cycle, location of the surface, or proximity to active regions. The only effects so far detected are the decrease in cell size and the lengthening of lifetime in the most intense magnetic

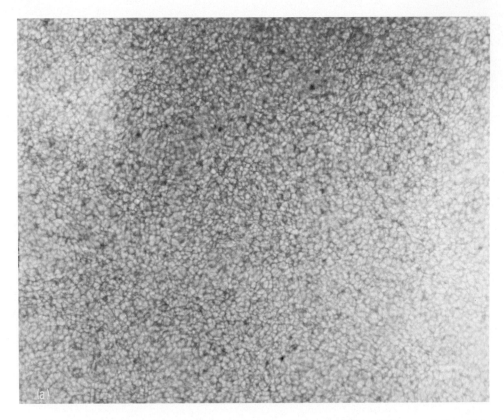

FIGURE 5-1.—Ground-based observations of solar granulation. (*a*) White-light granulation. This photograph was made with the vacuum telescope at Sacramento Peak Observatory and is of exceptional quality for a ground-based observation. It well illustrates the uniformity of the granulation pattern over a large area of the quiet sun. (Courtesy of R. Dunn, Sacramento Peak Observatory, Air Force Cambridge Research Laboratories.)

fields of sunspots. As discussed in section 3.2, the atmosphere becomes convectively unstable as we move upward in the region below the photosphere because of a steepening of the temperature gradient, caused primarily by the opacity increase. As a bubble of fluid moves upward, the temperature external to the bubble drops off more rapidly than the internal temperature. The result is a decreasing density within the bubble relative to its environment, causing it to be buoyed farther upward. Quantitatively, the condition for instability is stated by equation (3–11), the Schwarzschild condition. The bubble will continue to move upward to the region where the atmosphere again becomes stable, and we anticipate that an overshoot above this region will occur. Because the existence of this convective instability is independent of the presence of solar magnetic fields, granulation certainly should be regarded as a basic atmospheric process of the quiet sun.

|←——— 48 arcsec ———→|

FIGURE 5–1 (concluded).—Ground-based observations of solar granulation. (b) Large quiet region of solar granulation. Compared with (a), this photograph has a somewhat lower resolution but is still good for a ground-based observation. Individual cells and the separating dark channels are evident. (Courtesy of S. Smith and B. Nolan, Lockheed Solar Observatory.)

The recombination of hydrogen, which is partially responsible for granulation, occurs primarily in a relatively thin zone just below the photosphere. This recombination zone is shown in figure 5–4 where the energy that is stored in ionization relative to the total energy (thermal plus ionization) is plotted as a function of height. The gas is highly unstable in the region where the ionization energy is liberated rapidly with increasing height, from approximately −300 to 0 km. The thickness of this region (300 km) is approximately the same as the atmospheric scale height immediately below the photosphere (400 km). Thus, the scale of the granulation pattern (1800 km) is approximately four to five times the scale height, which is in agreement with existing theories of solar convection (Simon and Weiss, 1968).

TABLE 5–I.—Observations on Granulation Characteristics

Characteristic	Magnitude	Source
Mean intercell distance_____	2000 km (2.7 arcsec)	Mattig et al. (1969) and Leighton (1963)
	1800 km (2.5 arcsec)	Bray and Loughhead (1967)
	1100 km (1.5 arcsec)	Namba and Diemel (1969)
Width of dark lane between granules	<350 km (<0.48 arcsec)	Bray and Loughhead (1967) and Leighton (1963)
	250 km (0.34 arcsec)	Namba and Diemel (1969)
Mean lifetime of cell_____	10 min	Bray and Loughhead (1967)
	8.6 min	Bahng and Schwarzschild (1961)
Distance from limb to where granulation disappears	5 arcsec ($\cos \theta = 0.1$)	Bray and Loughhead (1967)
Variation in white-light rms intensity:		
at disk center, $\theta = 0$_____	14 percent	Edmonds (1962)
at maximum value, $\theta = 54°$_____	20.5 percent	Edmonds (1962)
Cell center-to-edge variation in temperature	>100 K	Bray and Loughhead (1967)
	≈2000 K (at h(HSRA)$\simeq$ −30 km)	Wilson (1969a and b)
Maximum rms temperature variation	$\simeq$600 K (at h(HSRA)$\simeq$ −30 km)	Wilson (1969a and b)
Vertical velocity of convective motion	≈0.3 km/sec	Zirin (1966)
	0.45 km/sec (rms)	Beckers and Parnell (1969)
	2.2 km/sec (spectrogram peak to peak)	Kirk and Livingston (1968)
	2.3 to 3.2 km/sec	de Jager and Neven (1968)
	≈3 km/sec ($h \approx 0$); very small ($h \gtrsim 150$ km)	Lambert and Mallia (1968)

Center-to-limb observations of the rms white-light continuum fluctuations also indicate that the observed granulation arises from a very shallow layer at the top of the convection zone. A peak in these fluctuations is observed at 53° (fig. 5–5(*a*)). Models generated by Wilson (1969*a* and *b*) to match these data (fig. 5–5(*b*)) are characterized by the following:

(1) a sharp peak (less than 80 km wide) in ΔT_{rms} at approximately −30 km (250 km below the HSRA height where $\tau_{5000} = 0.03$, as given by Wilson),

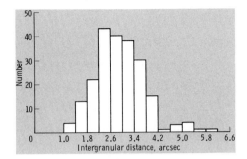

FIGURE 5–2.—Distribution of solar granulation size. (From Bray and Loughhead, 1967; copyright 1967, Chapman & Hall.)

(2) a surprisingly large value for the maximum ΔT_{rms} of 660 K, and

(3) a correspondingly large value for the maximum ΔT of 2000 K between hot and cold regions.

Closer to the limb, the granulation pattern becomes foreshortened and is not as well defined. However, granulation is still discernible to within 5 arcsec of the limb, where $\cos \theta = 0.10$ (fig. 5–6). At this height, the optical depth along the line of sight becomes unity at $\tau_{5000} \simeq \cos \theta \approx 0.1$, because the optical depth along the line of sight is approximately $\tau / \cos \theta$. Thus, the granule motion overshoots to a height of at least 140 km (HSRA) in the photosphere where the atmosphere is supposed to be convectively stable. Further evidence for an appreciable convective overshoot has been obtained from high-resolution spectrograms in three lines formed at various heights in the photosphere (Frazier, 1968a and b). The velocity and intensity fluctuations were observed for 55 min at 20-sec intervals. Velocity fluctuations in the 6371-Å line of Si II, formed between roughly -30 and $+90$ km (HSRA), show that 61 to 75 percent of the power in macroscopic gas motion is coherent and is in phase with the underlying granulation. Most important, 3.5 percent of this power is observed to penetrate all the way to the height of the temperature minimum. This represents an unexpectedly large amount of convective power transferred directly into the chromosphere. The convective velocity fluctuations are observed to be coherent and almost in phase at all three levels of line formation. Thus, an upward surging granulation cell at the surface of the convection zone displaces a large column of photospheric gas above it, coherently and in phase.

It is usually assumed, as we have done in our discussion to this point, that the atmosphere above the convection zone is convectively stable. The Schwarzschild condition for convective instability

$$\left| \frac{dT}{dr} \right|_{\mathrm{ad}} < \left| \frac{dT}{dr} \right|_{\mathrm{rad}} \tag{3–11}$$

is satisfied up to a height of zero (8 km in the HSRA). However, the Schwarzschild condition assumes that a bubble of fluid is displaced adiabatically. This is not strictly true for the gas motions in the solar atmosphere. If the assumption of adiabatic change is not made, it is found that convective instability will occur not

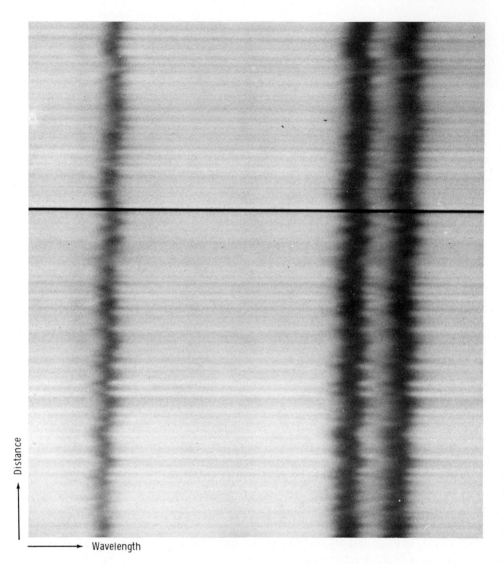

Distance →

Wavelength →

FIGURE 5–3.—High-resolution spectrogram. The three absorption lines shown are, from left to right, Fe I 5187.917, Ti II 5188.698, and Ca I 5188.852. The bright horizontal streaks are caused by the relatively bright continuum emission of granules dispersed in wavelength. The irregularities of the lines result from Doppler shifts induced by granular motion. A correspondence between the bright emission (horizontal bright lines indicating upward-moving material) and sharp Doppler shifts to the blue (left) can be seen. However, this correspondence is only approximate because the motion of the vertical oscillations partially masks the vertical velocities of the convective motion. There is some indication that the downward velocities (shifted to the right) are relatively larger than and confined to smaller areas than the upward velocities. (Courtesy of J. Evans, Sacramento Peak Observatory, Air Force Cambridge Research Laboratories.)

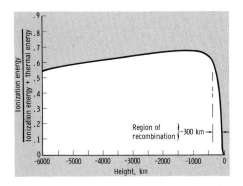

FIGURE 5–4.—Fraction of energy in ionization versus height.

only when the Schwarzschild condition is satisfied but also when the gas is thermally
unstable (Defouw, 1970a and b). That is, even though the temperature gradient
is positive in the chromosphere, the gas is convectively unstable if the net rate of
energy loss by radiation per mass of material increases with a decrease in temperature (thermally unstable). To quantitate thermal instability, we define $\mathcal{L}(\rho, T)$,
the energy loss function, as the rate of energy loss minus the rate of energy gain
per unit mass (Field, 1965). This function can be assumed to be independent of
pressure and not coupled to the radiation field by the radiation transfer equations
if the gas is optically thin. Thus, the change in the energy loss function is

$$d\mathcal{L} = \left(\frac{\partial \mathcal{L}}{\partial T}\right)_{\rho} dT + \left(\frac{\partial \mathcal{L}}{\partial \rho}\right)_{T} d\rho \qquad (5\text{–}1)$$

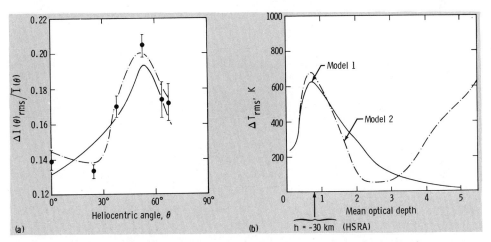

FIGURE 5–5.—Observed white-light continuum intensity fluctuations and calculated temperature
fluctuation of granulation. The intensity fluctuations as a function of distance from sun center
obtained from Project Stratoscope data (Edmonds, 1962). The peak is at 53°. The curves
are for two models generated by Wilson (1969a and b). (b) The corresponding temperature
fluctuations of these two models.

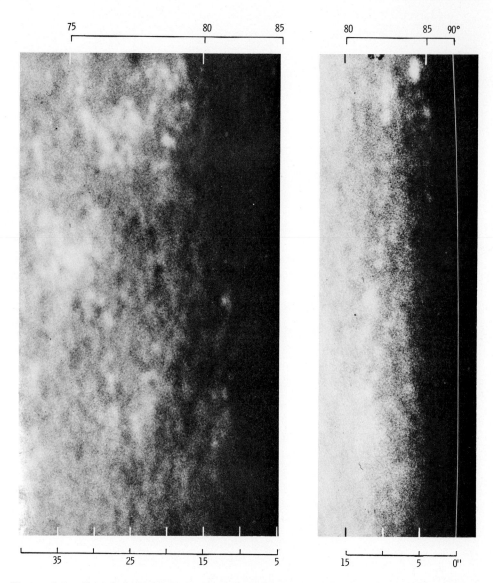

FIGURE 5-6.—Granulation at the solar limb. Both prints were made from a negative which was produced by the 5-inch photoheliograph at Sydney, Australia. The white line at 90° shows the portion of the limb derived from the negative. (From Bray and Loughhead, 1967; copyright 1967, Chapman & Hall.)

Using the perfect-gas relation

$$d\left(\frac{P}{\rho T}\right)=0 \qquad (5-2)$$

the rate of change of the energy loss function with temperature at constant pressure
is

$$\left(\frac{\partial \mathcal{L}}{\partial T}\right)_P = \left(\frac{\partial \mathcal{L}}{\partial T}\right)_\rho - \frac{\rho_0}{T_0}\left(\frac{\partial \mathcal{L}}{\partial \rho}\right)_T \qquad (5\text{-}3)$$

where the zero subscripts denote initial values. The gas will be thermally unstable if

$$\left(\frac{\partial \mathcal{L}}{\partial T}\right)_\rho - \frac{\rho_0}{T_0}\left(\frac{\partial \mathcal{L}}{\partial \rho}\right)_T < 0 \qquad (5\text{-}4)$$

Because the radiation loss rate can increase with density (radiative recombination
emission depends on the rate of binary collisions), $(\partial \mathcal{L}/\partial \rho)_T$ can be positive which
tends to produce thermal instability. The photosphere and the chromosphere, up
to the height where $T_e \approx 17\,500$ K, are both convectively and thermally stable
(Defouw, 1970b). Above this height thermal instability produces convective instability. Although no large velocity pattern has been identified with this phenomenon, Defouw suggests that convective instability could be a major factor in the
production of spicules and in the origin of the chromospheric temperature structure.
These points are considered in following sections.

Supergranulation

The second type of organized velocity pattern in the solar atmosphere, supergranulation, is of a more subtle nature observationally than normal granulation,
and only recently have we come to know its characteristics. Cellular motions in the
photosphere on a scale much larger than granulation were first detected many years
ago (Hart, 1956) and detailed observations subsequently were made (Leighton
et al., 1962). The technique of making a velocity-canceled spectroheliogram, per-
fected by Leighton, allows us to observe supergranulation directly. In figure 2–11
numerous velocity cells can be seen and they become more pronounced as we look
toward the limb. Because we are observing line-of-sight velocities, the velocities
are principally horizontal. The center of the disk appears nearly uniform, implying
that the vertical velocities are relatively small. The velocity cells themselves appear
to be almost symmetrical structures which become foreshortened as we move to
the limb. Close examination reveals that the dark part (receding velocities) of each
cell is toward the limb and the light side is toward sun center. Thus, there is an
outward expansion of gas from center to edge at the top of each cell. Because of its
similarity to granulation but larger length and time scales, this velocity pattern
has quite appropriately been termed "supergranulation."

The physical parameters of supergranulation evaluated by Leighton et al.
(1962) are in agreement with the results of subsequent investigations. They found
the average intercell spacing to be approximately 32 000 km with a range in values
extending from 20 000 to 54 000 km (fig. 5–7). Thus, the length scale is about
18 times larger than normal granulation. The lifetime, which is difficult to determine, has been assumed to be 20 hours (the approximate measured lifetime of the
chromospheric network). The principal basis for this assumption is the established

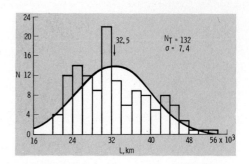

FIGURE 5–7.—Distribution of supergranulation size. (From Simon and Leighton, 1964; copyright 1964, University of Chicago Press.)

close connection between the chromospheric network and supergranulation. The average peak horizontal velocities within a cell are approximately 0.3 to 0.5 km/sec. This horizontal velocity increases slightly with depth (Deubner, 1971), as illustrated in figure 5–8. Because granulation and supergranulation coexist in the atmosphere, we might expect granulation cells to be swept toward the supergranular boundaries; evidence of this is observed (Simon, 1967). The upward velocities in the central region of a cell are relatively small, approximately 0.1 km/sec (Simon and Leighton, 1964, and Frazier, 1970). It is natural to anticipate that the material in the convective flow would return to deeper layers uniformly along the perimeter of each cell. However, in the low photosphere, "downdrafts" or small isolated areas of downward flow of approximately 0.1 km/sec are observed. These areas are primarily at the vertices of several cells (Frazier, 1970). Unlike the horizontal flow, the velocities of the vertical flow increase with altitude (Deubner, 1971). At the higher altitudes where $H\alpha\pm0.7$ Å and $H\beta\pm0.4$ Å are formed, downward velocities of 1 to 2 km/sec are observed (Simon and Leighton, 1964). From the continuity of mass flow ($\rho V \times area = constant$) and from the rapid decrease in density that occurs with height in the low chromosphere, we have a possible rationale for these observed changes.

In contrast to granulation, supergranulation does not appear as a brightness pattern, and the scale of the convection implies that the origin of its convective instability is at much lower depths. It has been suggested by Simon and Leighton that this convective stability is due to the recombination of He^+, which occurs at depths of 8000 to 2000 km, and He^{2+}, which occurs at depths of 20 000 to 10 000 km (fig. 3–3). A crude estimate of the diameter-to-depth ratio for an average cell shows granulation and supergranulation to be similar. For granulation, the intercell spacing is 1800 km and the effective depth of formation is 400 km, the scale height immediately below the photosphere. This depth-to-diameter ratio for granulation (4.5) and a cell size of 32 000 km for supergranulation yield a depth of 7100 km for supergranulation. If this is used as the effective depth of formation of supergranulation, it is seen to coincide with the recombination of He^+ (fig. 3–3). This depth is consistent with the time scale of supergranulation and with the approximate magnitude of upward velocity at cell center. Assuming nonstationary

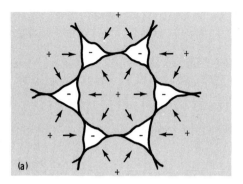 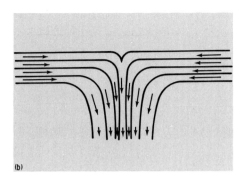

FIGURE 5–8.—Flow within solar granulation cells. (*a*) Top view; downflow is concentrated at vertices of cells. Direction of flow is indicated as upward (+), downward (−), and horizontal (arrow). (*b*) Vertical section of flow in region of vertex of several cells. Length of arrow denotes magnitude of velocity.

convection, the depth of formation is approximately 20 hours×0.1 km/sec = 7200 km. However, it is more compatible with existing theories of convection to associate the depth of formation with the scale height, which is equal to 7100 km at a depth of approximately 14 000 km. This coincides with the recombination of He^{2+} (fig. 3–3). In either case, because of the relatively small amount of helium present, a proportionately smaller amount of thermal energy is liberated by helium recombination when a fluid element moves to the surface. In addition, the fluid element takes much longer to rise from depth than in normal granulation. Thus, the temperature and brightness patterns would not be significantly perturbed. However, because of the lack of an adequate theory of solar convection, the association of supergranulation with helium recombination is tentative.

Granulation and supergranulation are similar in that both are driven by convective instabilities in the convection zone and their motions penetrate appreciably into the stable atmosphere above. It is quite remarkable that the convective processes manifest only those two distinct characteristic sizes, rather than a complete continuous range. Based on a crude model of the convection zone, it has been suggested that a third characteristic convective cell size of approximately 300 000 km exists (Simon and Weiss, 1968). Such giant cells or "hypergranulation" may explain the observed concentrations of active regions into complexes of activity (Bumba and Howard, 1965). Horizontal velocities of approximately 0.03 km/sec and lifetimes of about 14 months have been attributed to it (Bumba, 1967). We shall see in the following sections that, of these three types of granulation, supergranulation plays the fundamental role in establishing the magnetic structure of the nonuniform quiet chromosphere.

Vertical Oscillations

Granulation and supergranulation are both convective phenomena with which we have everyday experience such as building cumulus clouds or ascending smoke columns. However, supergranulation is not as readily anticipated nor as easily observed as granulation, and its origin and relation to other quiet-sun phenomena are open questions of fundamental importance. Equally intriguing and difficult to observe are the vertical atmospheric oscillations discovered approximately the same time as supergranulation (Leighton, 1960).[1] Physically, these oscillations of the solar surface are crudely analogous to the sloshing of waves on an ocean surface. In contrast to supergranulation, the oscillations are best seen at sun center because of their primarily vertical motion. The period of these oscillations is approximately 5 min and they occur in bursts that last many complete cycles. Their horizontal scale is approximately one to three times that of granulation and they have a peak velocity in the photosphere of approximately 0.4 km/sec. These vertical motions can be considered as only a perturbation of the quiescent atmosphere. The 5-min period and peak velocity of 0.4 km/sec, which is 1/18 of the photospheric sound speed, imply a displacement of only 1/5 of a scale height and an acceleration of only 1/30 of the local gravity.

The details of the causes and the effects of the oscillations are not well understood. Some of the mechanical energy of the convection zone is converted into the ordered motion of oscillations in the photosphere and chromosphere. It is possible that the buffeting turbulent motions underlying the photosphere have a wide range of frequencies and that the solar atmosphere acts as a filter by selecting and amplifying those close to a 5-min period. The degree to which this resonance amplification is dependent only on local conditions (traveling waves), or is a property of the total atmosphere having upper and lower boundary conditions (standing waves), is a basic question. It is also important to determine what role these oscillations play in transporting mechanical energy out of the convection zone to provide a non-radiative source for heating the upper atmosphere. The latter question is considered in section 5.2.

When we observe a "point" on the sun at a given wavelength, we are actually observing the radiation emitted from an approximately cylindrical volume (fig. 5–9). The cross section of the cylinder is set by the aperture of the instrument or the atmospheric seeing, whichever is limiting. The length is defined by the distance over which τ_λ changes from much less than 1 to much greater than 1; that is, the characteristic height of the contribution function at the wavelength of the observation. To make accurate observations of vertical oscillations, the velocity must be nearly uniform throughout the observed volume. Instruments which have a 1-arcsec resolution (aperture size and seeing effects combined) will be capable of resolving an oscillation with a horizontal wavelength no smaller than approximately 2300 km (π times 730 km). Also, lines of weak or moderate strength formed in the low

---

[1] Because vertical oscillations are thought to play an important role in the heating of the atmosphere and they have been under investigation for only a relatively short time, the current level of research effort in this area is high. Correspondingly, a more detailed discussion of oscillations is presented here.

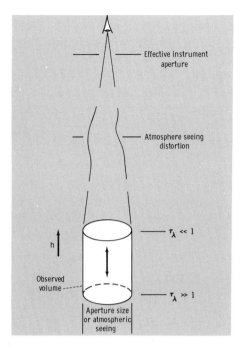

FIGURE 5–9.—Observation of an oscillating volume on the solar surface.

photosphere have contribution functions whose vertical scale is usually small compared to the scale for vertical velocity change. However, this is not the case for stronger lines formed in the chromosphere. Thus, extreme care must be exercised in interpreting the observations. We must always ask if the velocity is nearly uniform throughout the observed volume!

An excellent example of velocity-time histories for many points along a 2-arcmin line is shown in figure 5–10. Several features of vertical oscillations are well illustrated here. First, oscillations are almost always present to some degree. When large oscillations are observed, they usually begin and end with small amplitudes. That is, they do not start abruptly, as if excited by a single convective piston immediately below, and then decay. Rather, it appears that a steady oscillation is always present and transient "wave trains," smoothly modulated in amplitude, are superposed. The phase lifetime of the oscillation is considerably larger than the amplitude lifetime. Secondly, large lengths along the solar surface sometimes oscillate in phase. Although many points 3 to 6 arcsec apart oscillate independently of one another, phase coherence sometimes exists over 30 to 60 arcsec (22 000 to 44 000 km). These first two observations are consistent with those of Howard et al. (1968). Thirdly, horizontally moving waves, as detected by the motion of peak amplitudes, do exist. In figure 5–10, horizontal phase velocities of approximately 100 km/sec (Musman and Rust, 1970) are evident. These horizontal phase velocities can be followed over 30 to 50 arcsec. In figure 5–10, for example, they can be followed from 78 to 48 arcsec at 8 min, from 12 to 72 arcsec at 63 min, and from

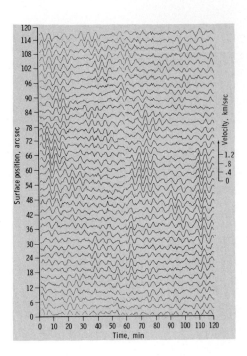

FIGURE 5–10.—Vertical velocity time history
for points on the solar surface separated by
intervals of 3 arcsec (2200 km). These
observed time histories were made by
Musman and Rust (1970) at the Sacramento Peak Observatory using the point-
scanning photoelectric Doppler-Zeeman
analyzer. Line shifts were measured to an
rms accuracy of 0.025 km/sec. An aperture
of 6 arcsec was used and a time resolution
of 35 sec was obtained. The observations
were made on January 7, 1969, on a region
of little activity close to the center of the
disk. (From Musman and Rust, 1970;
copyright 1970, D. Reidel.)

18 to 68 arcsec at 110 min. Lastly, velocity amplitudes of the oscillations range
from 0.2 to 0.6 km/sec.

The characteristics of the transient wave trains can be analyzed by averaging
data like those found in figure 5–10. In figure 5–11, the results of superposing
hundreds of velocity wave trains are shown with the accompanying average intensity oscillations in two absorption lines and in the continuum. It is seen that the
velocity and intensity oscillations have a period of approximately 5 min. Table 5–II
shows that a period of approximately 300 sec is usually observed and that it decreases with height. The decrease in amplitudes with time of the oscillation in
figure 5–11 is partially because of the superposed wave trains which have slightly
different periods slowly moving out of phase.

In figure 5–11, the continuum and the Fe I 5250 wing brightness oscillation
lead the velocity oscillation by significantly less than 90°. This is also observed to
be true for other lines formed low in the photosphere (Tanenbaum et al., 1969).
Oscillations of the Fe I 5250 core brightness and the Ca II $K232$ line, formed in
the chromosphere, lead the velocity oscillations by slightly more than 90°. The
oscillation of Fe I 6355, formed close to the temperature minimum, leads the
velocity by 117° (Frazier, 1968a). The phase lead for the intensity of Ca II $K1$ over
the velocity observed in two weak Fe I lines is equal to 90° (Jensen and Orrall,
1963). This variation with height of the relative phase of velocity and with intensity
changes should give insight into the nature of the oscillations. It is used to support

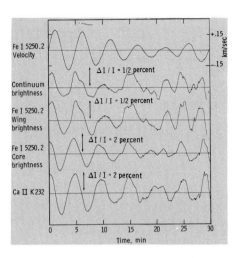

Fe I 5250.2 Velocity

Continuum brightness

Fe I 5250.2 Wing brightness

Fe I 5250.2 Core brightness

Ca II K232

FIGURE 5–11.—Superposed velocity and brightness oscillations. The velocity-time history was made by superposing several hundred separate wave trains from velocity-time histories such as those displayed in figure 5–10. The start of a wave train was defined by an upward velocity of greater than 0.1 km/sec (Tanenbaum et al., 1969). The brightness oscillations corresponding in time to the velocity wave trains were then also superposed. All of these brightness curves were synchronized with the Fe I 5250 velocity curve. The observations were made using a magnetograph with a 2.4-arcsec aperture at the Kitt Peak National Observatory. (From Tanenbaum et al., 1969; copyright 1969, D. Reidel.)

the contention that the oscillations are traveling waves in the photosphere and standing waves in the chromosphere (Tanenbaum et al., 1969). If the intensity of emission were in phase with the adiabatic temperature fluctuations of an oscillating element, which was always in pressure equilibrium with its surroundings, the intensity fluctuation would lead the vertical displacement by 180° and the velocity

TABLE 5–II.—Observations on Period of Vertical Oscillations

Period, sec	Source
$\simeq$300	Musman and Rust (1970)
300±6 "carrier"—several sidebands of varying power separated by 8.5×10⁻⁴ Hz (≈77 sec)	Gonczi and Roddier (1969)
306±6 (C I 5380)	Tanenbaum et al. (1969)
298±2 (Fe I 5250)	
288±6 (Na I 5896)	
280±11 (Mg I 5173)	
265 and 345 (2 peaks—same at 3 altitudes)	Frazier (1968a and b)
≈330 (several other peaks from 200 to 400)	Howard (1967)
300±54 (period decreases with height and as spectrum becomes broader)	Orrall (1965 and 1966)
273 (Fe I 3931 and Fe I 3937)	Jensen and Orrall (1963)
250 (Ca II K1 and Ca II K2)	
170 (Ca II K3)	
$\simeq$290 (in low photosphere and decreases slightly with altitude)	Noyes and Leighton (1963)
200 to 300 with mean value of 242 (decreases with altitude)	Evans and Michard (1962c)
296 (Fe I 5250)	Howard (1962)
296±3 (several photospheric lines)	Leighton et al. (1962)

by 90°. However, the following factors also must be considered in the interpretation of these data.

(1) The relaxation time for temperature perturbations is not infinite (adiabatic), but in the low photosphere it can be the same magnitude or much smaller than the period of oscillation.

(2) The intensity changes can be simply correlated with the temperature and density changes only for idealized collisionally controlled radiation production. For photoelectrically controlled radiation production and intermediate cases, the correlation is difficult to determine.

(3) The observed intensity fluctuations arise geometrically from the integrated effect of source function and optical depth variations all the way along the line of sight, not simply by the changes calculated following one fluid element.

(4) The pressure of an oscillating element can differ from that of its surroundings, as in a sound wave.

(5) The background continuum radiation intensity is not steady but includes the variations caused by evolving granulation cells.

These difficulties so far have precluded a rigorous interpretation of the observed phase relation for velocity and intensity oscillations through the use of realistic atmospheric models.

The type of data illustrated in figure 5–10 can be analyzed in a second way. Figure 5–12 (a) displays the time-autocorrelation functions, $C(\Delta t)$, for lines formed at three different heights and observed with exceptionally small apertures. If we start observing the vertical velocity of an element in steady-state oscillation at time t, we would expect that the product $v(t)v(t+\Delta t)$, normalized by $1/v^2(t)$, would oscillate between ± 1 with increasing Δt. The time-autocorrelation function averages the product $v(t)v(t+\Delta t)$ over the area of the observation and is also normalized to unity. In this way a measure of the covariance of the mean velocity field with time is obtained

$$C(\Delta t) = \frac{\langle\langle v(\mathbf{r}, t)v(\mathbf{r}, t+\Delta t)\rangle\rangle}{\langle\langle v^2(\mathbf{r}, t)\rangle\rangle} \tag{5-5}$$

$$C(\Delta t) = \frac{\int_0^{y_0}\int_0^{x_0} v(x, y, t)v(x, y, t+\Delta t)\, dx\, dy}{\int_0^{y_0}\int_0^{x_0} v^2(x, y, t)\, dx\, dy} \tag{5-6}$$

where $\mathbf{r}$ is the position vector on the solar surface, x and y are coordinates of a Cartesian coordinate system in which z is parallel to the local vertical, and the integrals are carried out over the area under observation $(x_0 y_0)$. These integrals become summations when the data are obtained from a large number of discrete regions inside the observed area. As seen in figure 5–12 (a), the oscillatory character

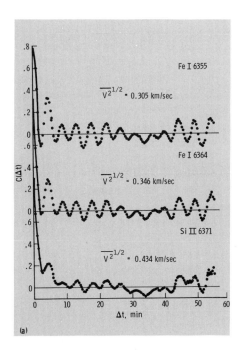

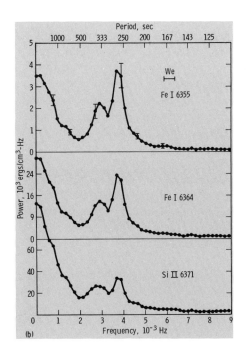

FIGURE 5–12.—Time autocorrelation of line-of-sight velocities and power spectra. The velocity data for these curves were obtained using the vertical spectrograph at the Kitt Peak National Observatory. The data were obtained from 13 strips, 170 by 6800 km, spaced 510 km apart and taken every 20 sec (Frazier, 1968a). The height of formation and approximate vertical scale of the contribution functions (HSRA) for the three lines investigated are Si II 6371, 30/120 km; Fe I 6364, 100/240 km; and Fe I 6355, 350/160 km, respectively. The observations were made on May 19, 1965, at the sun center when it was free of activity. The rms velocity amplitudes are given in figure 5–12(a). The 50-percent confidence limits and instrument resolution (We) are shown in figure 5–12(b) where the ordinates are kinetic energy, $\rho v^2/2$, per frequency interval. In both figures, the autocorrelation was calculated by separately averaging the data from the 13 strips over the x direction and then averaging the results, which essentially average over the y direction. (Data from Frazier, 1968a; copyright 1968, University of Chicago Press.)

is very evident even though $C(\Delta t)$ has decreased to 0.1 after only two cycles. This rapid initial damping is a result of the presence of convective velocities, which are not oscillatory, as well as the oscillations at all points not remaining in phase. However, after this initial damping, a most remarkable feature that appears is a long-term phase persistence of the oscillations; that is, a steady-state resonance. Twelve cycles lasting the total observing period of 55 min are easily distinguished. Also notable is an increase in amplitude after 40 min. Similar long-term modulation of the time-autocorrelation function, obtained using other data, is also observed. However, this modulation is not reproducible, even after many hours of observation (Howard, 1967).

The power spectrum, $\rho v^2/2$ per unit frequency interval, as a function of frequency, is shown in figure 5–12(b). The presence of appreciable low-frequency power, attributed to convective motions, is present for periods greater than 8 min, the approximate lifetime of a convection cell. It is seen that this power is relatively large in the Si II 6371 line formed low in the photosphere. The most interesting feature of these power spectra, however, is that the 300-sec oscillation is really composed of two components that do not change period with height: (1) a sharp, strong component at 265 sec and (2) a broader, relatively weak component at 345 sec. The 265-sec component increases in relative strength with height. The combination of these two components should produce a net oscillation with a 300-sec period modulated by a beating between the two components, with periods of 19 min in the initial data (fig. 5–10) and 38 min in the time-autocorrelation curves (fig. 5–12(a)). Consistent with this are the observations of Gonczi and Roddier (1969) which suggest that the lifetime of phase oscillation is much longer than that of the amplitude and is probably greater than 1 hour. Also, the amplitude is modulated such that the oscillation appears to come in wave trains about 11 min long and approximately 20 min apart. Thus, Frazier's small aperture (170 km) data, having two components, present a coherent picture of the oscillations. However, power spectra of observations acquired with significantly larger effective apertures, hence, low resolution, do not confirm these results. In figure 5–13 the power spectrum resembles a modulated wave consisting of a strong 300-sec peak that is always present, like a carrier wave, and of side peaks of lesser strength that resemble sidebands. Other observations show 6 to 10 peaks between 200 and 400 sec, often with none at 300 sec (Howard, 1967). To uniquely determine the detailed power spectrum of the oscillations, additional observations are required which simultaneously have an effective spatial resolution significantly higher than even that of Frazier's, a large area of observation (many wavelengths), high time resolution (a small fraction of a period), and long periods of data acquisition (many periods) to increase the statistical validity of the results.

The general characteristics of the variation in the power spectrum with height are better established (figs. 5–12(b) and 5–14). In the low photosphere, the power

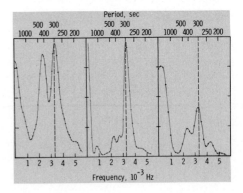

FIGURE 5–13.—Power spectra of oscillations. These observations were made using the Kitt Peak McMath solar telescope (Gonczi and Roddier, 1969). The Sr I 4607 line was used with an aperture between 3.6 and 10 arcsec in diameter. The lifetimes of the three recordings are, from left to right, respectively, 95, 120, and 75 min. (From Gonczi and Roddier, 1969; copyright 1969, D. Reidel.)

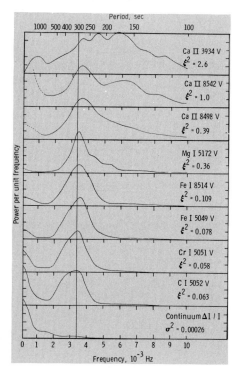

FIGURE 5–14.—Power spectra of oscillations as a function of height. The power is normalized to a maximum of unity for each line. The value of $\xi^2 = 2 \langle v^2 \rangle$, twice the peak energy per unit mass, is given for each line in (km/sec)^2. The lines are arranged from bottom to top in order of increasing height of formation in the atmosphere. The continuum is formed at $h \approx 0$ and Ca II 3934 (Ca $K3$) at $h \simeq 2000$ km. The data sources are as follows: for 3934, Orrall (1966); for 8542, 4898, 5172, and 8514, Evans et al. (1963); and for 5049, 5051, 5052, and the continuum, Edmonds et al. (1965). The effects of slow changes in the velocity field (frequency $<10^{-3}$ Hz) have been removed from the Ca $K3$ data before plotting. (From Noyes, 1967; copyright 1967, Academic Press.)

spectrum is dominated by convective power with periods greater than 8 min. As we move up toward the temperature minimum, the power centered around the 5-min oscillations becomes prominent and sharply peaked. In moving up to approximately a 2000-km altitude in the chromosphere, the resonance power spreads over a wider range of frequencies, shifts toward shorter periods, and acquires several individual peaks (Ca II 3934 or $K3$ in fig. 5–14). Also, in Ca II $K3$ a peak at approximately 18 to 20 min is apparent. It is to be noted that slow changes in the velocity field (frequency $<10^{-3}$ Hz) have been removed from the data (Orrall, 1966). The power spectrum of Hα, formed in approximately the same region of the chromosphere as Ca II $K3$, also displays a low-frequency peak (15-min period) and is associated with oscillations at supergranulation boundaries (Elliott, 1969).

The average velocity of the oscillations in the photosphere is within the range of 0.1 to 0.4 km/sec and increases with decreasing aperture size (fig. 5–15). The mean amplitude for the smallest aperture is 0.4 km/sec. To date, a correlation between amplitude and period of oscillation has not been discovered. However, oscillation amplitudes have been observed to decrease with the presence of medium-strength magnetic fields; a decrease of 25 percent for fields greater than 80 gauss (Howard, 1967) and a decrease of 33 percent for fields greater than 100 gauss (Deubner, 1967) have been observed. As noted in figure 5–14, the amplitudes also

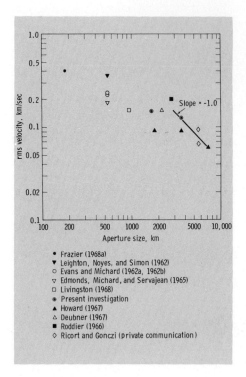

FIGURE 5–15.—Observed amplitude of rms velocity as a function of aperture size. In this summary of data, aperture size is the length of a square aperture equivalent to that actually used, equal in area to the circular one employed, or defined by the effective instrument resolution when an aperture was not used (Tanenbaum et al., 1969). The rms velocity is inversely proportional to aperture size for apertures larger than approximately 3000 km, as indicated by the straight line. (From Tanenbaum et al., 1969; copyright 1969, D. Reidel.)

increase with height. At the region of Hα formation, the peak velocity is 3.0 km/sec, giving an rms value of 2.1 km/sec (Deubner, 1969). Even though the energy per unit mass of oscillating elements increases with height, the energy per unit volume rapidly decreases because of the sharp decrease in density. Assuming an rms velocity of 0.4 km/sec and a density of 10^{-8} gram/cm³ (corresponding to a height of approximately 200 km), a mean kinetic energy density, $\langle \rho v^2/2 \rangle$, of 8 ergs/cm³ is calculated. At 2000 km, an rms velocity of 2 km/sec and a density of 2×10^{-13} gram/cm³ are assumed. A mean energy density of 2×10^{-3} erg/cm³ results which is a factor of 2.5×10^{-4} lower than that at 200 km.

Analogous to the periodicity in time, the vertical oscillations of the solar atmosphere also display a periodicity in space. In figure 5–16, oscillations in both space and time are evident. The vertical scale measures the magnitude of the autocorrelation function, which has been generalized from that previously used to include covariance with position on the solar surface as well.

$$C(\Delta \mathbf{r}, \Delta t) = \frac{\langle\langle\langle v(\mathbf{r}+\Delta \mathbf{r}, t+\Delta t)v(\mathbf{r}, t)\rangle_x\rangle_y\rangle_t}{\langle\langle\langle v^2(\mathbf{r}, t)\rangle_x\rangle_y\rangle_t} \qquad (5\text{–}7)$$

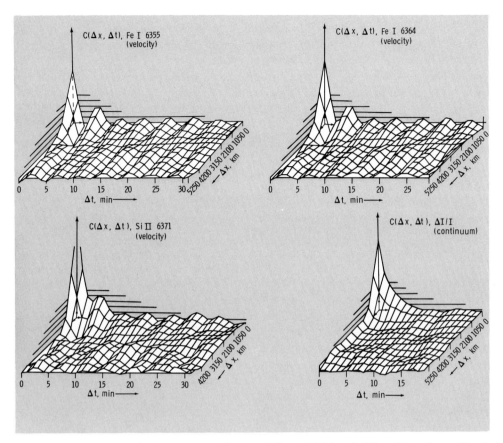

FIGURE 5–16.—Space and time autocorrelation of line-of-sight velocities. The observational parameters are the same as figure 5–12, but the correlation in space has been added. The autocorrelation for space is two dimensional. The autocorrelation was computed for one dimension only (x) at all values of the second dimension (y) and the resulting functions were averaged over y. The effective aperture was 170 km and the grid size was 510 km (Frazier, 1968a). The relative peak at the origin is partially attributed to the convective component which decreases in magnitude with height. The approximate heights of line formation are as follows: for Fe I 6355, 350 km; for Fe I 6364, 100 km; for Si II 6371, 30 km; and for continuum, 0 km. (From Frazier, 1968b; copyright 1968, Springer-Verlag.)

$$C\left(\Delta x,\,\Delta y,\,\Delta t\right) = \frac{\displaystyle\int_0^{t_0}\int_0^{y_0}\int_0^{x_0} v\left(x+\Delta x,\,y+\Delta y,\,t+\Delta t\right)v\left(x,\,y,\,t\right)\,dx\,dy\,dt}{\displaystyle\int_0^{t_0}\int_0^{y_0}\int_0^{x_0} v^2\left(x,\,y,\,t\right)\,dx\,dy\,dt} \tag{5-8}$$

where t_0 is the time duration of the observation. In the preparation of figure 5–16, finite summations over a grid pattern rather than integrals were used, Δy was zero in the calculations, and the results were subsequently averaged over all values of y. The rapid drop in the autocorrelation function as we move away from the origin is partially because of the presence of convective velocities and, for $\Delta x = 0$, oscillations at all positions not remaining in phase. In a corresponding manner for $\Delta t = 0$, oscillations at all points in time do not remain in phase for increasing Δx. That is, in the same way in which the periodicity in time is not the same at all points in space, the periodicity in space is not the same at all points in time. Also of interest in figure 5–16 is the uniform interweaving of the ridges formed by the cyclic variation of the autocorrelation function with Δx and Δt. Lastly, it is seen that the spatial wavelength of the observed oscillations is of the same size as the total scale of Δx, 4000 to 6000 km.

The time history of vertical velocities along a line across the solar surface is shown in figure 5–17 (Deubner, 1967). It is seen that the periodicity in time is much more definite than the periodicity in space. The mean linear distance between oscillating elements, averaged over many Doppler records like figure 5–17 by Deubner, is about 6 arcsec (4400 km). The distance is 9 arcsec (6600 km) if the weakest oscillations are neglected. The mean lifetime of the oscillations, obtained by tracing an oscillating element through as many cycles as are clearly recognizable, is 20 min, or 27 min when weaker oscillations are neglected. These times are about 60 percent larger in active regions. The most frequent lifetime for the stronger oscillations, both in and out of active regions, is 15 min. These times are compatible with the previously mentioned estimate of wave-train duration and with those apparent in figure 5–10. Unlike the data of figure 5–10, no high-velocity lateral propagation of disturbances (100 km/sec) were observed. However, disturbances were observed to propagate with essentially the speed of sound, 6 km/sec. A characteristic of fundamental importance, clearly illustrated in figure 5–17, is that oscillations usually begin and end with small amplitudes. From this characteristic, Deubner suggests that each oscillation is not excited by a single rising granule nor independent of adjacent elements. Rather, the oscillations consist of interwoven standing waves in which mutual interference of adjacent elements produces the observed 15- to 20-min modulation of amplitude. The accompanying variations of magnetic field are also shown in figure 5–17. They are seen to correspond only roughly to the stronger velocity oscillations. Magnetic-field oscillations also have been measured by Severnyi (1967), who found them to be less than 5 gauss in amplitude and to have a period of approximately 9 min.

The two-dimensional character of the oscillation field is clearly illustrated in figure 5–18. The oscillating cells are irregular in outline and cover almost the total surface. Despite the lack of spatial uniformity, the mean cell size of 7 to 8 arcsec (5100 to 5800 km) is well defined (Deubner, 1969). This is significantly larger than earlier estimates of element size: 1700 to 3500 km by Leighton et al. (1962); and 2000 to 3000 km by Evans and Michard (1962c). On the other hand, it is smaller than the spatial coherence length of 7700±2300 km determined by Howard et al.

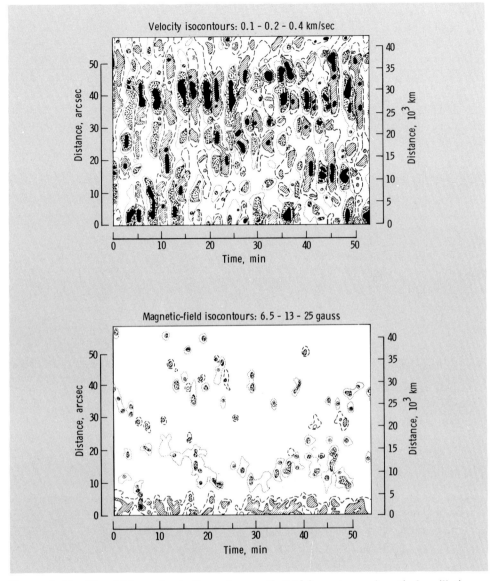

FIGURE 5–17.—Time history of velocity and magnetic-field isocontours of vertical oscillations. The data were obtained with the Capri magnetograph of the Fraunhofer Institute, Freiburg, Germany. Using the Fe I 5250 line and a 3-arcsec square aperture, 65 repetitive scans of 52-sec duration each were made parallel to the solar axis (Deubner, 1967). The line-of-sight velocities and longitudinal magnetic fields are shown as measured along a line free of activity at the center of the disk on October 4, 1966. The dotted velocity isocontours are upward velocities and the hatched are downward. The dotted magnetic-field isocontours are south polarity; the hatched are north. (From Deubner, 1967; copyright 1967, D. Reidel.)

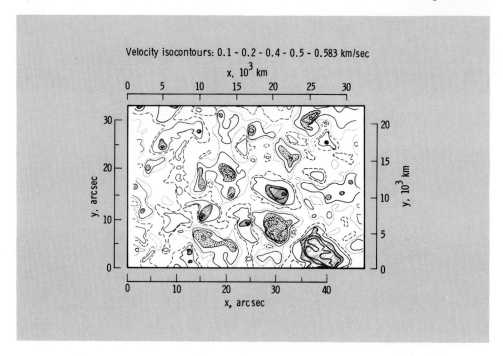

FIGURE 5–18.—Two-dimensional velocity isocontours. Using the same instrument as discussed
in figure 5–17, an area of 65 by 92 arcsec at sun center has been scanned in 450 sec (Deubner,
1969). The hatched and dotted regions are of opposite velocities. (From Deubner, 1969;
copyright 1969, D. Reidel.)

(1968), using an autocorrelation analysis. In figure 5–18, it is seen that a group
of adjacent cells oscillating in phase could be taken for one cell, if observed under
relatively low resolution. Numerous locations exist in which the coherence in phase
covers a much larger area than the coherence in amplitude. This characteristic has
also been observed by Gonczi and Roddier (1969).

Analogous to the one-dimensional power spectrum of figure 5–14, a two-
dimensional power spectral density can be obtained by taking the Fourier transform
of the autocorrelation function, $C(\Delta\mathbf{r}, \Delta t)$ (Jennison, 1961, or Phillips, 1966). The
three-dimensional Fourier transform of the autocorrelation function is

$$F(\mathbf{k}, \omega) = \int_{\Delta\mathbf{r}} \int d(\Delta\mathbf{r}) \int_{-\infty}^{+\infty} C(\Delta\mathbf{r}, \Delta t) \exp\left[-i(\mathbf{k}\cdot\Delta\mathbf{r} - \omega t)\right] d(\Delta t) \qquad (5\text{–}9)$$

where $\mathbf{k}$ is the two-dimensional horizontal wave number, equal in magnitude to
2π over the wavelength, and ω is the angular frequency. Because there is no preferred horizontal direction, $C(\Delta\mathbf{r}, \Delta t)$ is azimuthally symmetric. Thus, by defining
$\Delta\mathbf{r}$ in cylindrical coordinates $(\Delta r, \Delta\theta)$, we can immediately integrate over $\Delta\theta$. Also,
if we assume that the statistical properties of the oscillation are constant in time,

characteristic of a stationary wave field, $C(\Delta \mathbf{r}, \Delta t) = C(\Delta \mathbf{r}, -\Delta t)$. With these simplifications, the transform becomes (Frazier, 1968b)

$$F(k, \omega) = 4\pi \int_0^\infty \Delta r \, d(\Delta r) \int_0^\infty C(\Delta r, \Delta t) J_0(k \, \Delta r) \cos(\omega \, \Delta t) \, d(\Delta t) \quad (5\text{-}10)$$

where J_0 is the zeroth-order Bessel function of the first kind.

In figure 5–19, the isocontours of the power spectral density in the k-ω plane, equal to $kF(k, \omega)$, are plotted for the autocorrelation functions of figure 5–16. The distinct separation between the oscillatory power density and the convective power density is very evident. It is seen that the convective power decreases relative to the oscillatory power with increasing height (continuum→Si II 6371→Fe II 6364→ Fe II 6355). Also, the wavelength for the peak convective power density is approximately 2500 to 3000 km and decreases slightly with increasing altitude. This wavelength is considerably larger than the average cell spacing of 1800 km as found by Bray and Loughhead (1967). The location of the two peaks in oscillatory power remains essentially unchanged with height (265 sec/5000 km and 345 sec/5000 km). In figure 5–20, the power spectral densities obtained from observations made with appreciably larger aperture sizes than in figure 5–19 are shown. The merging of the two oscillatory peaks into one and the appearance of power at longer spatial wavelengths are apparent. This leads us to wonder at what wavelength below 5000 km the peak power would appear if the resolution of the observation were not limited by atmospheric seeing and could be greatly improved. Also shown in figure 5–19 are the calculated wavelengths and frequencies for several different hydrodynamic modes of oscillation. The straight line running through the origin represents acoustic waves propagating horizontally ($\omega = V_0 k$). The curved line is the boundary between transient waves and acoustic waves as modified by gravitation. From the results shown in figure 5–19, Frazier (1968b) concludes that the oscillations are primarily standing resonant acoustic waves and that the gravity mode was not observed. The existence of standing waves is supported by his observation that there is negligible phase lag between velocities in the low photosphere and upper photosphere. The various possible modes of oscillation are now described analytically.

Theoretical efforts to correctly describe vertical oscillations generally seek to discover resonant modes of the atmosphere which produce power spectra in the k-ω plane matching those observed, or which could exist but are not presently observed. The basic hydrodynamic equations are combined with a model atmosphere, and resonant modes are computed. The complexity of the calculations requires that simplifying assumptions be made. As is often true, the nature of the assumptions significantly influences the nature of the results.

The first basic hydrodynamic equation is the conservation of mass, which equates the net rate of mass flow out of a unit volume to the negative of the time rate of change of density

$$\nabla \cdot \rho \mathbf{V} = -\frac{\partial \rho}{\partial t} \quad (5\text{-}11)$$

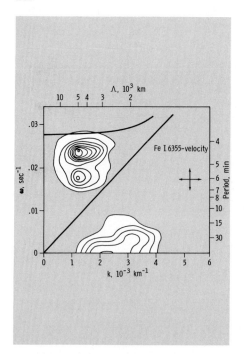

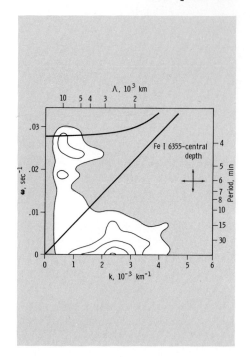

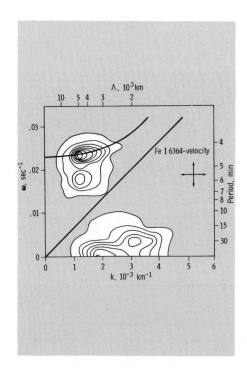

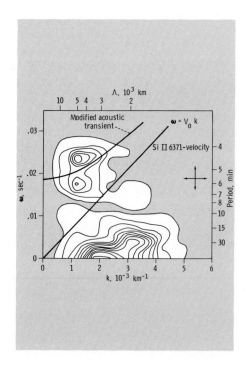

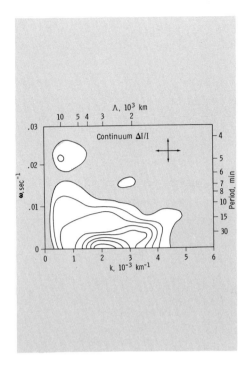

FIGURE 5–19.—The power spectrum $P(k, \omega)$ of vertical oscillations observed with a 170-km effective aperture size. The values of the spatial wavelength Λ and the period are shown for the corresponding values of k and ω. The power density in the $k-\omega$ plane is indicated by isocontours. The density is calculated by taking the Fourier transforms of the velocity autocorrelation functions shown in figure 5–16 (Frazier, 1968b). The straight lines on the power spectra, calculated by Frazier, represent acoustic waves propagating horizontally, calculated from linear hydrodynamic theory. The curved lines are boundaries between the acoustic waves, as modified by gravitation, and the transient waves. Local physical parameters were used at all three altitudes and the radiative relaxation times were included explicitly following Souffrin (1966). (From Frazier, 1968b; copyright 1968, Springer-Verlag.)

where **V** is the macroscopic velocity of the gas. The conservation of momentum equates the inertial force to the restoring forces which can promote oscillations. These restoring forces could be:

(1) Pressure gradients which differ from those of the static atmosphere and can lead to pure acoustic waves in the limit of high frequency.

(2) Buoyancy forces which, unlike those leading to convection, oppose the direction of motion and can lead to gravity waves at low frequencies.

(3) Magnetic forces which are relatively small in the photosphere and low chromosphere of the quiet sun. They will not be considered further until the next section where it will be seen that they lead to Alfvén and other hydromagnetic waves which may be of importance in carrying non-radiative energy into the upper atmosphere.

Thus, our equation for the conservation of momentum is

$$\rho \frac{D\mathbf{V}}{Dt} = -\nabla p + \rho \mathbf{g} \qquad (5\text{-}12)$$

where **g** is the gravity vector directed downward and where the substantial derivative, $D(\ )/Dt$, yields the total time rate of change of a quantity which is a function of both time and position. It describes the time rate of change experienced by an

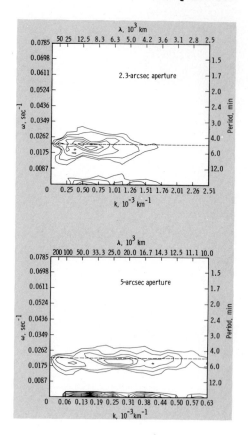

FIGURE 5–20.—The power spectrum $P(k, \omega)$ of vertical oscillations observed with effective aperture sizes of 1800 and 3600 km. (From Tanenbaum et al., 1969; copyright 1969, D. Reidel.)

observer moving with a fluid element. That is,

$$\frac{D\mathbf{V}}{Dt} = \frac{\partial \mathbf{V}}{\partial t} + \mathbf{V} \cdot \nabla \mathbf{V} \tag{5–13}$$

In equation (5–12) the viscous forces, which vary as $\nabla^2 \mathbf{V}$, have been assumed to be negligible because of the large physical lengths involved in the velocity gradients (Souffrin, 1966). The conservation of energy relation follows directly from the first law of thermodynamics which states that the change in internal energy of a fluid element is equal to the net heat added to it minus the work done by it.

$$C_v \frac{DT}{Dt} = -\mathcal{L} - p \frac{D(1/\rho)}{Dt} \tag{5–14}$$

where C_v is the energy required to raise the temperature 1 K per unit mass (the specific heat at constant volume) and where $\mathcal{L}$ is the net heat lost per unit mass and time by radiation (the heat-loss function defined in eq. (5–1)). The last relation to be used is the perfect-gas law (eq. (3–14)) which, using a relation also derived from the first law of thermodynamics, can be written as

$$p = \rho(\gamma - 1)C_v T \tag{5-15}$$

When the perfect-gas law is combined with equation (5–14), the conservation of energy is

$$\frac{1}{T}\frac{DT}{Dt} = -\frac{1}{\tau_R} + \frac{(\gamma - 1)}{\rho}\frac{D\rho}{Dt} \tag{5-16}$$

where τ_R is the characteristic radiative lifetime of a thermal perturbation at constant density

$$\tau_R \equiv \frac{C_v T}{\mathcal{L}} \tag{5-17}$$

Another conceptually useful expression for the conservation of energy also follows directly from equations (5–15) and (5–16). Assuming γ to be constant,

$$\frac{D\ln(p\rho^{-\gamma})}{Dt} = -\frac{1}{\tau_R} \tag{5-18}$$

As we follow a fluid element, the degree to which $p\rho^{-\gamma}$ changes is dependent upon the magnitude of τ_R. When τ_R is large relative to the characteristic time for fluid property changes $(1/\omega)$, the variations are nearly adiabatic $(p\rho^{-\gamma} = \text{constant})$. It will be seen that the assumption of adiabatic change $(\tau_R \to \infty)$ is valid in the chromosphere but not in the low photosphere.

In solving the conservation equations (5–11), (5–12), and (5–18) for the values of the dependent variables p, ρ, and $\mathbf{V}$, additional assumptions are often made. In addition to adiabatic variations, it usually is assumed that the variations in p and ρ are small relative to their static values $(\mathbf{V} = 0)$. Our previous discussion, which showed that the oscillations are only a perturbation of the quiescent atmosphere, indicates that this is a good assumption. Two other simplifications are usually made. First, because there is no preferred horizontal direction, only two spatial dimensions need to be considered, one horizontal (x), and one vertical (z). Second, all perturbations vary harmonically in time and either harmonically or exponentially in space. Thus,

$$p = p_0 + p_1$$

$$\rho = \rho_0 + \rho_1 \tag{5-19}$$

$$\mathbf{V} = \{\text{zero}\} + u\mathbf{e}_x + v\mathbf{e}_z$$

and

$$\frac{p_1}{\bar{p}} = \frac{\rho_1}{\bar{\rho}} = \frac{u}{\bar{u}} = \frac{v}{\bar{v}} = \exp\left[i(\omega t - K_x x - K_z z)\right] \tag{5-20}$$

where the subscripts 0 and 1 denote static (zeroth order) and perturbation quantities caused by the oscillations (first order), respectively; $\mathbf{e}_x$ and $\mathbf{e}_z$ are unit vectors in the x and z directions; $\bar{p}$, $\bar{\rho}$, $\bar{u}$, and $\bar{v}$ are complex constants which define the relative magnitude and phase between the variations; and K_x and K_z are complex wave numbers which define spatial variations (oscillations and attenuations). The assumption that ω has no imaginary component is equivalent to assuming steady-state oscillations. When these expressions for the dependent variables (eqs. (5–19) and (5–20)) are substituted into the conservation equations, one zeroth-order and four first-order equations result. The zeroth-order equation is that previously encountered for a static atmosphere.

$$p_0 \sim \exp\,(-z/H) \qquad\qquad (5\text{–}21)$$

where

$$H = (\gamma - 1)C_v T/g = V_0^2/\gamma g \qquad\qquad (5\text{–}22)$$

Here V_0 is the local speed of sound. The first-order equations determine the relative magnitudes of pressure and density variations of the horizontal and vertical motion in the form of relations for $\bar{p}$, $\bar{\rho}$, $\bar{u}$, and $\bar{v}$ called "polarization relations." They also yield a relation between frequency and wave number called the dispersion relation, which is of prime interest in our discussion here.[2]

$$\omega^4 - \omega^2 V_0^2 (K_x^2 + K_z^2) + (\gamma - 1)g^2 K_x^2 + i\gamma g \omega^2 K_z = 0 \qquad\qquad (5\text{–}23)$$

In solving the first-order equations and arriving at equation (5–23), it has been assumed the ρ_0 also varies as $\exp\,(-z/H)$. This is equivalent to assuming that

$$\frac{\partial \ln \rho_0}{\partial z} \gg \frac{\partial \ln T_0}{\partial z} \qquad\qquad (5\text{–}24)$$

and, in a strict sense, that the atmosphere is isothermal, which is valid only in the region of the temperature minimum.

To extract physically meaningful information from the dispersion relation, we examine the real and imaginary parts of equation (5–23) separately. Consistent with our assumption of no preferred horizontal direction or variations of the static atmosphere in the vertical direction only, we assume that the only attenuation of the wave motion is in the z direction. Thus,

$$K_x = k_x \qquad\qquad (5\text{–}25)$$

where k_x is real. Setting the imaginary part of equation (5–23) to zero now requires

$$K_z = k_z + i/2H \qquad\qquad (5\text{–}26)$$

where k_z is real. This, in turn, implies that the kinetic energy density $\rho_0 (u^2 + v^2)/2$ is invariant with height. This conclusion is only as valid as the assumptions which have led to it. The dispersion relation now becomes

$$\omega^2 k_z^2 = \omega^2 (\omega^2 - \omega_a^2)/V_0^2 + (\omega_g^2 - \omega^2)k_x^2 \qquad\qquad (5\text{–}27)$$

---

[2] For a more detailed discussion of the derivations and resulting relations, see Hines (1960), Whitaker (1963), Moore and Spiegel (1964), and Stein (1967).

where

$$\omega_a = \frac{1}{2}\frac{V_0}{H} \qquad = \frac{\gamma g}{2V_0} \qquad\qquad \text{acoustic wave frequency} \qquad (5\text{--}28)$$

$$\omega_g = \frac{(\gamma-1)^{1/2}}{\gamma}\frac{V_0}{H} = \frac{(\gamma-1)^{1/2}g}{V_0} \qquad \text{gravity wave frequency} \qquad (5\text{--}29)$$

Because γ is less than 2, ω_g is always less than ω_a. Using values representative of the region of the temperature minimum, it is seen that ω_a and ω_g are of the same magnitude as the observed oscillations. For $\gamma = 1.2$ and $V_0 = 7$ km/sec, $\omega_a = 2.35 \times 10^{-2}$ sec^{-1} and $\omega_g = 1.75 \times 10^{-2}$ sec^{-1}, which yields periods of 267 and 359 sec, respectively.

The velocity of phase propagation, V_ϕ, is seen to be ω/k from equation (5–20), where $k = (k_x{}^2 + k_z{}^2)^{1/2}$. Thus, the dispersion relation can be written in the alternate form

$$\left(\frac{V_\phi}{V_0}\right)^2 = \frac{1 - \left(\dfrac{\omega_g}{\omega}\right)^2 \sin^2\theta}{1 - \left(\dfrac{\omega_a}{\omega}\right)^2} \qquad\qquad (5\text{--}30)$$

where θ is the angle of phase propagation relative to the vertical direction, $k_z = k \cos\theta$. This reveals that the wave motion can take on several different characteristics depending upon the frequency. For $\omega > \omega_a$, the phase velocity is real and the waves are termed "acoustic waves." When $\omega \gg \omega_a$, the phase velocity approaches the speed of sound and is independent of direction. This is equivalent to the near absence of gravity in that both ω_a/ω and ω_g/ω approach zero.

For $\omega < \omega_g \sin\theta$ ($\omega < \omega_g$ for horizontal phase propagation only), the phase velocity is again real. Waves in this regime are termed "internal gravity waves." The term "internal" has been used to make the distinction between these waves and those which do not have any vertical phase propagation ($k_z = 0$), like water surface waves. For frequencies in the range $\omega_a > \omega > \omega_g \sin\theta$, the phase velocity is imaginary. Waves of this type are evanescent and are attenuated or dissipated rather than propagated. In this case k_x or k_z must be imaginary in equation (5–27), and equation (5–23) should be reexamined. It is important to note that the standard nomenclature presented here can be misleading. That is, buoyancy forces and pressure gradients play a role in both internal gravity waves and acoustic waves, and both types of waves, as discussed here, are really internal.

The diagnostic diagram, which has previously been used to present observational results (figs. 5–19 and 5–20), can also be used to depict the results of the theoretical analysis (eqs. (5–27) to (5–30)). The condition of pure horizontal phase propagation ($k_z = 0$) yields two values of ω for each value of k_x, as shown in figure 5–21. The diagnostic diagram is therefore divided into three regions corresponding to acoustic waves, evanescent waves, and gravity waves. Acoustic waves can exist above the upper line corresponding to $k_z = 0$. As k_x becomes very large (short

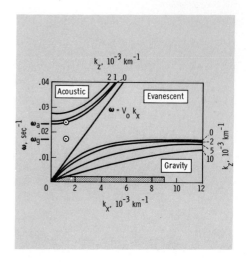

FIGURE 5-21.—Diagnostic diagram for region of the temperature minimum. The parameters for the above diagram are $T = 5000$ K and $\gamma = 1.20$. These yield $V_0 = 7.06$ km/sec, $\omega_a = 0.0233$ sec^{-1}, and $\omega_g = 0.0174$ sec^{-1}. The two lines corresponding to $k_z = 0$ divide the diagram into three regions: acoustic, evanescent, and gravity waves. The shaded region at the bottom defines the values of ω and k_z where solar granulation is found. The two locations marked by $\odot$ are those of maximum spectral power density found by Frazier (1968b). (From Whitaker, 1963; copyright 1963, University of Chicago Press.)

wavelengths), the frequency of acoustic waves approaches $V_0 k_x$ and a phase velocity of V_0. Gravity waves can exist below the lower line corresponding to $k_z = 0$. It is seen that the largest possible value of ω approaches ω_g for very large k_x (short wavelengths). As k_x becomes very large, the phase velocity approaches zero. In the region between acoustic and gravity waves, k_z and V_ϕ are imaginary and any wave motion, once initiated, will be evanescent. The dispersion relation can also be plotted as shown in figure 5-22. The advantage of plotting surfaces of constant ω in the k_x-k_z plane (slowness surfaces) is that the direction of energy propagation or group velocity is easily identified. In figure 5-22, the energy propagation is in the direction normal to a line of constant ω and in the direction of increasing ω. For acoustic waves (elliptic sections), the directions of phase propagation ($\mathbf{k}$) and of energy propagation are approximately the same. However, for gravity waves (hyperbolic sections), the two directions can differ by as much as 90°. In particular, the vertical component of phase propagation will always be opposite to that of energy propagation.

The above analysis has made the simplifying assumption that the atmosphere is isothermal. When this assumption is removed, a significant effect on gravity waves results. The new frequency, corresponding to ω_g but with the atmospheric temperature gradient included, is the Brunt-Väisälä frequency, ω_B. Its value is a limiting case obtained by neglecting the pressure gradient perturbation relative to the density perturbation (pressure force relative to buoyancy force). It can be pictured in a fashion similar to convection cell formation (fig. 2-4). However, because the gas above the convection zone is stable, a rising cell of gas becomes more dense than its surroundings and is accelerated downward. Correspondingly, cells moving downward become buoyant and oscillations result. Letting z represent the vertical displacement of a cell from static equilibrium, the balance between inertial force and buoyancy force per unit volume is

$$\rho' \frac{\partial^2 z}{\partial t^2} = g(\rho - \rho') \tag{5-31}$$

where ρ' and ρ are the gas densities inside and outside the cell, respectively. The change in these densities from their initial value of ρ_0, as a result of the displacement, z, is

$$\rho - \rho_0 = \left(\frac{\partial \rho}{\partial z}\right)_{\text{at}} z \tag{5-32}$$

$$\rho' - \rho_0 = \left(\frac{\partial \rho}{\partial z}\right)_{\text{ad}} z \tag{5-33}$$

where the partial derivatives are the rates of change in the atmosphere (at) and for adiabatic (ad) variations, respectively. Using the perfect-gas relation and the assumption that the pressure inside and outside the cell are the same (neglect of the pressure perturbation), the force balance becomes

$$\frac{\partial^2 z}{\partial t^2} + \frac{g}{T} \left\{ \left(\frac{\partial T}{\partial z}\right)_{\text{at}} - \left(\frac{\partial T}{\partial z}\right)_{\text{ad}} \right\} z = 0 \tag{5-34}$$

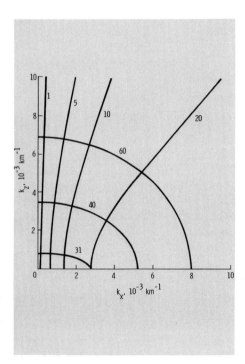

FIGURE 5–22.—Slowness surfaces. The values of k_x and k_z are shown for several values of ω which satisfy the dispersion relation in equation (5–27). The values of ω (shown next to each curve) are in units of 10^{-3} sec^{-1}. The values used in the computations are $T = 5000$ K, $\omega_a = 0.304$ sec^{-1}, and $\omega_g = 0.298$ sec^{-1}. The acoustic waves ($\omega > \omega_a$) correspond to elliptic sections and the gravity waves ($\omega < \omega_g$) to hyperbolic sections. The energy of the oscillations propagates in the direction and with the speed of the group velocity:

$$\nabla_k \omega = \left(\frac{\partial \omega}{\partial k_x}\right) \mathbf{e}_x + \left(\frac{\partial \omega}{\partial k_z}\right) \mathbf{e}_z$$

Because their velocity is the gradient of ω in k space, it is perpendicular to the slowness surfaces and in the direction of increasing ω. (For a detailed treatment, see Hines, 1960.) (From Stein, 1967; copyright 1967, D. Reidel.)

The coefficient of z is the square of the oscillation frequency which, for an atmospheric pressure that varies as exp $(-z/H)$, can be expressed as

$$\omega_B{}^2 = \omega_g{}^2 + \frac{g}{T}\left(\frac{\partial T}{\partial z}\right)_{at} \tag{5-35}$$

This value of ω_B replaces ω_g in our previously derived dispersion relation (eq. (5-27)). The acoustic wave frequency ω_a is unaffected to first order by a temperature gradient. From equation (5-35), it is clear that the value of the atmospheric temperature gradient determines the nature of the gravity waves. When the temperature gradient is large and negative, $\omega_B{}^2$ can be less than zero so that a gas-cell displacement is convectively unstable, as in the convection zone. In the photosphere where the temperature gradient is still negative but the gas is stable, the upper limit to gravity wave frequency ω_B is less than ω_g. However, above the temperature minimum the positive temperature gradient increases ω_B above ω_g and the possibility of propagation of gravity waves is more favorable.

A second simplifying assumption used throughout the above analysis is that the ratio $p/\rho T$ (equal to $(\gamma-1)C_v$, eq. (5-15)) is a constant; that is, that the perfect-gas law is valid. This effectively neglects the effect of changes in the degree of ionization with changes in temperature and pressure. When changes in the degree of ionization are included (Thomas et al., 1971), the Brunt-Väisälä frequency is

$$\omega_B{}^2 = g\beta\left[\left(\frac{\partial T}{\partial z}\right)_{at} - \left(\frac{\partial T}{\partial z}\right)_{ad}\right] \tag{5-36}$$

where β is the coefficient of thermal expansion

$$\beta = -\frac{1}{\rho}\left(\frac{\partial \rho}{\partial T}\right)_p \tag{5-37}$$

and

$$\left(\frac{\partial T}{\partial z}\right)_{ad} = -\beta T g/C_p \tag{5-38}$$

Only for a perfect gas is β equal to $1/T$, and is ω_B given by equation (5-35). As we shall discuss shortly, a major effect of including hydrogen ionization in the calculations is that $\omega_B{}^2$ has a broad peak around the temperature minimum. This resembles a potential well that can trap gravity waves. When hydrogen ionization is included along with a model of the solar atmosphere, the difficulty of obtaining a diagnostic diagram like figure 5-21 is greatly increased. However, by considering only horizontal propagation $(k_z=0)$, the division between acoustic, gravity, and evanescent waves can still be obtained. It is possible to combine the conservation equations into one of the form (Clark et al., 1971)

$$\frac{d^2Q}{dz^2} + F(k_x, \omega, z)Q = 0 \tag{5-39}$$

where

$$Q^2 = \frac{\rho v^2}{\left| \dfrac{1}{V_\phi{}^2} - \dfrac{1}{V_0{}^2} \right|} \qquad (5\text{–}40)$$

If $F > 0$, the z dependence of the dynamical quantity Q is oscillatory, and propagating waves can exist. If $F < 0$, Q varies exponentially with z and the waves are evanescent. In figure 5–23, the atmospheric layers in which propagation can exist are shown for 300-sec-period oscillations and several horizontal wavelengths. The calculations were made using a piecewise continuous idealized model of the BCA. Although the details of figure 5–23 will change with the model employed and with the manner in which the calculations are made, its general features will not vary greatly and it serves as an excellent summary of the wave propagation characteristics of the solar atmosphere. Gravity waves can exist primarily for horizontal wavelengths of 2000 km or less. If they can be trapped in the regions shown, standing as well as propagating waves can exist. For horizontal wavelengths of 1000 km, the evanescent layer at 1500 km is thin, and the tunneling of waves through it may effectively join the two propagating layers. At horizontal wavelengths of 3000 km and greater, the gravity waves in the photosphere and chromosphere above 200 km are no longer possible, but acoustic waves in the convection zone, low photosphere, and middle chromosphere (>1800 km) can exist. Thus, the tendency for oscillations to require short wavelengths (large k_x) for gravity waves and longer wavelengths (small k_x) for acoustic waves again appears.

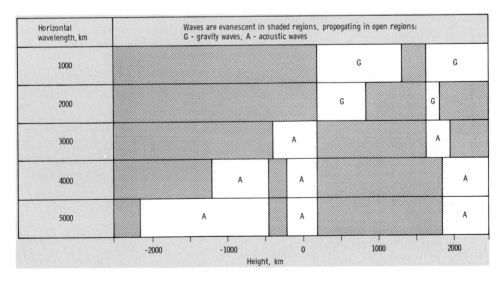

FIGURE 5–23.—Propagating and evanescent regions for 300-sec-period waves in the solar atmosphere. The evanescent regions are those where $k_z{}^2 < 0$. (Data from Clark et al., 1971.)

Before consideration of the relation between theoretical and observational results, we will discuss some significant effects encountered by removing the adiabatic change assumption used in analyzing both types of waves. If the characteristic time of relaxation of thermal perturbations, τ_R, is approximately the same size as, or much less than, the characteristic lifetime of the perturbation $1/\omega$, the changes in the gas are no longer adiabatic and the atmosphere tends to be neutrally stable. That is, when an element of gas is displaced, it will achieve thermal equilibrium with its new environment before buoyancy or pressure-gradient restoring forces exert appreciable effect. The thermal relaxation time for a perturbation in an infinite homogeneous medium is (Spiegel, 1957)

$$\tau_R{}^{-1} = \frac{16\sigma\kappa T^3}{C_p}\ (1 - \tau_e \cot^{-1} \tau_e) \tag{5-41}$$

where τ_e is the effective optical depth for radiative relaxation of the thermal perturbation. The term $\tau_e \cot^{-1} \tau_e$ accounts for absorption and reemission of radiation and it tends to smooth out the perturbation. For $\tau_e \ll 1$, $\tau_R \simeq C_p/16\sigma\kappa T^3$. However, when radiation diffusion is dominant in inhibiting the thermal relaxation, $\tau_e \gg 1$ and $\tau_R \simeq 3\tau_e{}^2\tau_R\,(\tau_e = 0)$. For waves with only horizontal-phase propagation in an infinite homogeneous medium, τ_e is simply the horizontal size of the perturbation, $\Lambda/2\pi$, divided by the photon mean free path, $1/\rho\kappa$. That is, the optical thickness of the perturbation τ_p is

$$\tau_p = \Lambda\rho\kappa/2\pi \tag{5-42}$$

where Λ is the horizontal wavelength. In this case, the perturbations are smoothed out horizontally. However, in the solar atmosphere τ_e cannot be greater than τ, the optical depth of the atmosphere, because a perturbation can exchange radiation with its environment in the vertical direction as well. In this case, a crude approximation for τ_e (Ulrich, 1970) is

$$\frac{1}{\tau_e{}^2} = \frac{1}{\tau^2} + \frac{1}{\tau_p{}^2} \tag{5-43}$$

A plot of τ_R as a function of height is shown in figure 5–24. Over a large part of the photosphere (0 to 250 km), τ_R is less than $300/2\pi$ sec and adiabatic oscillations are therefore impossible. Primarily because of the rapid decrease of the opacity (κ) with height, however, τ_R becomes large in the upper photosphere and low chromosphere. At 1000 km, τ_R starts to decrease but the large increase in C_p, resulting from the onset of hydrogen ionization, causes a second maximum. Then, τ_R rapidly decreases again because of increases in both κ and T. Over the full range of this curve, $\tau_p{}^2$ is much larger than τ^2 for $\Lambda = 5000$ km, so that $\tau_e \simeq \tau$. Thus, diffusion of radiation is important only in the convection zone. If $\Lambda \rightarrow 0$, then $\tau_e \rightarrow 0$ and radiation diffusion does not play a significant role in any part of the atmosphere. Below the photosphere and for increasing τ, τ_R rapidly increases as $3\tau^2\tau_R\,(\tau_e = 0)$. Thus, thermal relaxation inhibits oscillations at the surface of the convection zone and low photosphere, but not below.

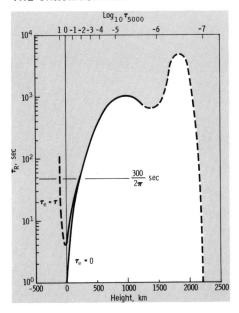

Figure 5–24.—Thermal relaxation time of the solar atmosphere. Spiegel's formula (eq. (5–41)) is used to calculate τ_R for effective optical depths of a perturbation equal to either zero or τ, the optical depth of the atmosphere. The Bilderberg continuum atmosphere is used with the values of C_p as given by Thomas et al. (1971). The value of κ at 5000 Å was used. The dotted lines indicate regions in which direct application of the formula is invalid but the general trend of τ_R is correct.

The effect of a nonzero value for $1/\tau_R$ on the diagnostic diagram can be investigated by again looking for the divisions between acoustic, evanescent, and gravity wave regions defined by the condition $k_z=0$. For $k_z=0$ in the dispersion relation derived under the adiabatic and isothermal atmosphere assumptions in equation (5–27), we find

$$k_x^2 = \frac{\omega^2-\omega_a^2}{\omega^2-\omega_B^2}\left(\frac{\omega}{V_0}\right)^2 \tag{5–44}$$

When the adiabatic assumption is removed, the corresponding relation is (Ulrich, 1970)

$$k_x^2 = \frac{\omega^2-\omega_a^2+\left(\gamma-\dfrac{\omega_a^2}{\omega^2}\right)\tau_R^{-2}}{\omega^2-\omega_B^2+\tau_R^{-2}}\left(\frac{\omega}{V_0}\right)^2 \tag{5–45}$$

The diagnostic diagram is shown in figure 5–25 and should be compared with figure 5–21. It is seen that the most pronounced effect of decreasing τ_R is to decrease the regions in which gravity waves can propagate. According to Souffrin (1967), gravity waves cannot exist if $\tau_R<1/\omega_B$. If the analysis is made allowing imaginary values of ω (transient oscillations), the condition for the nonpropagation of gravity waves is $\tau_R<1/2\omega_B$ (Stix, 1970). In the photosphere, ω_B is approximately 0.03 sec^{-1}. Therefore, τ_R must be greater than 33 sec for steady-state gravity waves to propagate. This corresponds to heights greater than approximately 200 km.

We now turn to the primary question that we seek to answer in this section. "What waves can exist in the solar atmosphere and can they be identified with

FIGURE 5–25.—Effect of thermal relaxation on the diagnostic diagram. The boundaries for the acoustic, evanescent, and gravity wave regions, defined by $k_z = 0$, are shown for three values of the nondimensional thermal relaxation time, $\tau_R V_0/H$. At a height of 300 km in the atmosphere (BCA), at a horizontal wavelength of 5000 km, and when $\tau_R = 1/\omega = 300/2\pi$ sec, we find $H = 110$ km, $V_0 = 7$ km/sec, and nondimensional values of $\omega H/V_0 = 0.33$, $\tau_R V_0/H = 3.0$, and $k_x H = 0.14$. In the diagram, this point is marked by $\odot$; the point corresponding to a wavelength of 1000 km is marked by $\boxdot$. It is seen that thermal relaxation has its most pronounced effect on gravity waves. At a horizontal wavelength of 1000 km and a height of 300 km (BCA), gravity waves are strongly inhibited unless $\tau_R V_0/H \approx 3.7$ or $\tau_R \approx 60$ sec. Therefore, 1000-km gravity waves are just possible at this altitude. (Data from Souffrin, 1967.)

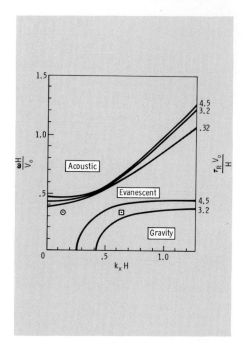

those observed?" In essence, there are two types of waves that we must consider: gravity waves in the photosphere and chromosphere, and acoustic waves in the convection zone (fig. 5–23). Do neither, one, or both of these waves exist?

In the diagnostic diagram, a most obvious distinction between the two waves is their horizontal wavelength, $2\pi/k_x$. Gravity waves have horizontal wavelengths of 2000 km or less, while acoustic wavelengths are 3000 km or greater. Because the shortest observed wavelength of peak spectral energy density is 5000 km (Frazier, 1968b; fig. 5–19), it would appear that acoustic waves are the only observable type. However, seeing limitations make it difficult, if not impossible, to observe horizontal wavelengths of 2000 km or less (corresponding to approximately 0.4-arcsec resolution). Therefore, it is possible that gravity waves of relatively short wavelengths exist but are not observable from the ground.

The two types of waves in the diagnostic diagram also differ in the frequencies at which they can exist. Acoustic waves are not greatly altered by thermal relaxation and, in the convection zone, the relaxation time becomes very long. Therefore, acoustic waves can match the observed frequencies. However, the upper limit for the frequency of gravity waves has been shown to be (Stix, 1970)

$$\omega_{\text{gravity}}^2 < \omega_B^2 - (1/2\tau_R)^2 \qquad (5\text{–}46)$$

This limiting frequency for transient waves is plotted in figure 5–26, where it is seen that the effects of thermal relaxation are limited to the first 200 km. Gravity waves cannot exist below 140 km and have an upper frequency limit of essentially

ω_B above 200 km. Using Souffrin's more restrictive criterion for the existence of steady-state gravity waves, $\omega_B{}^2 > 1/\tau_R{}^2$, it is seen in figure 5–25 that the atmosphere can support gravity waves of 1000-km wavelength at an altitude of 300 km. Thus, even though thermal relaxation tends to inhibit gravity waves in approximately the first 200 km of altitude, it does not affect them significantly above this height and up to approximately 2000 km, so that gravity waves can also match the observed frequencies. The reason for the small spatial extent of thermal relaxation effects is the rapid increase in τ_R in the low photosphere.

A factor which should be used in screening acoustic models is that negligible phase lag is observed between waves in the low photosphere and in the chromosphere. Thus, a way of trapping waves to produce standing waves must exist. It has been shown that acoustic waves in the convection zone are reflected downward close to the photosphere and back upward at depths of several thousand to several tens of thousands kilometers, depending upon the frequency and horizontal wavelength (Ulrich, 1970). Standing waves can be set up and, because the upper boundary is not perfectly reflecting, oscillatory energy will leak into the photosphere and chromosphere in the form of dissipating or evanescent waves. The decay length for these waves is long and, because the energy density is $\rho v^2/2$, the oscillatory velocity should tend to increase with height. Thus, the observed oscillations could be evanescent acoustic waves in phase with the relatively thick standing waves in the convection zone.

It is of interest to note that gravity waves can also account for a small height variation of phase. They can also set up standing waves in the photosphere and chromosphere. Figure 5–26 shows that a large "potential well" for trapping gravity waves exists between approximately 200 and 1200 km. This trapping of waves in the region of the temperature minimum has previously been attributed to temperature effects only (Kahn, 1961 and 1962—acoustic waves; and Uchida, 1965 and 1967—gravity waves). However, it has been shown that the formation of a potential well is the result of ionization effects which trap the gravity waves and that acoustic waves which could be trapped in the same region have frequencies higher than

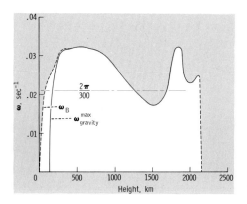

FIGURE 5–26.—Upper limit to gravity wave frequency as a function of height. The above is a plot of $[\omega_B{}^2 - (1/2\tau_R)^2]^{1/2}$ (eq. (5–46)). The Brunt-Väisälä, ω_B, is from Thomas et al. (1971) and includes the effect of hydrogen ionization which is important above 1400 km. The BCA was used in the calculations. Values of τ_R are from figure 5–24. It is seen that the range of approximately 200 to 1200 km can support gravity wave oscillations at the observed frequency. The rapid drop to zero above 2100 km is a result of the rapid decrease of τ_R at this altitude.

those observed (Thomas et al., 1971). The initial rise of the upper limit to gravity wave frequencies in the photosphere (fig. 5–26) results from the rise of ω_B, as the atmosphere changes from instability in the convection zone to stability above, and from the sharp rise of τ_R. In the range of 300 to 800 km, ω_B is very flat because the atmospheric temperature gradient is negligible and because the adiabatic temperature gradient is nearly constant. Using the expression for ω_B (eqs. (5–36) and (5–38)) and the variation of β and C_p shown in figure 5–27, it is seen that $\omega_B{}^2 \simeq (g\beta)^2 T/C_p$ and that this quantity is nearly constant around the temperature minimum (330 km in the BCA). The decrease of ω_B above 1000 km results from the hydrogen ionization which rapidly increases C_p (fig. 5–27). This decreases the adiabatic temperature gradient below the gradient in the atmosphere and causes a peak in β which, in turn, causes a second peak in ω_B at approximately 1800 km. Using a four-layer model of the atmosphere, Thomas et al. (1971) derived two characteristic periods for trapped gravity waves of 263 and 338 sec, both at 1500-km wavelength. It is interesting, but unexplained, that these periods are close to those found in the observations of Frazier (1968b), the majority of which were made in the low photosphere where thermal relaxation inhibits gravity wave oscillations. However, gravity waves could still exist in this region because the trapped gravity waves are really characteristic or eigenmodes of oscillation of a whole atmospheric layer. Regions above and below this layer, which are neutrally stable, are driven by its large-scale motions (Thomas, 1971, private communication) in a manner analogous to the strong convective power overshoot observed in the photosphere. This should be especially true in the regions only a few scale heights from the oscillating layer. Thus, gravity waves should exhibit a small height variation of phase over a large height range, if they were observed.

The two types of waves also can be compared by considering their possible means of excitation. It has been stated but not demonstrated that the oscillations in the convection zone are self-exciting; that is, once initiated by a small perturbation, they will tend to grow in time (Ulrich, 1970). Also, although the acoustic waves are only weakly coupled to the convective velocity field, they should receive significant energy input from it. On the other hand, gravity waves must depend only upon direct excitation by the underlying turbulent motions. Observationally,

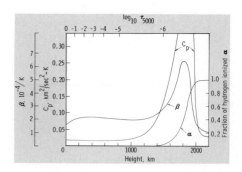

FIGURE 5–27.—Specific heat at constant pressure, coefficient of thermal expansion, and fraction of hydrogen ionized as a function of height. These values are based on the BCA. The major effect to note is the sharp peaking of β and especially of C_p, as α increases to unity between 1400 and 2000 km. (From Thomas et al., 1971; copyright 1971, D. Reidel.)

a one-to-one correspondence between an upward-surging granule and an overlying oscillation has not been found. However, it has been shown that a fully developed wave train will not be seen directly above the granule but rather at a distance of at least several wavelengths away (Clark et al., 1971). An observer over the granule experiences an upward thrust, a downward fall, and a slow return back up to his initial altitude. An observer several wavelengths to the side will experience many oscillations whose period slowly decreases with time. On the solar surface, one should observe the summation of the wave trains from many nearby granules.

Lastly, we must determine how well each theoretical model of the oscillations can be adapted to the real solar atmosphere which includes the horizontal non-homogeneities of the chromospheric network (sec. 5.3). We shall see that, in the convection zone and low photosphere, both the gas static and dynamic pressures are much greater than the magnetic-field pressure of the network so that the acoustic wave theory does not require significant modification. However, in the chromosphere the magnetic field along the network is able to restrict the gas motion primarily to the vertical direction, parallel to the field. Some effect of the network has been observed. The mean period of oscillation (observed in Ca II $K3$) is longer on the network ($K2$ bright) than off the network in a supergranule cell ($K2$ faint), primarily because of the appearance of a pronounced long-period tail (400 to 600 sec) in spectral power distribution (Orrall, 1966). Defouw (1970b) has suggested that the field-free regions of supergranule cells exhibit thermal-convective over-stability (self-exciting) but that the regions along the network do not. Consistent with this picture, Uchida (1967) analyzed standing gravity waves inside a flat cylindrical "cavity resonator" whose top and bottom are defined by the trough of the temperature minimum and whose walls are formed by the magnetically rein-forced supergranulation cell edges coincident with the chromospheric network. The effect of the network on gravity waves requires significantly further definition.

Current investigations of atmospheric oscillations are interesting and funda-mentally important. For now, we must conclude that acoustic waves are most likely the cause of the observed oscillations. However, gravity waves at short spatial wavelengths may also exist. To observe these waves, high spatial resolution observations are required which are not limited by the current levels of atmospheric seeing; that is, by the use of large vacuum telescopes or space platforms. Also, the role which both types of oscillations play in heating the atmosphere needs to be established. Do the oscillations act only as an intermediate energy storage or accumulator in the atmosphere, or do they participate directly in the nonradiative heating of the gas? We now turn to a discussion of this most important area.

5.2 THE TEMPERATURE RISE AND ATMOSPHERIC HEATING

It is natural to expect that the decrease in temperature from the core to the photosphere continues through the outer solar atmosphere. The hot solar interior transfers heat to the cold expanses of interplanetary space and a continuous decrease in temperature is consistent with our previous experience. However, the temperature rises abruptly in the chromosphere to very high values in the corona. Where we expect a cool, nonemitting, and thin outer sheath we find a hot, luminous, and extensive outer envelope (fig. 2–18). As shown in figure 5–28, the temperature rises abruptly from photospheric values below 10^4 K to over 10^6 K, a value close to that found in the core, over a distance of approximately 2000 km. This apparent contradiction to our normal experience with heat transfer can exist because the gas above the low photosphere is optically thin in the range of visible and IR wavelengths, where most of the energy is radiated to space, and diffusion of radiant energy is no longer the primary transfer mechanism. Also, a mechanism is at work which converts a portion of the energy generated by the core into a nonradiative form which flows against the positive temperature gradient into the chromosphere and corona where it is dissipated. Generally, it is believed that this mechanism is the production of waves by the turbulent churning motions in the convection zone, the transport of mechanical energy upward by these waves, and the subsequent increase in atmospheric thermal energy as the waves dissipate. Although this nonradiative flux of energy is of fundamental importance in determining the structure of the observable solar atmosphere, it is only approximately 10^{-4} of the radiative flux $(L_\odot = 6.27 \times 10^{10}$ ergs/cm²-sec$)$.

Observations from space have given us the opportunity to investigate the characteristics of the abrupt temperature rise and the overlying high-temperature atmosphere. Much of the radiation emitted by the chromosphere and corona fall in the UV, XUV, and X-ray ranges. Recent space observations in these ranges have discovered some characteristics of the temperature profile that place constraints on the theories of nonradiative atmospheric heating. The models that have evolved, however, leave large uncertainties in the location of the rapid temperature rise, yield only order-of-magnitude estimates of energy fluxes, and propose several dif-

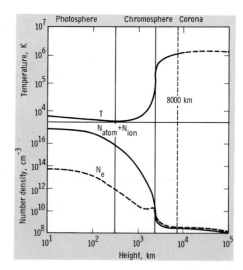

FIGURE 5–28.—Temperature and densities in the solar atmosphere. (Goldberg et al., 1968; copyright 1968, American Association for the Advancement of Science.)

ferent detailed mechanisms for nonradiative energy generation, propagation, and dissipation. One of the principal reasons for these uncertainties is that the chromosphere is not a spherically symmetric layer but, because of the low gas density and the presence of nonuniform magnetic fields, many structural nonuniformities exist. Significant increases in the spatial and spectral resolution of future observations should give us a much more detailed and accurate picture of this region and the nonradiative energy fluxes which influence it so strongly. In the following discussion, the temperature profile, energy fluxes, and the possible energy generation, propagation, and dissipation mechanisms are considered.

Temperature Profile

Once we assume the existence of a nonradiative energy input to the solar atmosphere, we can understand qualitatively the temperature rise as a consequence of the decrease in density with height. In the low photosphere, the density is high enough and the temperature is low enough that H^-, a very efficient absorber and emitter of continuum radiation, is formed. This ion efficiently radiates away the nonradiative energy input in the photosphere. Above the photosphere, where the density is substantially decreased, the rate of H-e collisions is less and the fraction of H^- present is greatly reduced. In this region the temperature will be driven up until the emission from excited and ionized states of H I is sufficient to balance the energy input. In the LTE photosphere, the rate of collisional ionization depends primarily on two body collisions and the rate of recombination depends on three body collisions. Thus, the degree of ionization will increase with decreasing gas density. However, in the lower chromosphere, the degree of hydrogen ionization becomes independent of density. Radiative recombination (two body) rather than collisional recombination (three body) balances the collisional ionization (two body) so that the ionization is density independent. As the hydrogen becomes almost fully ionized, the temperature increases further until the emissions from He I and He II balance the energy output. Eventually, at greater heights He II is also fully ionized. Now, because the Li and Be abundances are negligible and the elements of higher atomic number have abundances that are small relative to hydrogen and helium, much higher degrees of ionization are required for the energy emission to balance the energy input. Crudely, the ability of an ion of abundance A and unbalanced nuclear charge z to radiate is proportional to Az^4. Thus, when A is small, high temperatures and stages of ionization are required. The net result is that the temperature attempts to jump from the values characteristic of strong helium emission ($\approx 1/2 \times 10^5$ K) to values characteristic of highly ionized states of the heavier elements (C, N, O, etc., at $\approx 10^6$ K).

The characteristics of this temperature variation with height are shown in figure 5-29. Conceptually, we can divide this profile into two regions: the 10^5 to 10^6 K region, where the temperature gradient is so large that the downward conduction of heat determines the profile, and the 10^4 to 10^5 K region, where the effects of hydrogen and helium ionization are dominate. Observations indicate that an optical depth of unity in the H I Lyman continuum occurs at an electron tem-

FIGURE 5-29.—A hypothetical temperature profile of the solar atmosphere. Because of the large uncertainties that presently exist in our knowledge of this profile and the invalid assumption of a spherically symmetric outer atmosphere, the location of the transition region and the shape of the profile above the temperature minimum are approximations only. Nevertheless, the qualitative characteristics of the profile do illustrate some interesting and possibly real features. The profile below 1700 km is the HSRA profile. The hydrogen and helium plateaus are assumed to be approximately 200 km wide and at the temperature ranges suggested by Athay (Thomas and Athay, 1961). The hydrogen plateau is assumed to be centered at 2000 km. The part of the profile dominated by heat conduction (10^5 to 10^6 K) is assumed to start at 2500 km and its variation is that computed by Athay (1971). The greatest uncertainties are in the location and shape of the profile between 10^4 to 10^5 K.

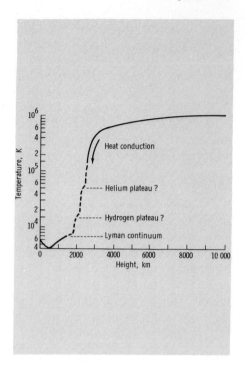

perature of approximately 8000 K (Noyes and Kalkofen, 1970, and Avrett, 1970). The scale height at this temperature is 280 km, but unit optical thickness in the Lyman continuum corresponds to only 50 km (HSRA). Thus, most of the gas 50 km above the height of 8000 K ($\approx$1800 km in the HSRA) is transparent to the Lyman continuum which must result from a sharp increase in the hydrogen ionization. This implies a steep temperature rise starting at approximately 1800 km. It also has been found that a plateau in this temperature rise should exist at approximately 15 000 K and be at least 200 km in width in order to be consistent with the observed Lyman-β line profile as well as the center-to-limb behavior of the C II resonance line (Avrett, 1970). Plateaus in the temperature rise also are predicted by energy considerations (Thomas and Athay, 1961). At conditions where the radiant energy loss is a strongly increasing function of temperature, the temperature rise tends to be relatively slow and a plateau results. When this loss begins to decrease with temperature, however, as might occur at the locations where either hydrogen or helium approach full ionization, the temperature rise should be rapid until a new source of strong emission is encountered. Athay points out the possibility of a plateau terminating at 12 000 to 14 000 K because of the strong bound-free emission of hydrogen, and a second plateau between approximately 40 000 to 60 000 K primarily caused by the Balmer-α emission of He II. Based on this same general reasoning, although differing in details, Defouw (1970b) predicts a transition from a gradual to a sharp temperature rise at approximately 17 500 K, the temperature where the rate of change of the heat-loss function with temperature (eq. (5–3)) becomes negative and the atmosphere becomes thermally unstable. Hence, both the observational and theoretical evidence point toward the existence of one or more plateaus below 10^5 K, but the details require appreciable clarification.

Energy Fluxes

Estimates of the energy fluxes associated with the heating of the solar atmosphere are shown in figure 5–30. The power inputs for each region of the atmosphere place constraints on theories which estimate the dissipation of wave energy. Because of theoretical or observational difficulties, most of the numerical values quoted are good to factors of 2 or 3 at best. We encounter four different types of energy fluxes when analyzing nonradiative heating. The first, $\mathbf{F}_r$, is the radiant energy flux emitted over and above the emission that would occur if no atmospheric heating existed. For the atmosphere as a whole, the total output of this flux is nearly balanced by the input of wave energy flux generated by the convective motions, $\mathbf{F}_w$. The thermal conductive flux, $\mathbf{F}_c$, is important in transferring energy between some adjacent regions. Lastly, the mechanical energy flux of gas motions, $\mathbf{F}_m$, distinct from $\mathbf{F}_w$, includes the energy flux in spicules, and the potential and kinetic energy in the solar wind. For a steady-state atmosphere, the time rate of change of energy density is zero. That is,

$$\nabla \cdot (\mathbf{F}_r + \mathbf{F}_w + \mathbf{F}_c + \mathbf{F}_m) = 0 \tag{5–47}$$

The values given in figure 5–30 are estimates of the four terms in equation (5–47), each integrated over the region considered.

$$\int_{h_1}^{h_2} \nabla \cdot \mathbf{F}_r \, dh + \int_{h_1}^{h_2} \nabla \cdot \mathbf{F}_w \, dh + \int_{h_1}^{h_2} \nabla \cdot \mathbf{F}_c \, dh + \int_{h_1}^{h_2} \nabla \cdot \mathbf{F}_m \, dh = 0 \tag{5–48}$$

Thus, as described, the power inputs should balance the power outputs for each region.

The enhancement of radiative output power ΔF_r in the photosphere and low chromosphere can be described in terms of the actual atmospheric temperature T and that which would exist if no wave flux dissipation existed and radiative equilibrium prevailed, T_0. Using equation (4–23) and the Planck function to represent the source function of H^-, an approximate expression for ΔF_r is (Athay, 1966b)[3]

$$\Delta F_r = 8\sigma T_0^3 \, \Delta T \, \Delta \tau^c \tag{5–49}$$

In this expression $\Delta T = T - T_0$, it is assumed that $\Delta T / T_0 \ll 1$, and $\Delta \tau^c$ is the optical depth over which H^- provides the dominate opacity and ΔT is nonzero. For $\Delta T = 200$ K and $\Delta \tau^c = 10^{-3}$, $\Delta F_r = 8 \times 10^6$ ergs/cm²-sec; these values are upper limits.

---

[3] The factor 8 in eq. (5–49) was originally 4 as derived by Osterbrock (1961). It was subsequently changed to 8 by Osterbrock to allow for ingoing as well as outgoing radiation.

Region and height, km	Power output, ergs/cm^2-sec			Power input, ergs/cm^2-sec		
	Radiation enhancement	Conduction to adjacent region	Mechanical energy	Wave flux dissipation	Conduction from adjacent region	Mechanical energy
Intermediate corona ≈ 100,000		↑ 4 x 10^4, to solar wind (Parker, 1963)	↑ 4 x 10^4, to potential and kinetic energy of solar wind (Kuperus, 1969)	? ↑		
Inner corona ≈ 2500	↑ 3 x 10^5, UV lines of ionized metals (Athay, 1966b)	5 x 10^5, to upper chromosphere (Athay, 1971) ↓		2 x 10^4, slow mode shocks with B = 2 gauss (Osterbrock, 1961)		2 x 10^5, from upper chromosphere spicules (Athay, 1971) ↑
Upper chromosphere ≈ 1000	↑ 3 x 10^5, H I Lyman-α line (Hintereggar, 1963)		↑ 2 x 10^5, to low corona spicules (Athay, 1971)	8 x 10^5, fast mode waves with B = 2 gauss (Osterbrock, 1961) ↑	↓ 5 x 10^5, from low corona (Athay, 1971)	
Middle chromosphere ≈ 500	↑ 1 x 10^6, H I Balmer lines (Athay, 1966b)			6 x 10^6, fast-mode waves with B = 2 gauss (Osterbrock, 1961) ↑		
Photosphere and low chromosphere 0	↑ < 8 x 10^6, H$^-$ continuum (Athay, 1966b)		↑ Gravity waves 4 x 10^7 (Whitaker, 1963)	2 x 10^7, fast mode waves with B = 2 gauss (Osterbrock, 1961) ↑		
Convection zone	↑ Acoustic waves 3 x 10^7 (Osterbrock, 1961 and Kuperus, 1969)	2 x 10^7 (Stein, 1968)	3 x 10^6 (Ulm-schneider, 1970)			

FIGURE 5–30.—Energy fluxes associated with nonradiative heating of the atmosphere. Because of the difficulties of the theories and interpretations of observations, most of these values are good to factors of 2 or 3 only. The height ranges shown are estimates of the regions in which the particular energy flux originates or is dissipated.

If negligible heating occurs below the temperature minimum at $\tau^c \approx 10^{-4}$ and ΔT is only 100 K, $\Delta F_c = 4 \times 10^5$ ergs/cm²-sec, 20 times smaller than the previous estimate. A careful consideration of the effects of line blanketing and departures from LTE in the H⁻ equilibrium (Cayril mechanism) predicts $T_0 = 4300 \pm 150$ K at $\tau_{5000} \approx 10^{-4}$, a value close to those of some model atmospheres (Athay, 1970). Because of the level of accuracy of current estimates of ΔT and $\Delta \tau^c$, we cannot rule out the possibility that the heating below the temperature minimum could be very small ($< 10^5$ ergs/cm²-sec). In the middle chromosphere, the Balmer lines of H I dominate the emission and contribute approximately 1×10^6 ergs/cm²-sec to the radiative flux. The values of height given in figure 5–30 for the boundaries of the regions are approximate only and depend greatly on the actual temperature profile. As we move up to higher temperatures in the chromosphere, sufficient energy becomes available by collision to appreciably excite H I; and its resonance line, $L\alpha$, becomes the dominate contributor (3×10^5 ergs/cm²-sec). Helium emission, although possibly dominate over narrow regions of height, is small relative to hydrogen emission in the chromosphere because of helium's relatively low abundance. In the inner corona, the combined emission in lines of many ionized metals contribute approximately the same as $L\alpha$ in the chromosphere, 3×10^5 ergs/cm²-sec. It will be shown in chapter 6 that the emission in the intermediate corona varies as N_e^2, which rapidly decreases with height. Thus, the emission above the inner corona is negligible. Summing up the radiation loss of all the regions, we see that the nonradiative heating supplied to the solar atmosphere must be approximately 1×10^7 ergs/cm²-sec.

An interesting and perhaps meaningful observation on the radiation loss is that, although it decreases with both increasing height and increasing mass density, it is roughly constant with changes in the ion density over four orders of magnitude (Athay, 1966b; fig. 5–31). It is tempting to conclude that the rate of dissipation of wave energy is directly proportional to the mass density of ions. However, it is possible that this result is fortuitous, and emphasizing it could obscure the real mechanisms at work. Also, there are other energy fluxes that can be of the same magnitude locally as the radiation loss and wave dissipation.

The rapid rise to coronal temperatures in the transition region between the chromosphere and the corona implies that an appreciable conductive flow of thermal energy back into the chromosphere exists. This conductive flux is equivalent to the temperature gradient times the thermal conductivity. Previously we have discussed the tendency for the temperature to jump abruptly from values characteristic of helium ionization to the very high values required for the low-abundance metals to be significant radiation emitters. Thus, we expect a very high temperature gradient in the transition zone and a correspondingly high conductive flux. This flux, in turn, tends to smooth the temperature jump. A second important effect of the high coronal temperatures is that the thermal conductivity is greatly increased, also tending to enhance the conductive flux. Because of their high thermal speed, the electrons rather than the ions are primarily responsible for the high rate

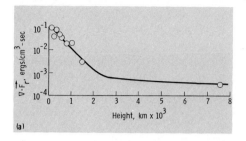

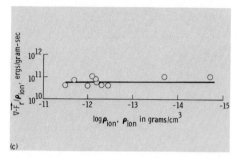

FIGURE 5–31.—Radiative energy loss as a function of height, total mass density, and ion mass density. All measurements cover the same height range. (*a*) Radiative loss per unit volume as a function of height. (*b*) Radiation loss per unit total mass as a function of total mass density. (*c*) Radiation loss per ion unit mass as a function of ion mass density. (From Athay, 1966*b*; copyright 1966, University of Chicago Press.)

of heat conduction. As the average thermal speed of the electrons (varying as $T_e^{1/2}$) is increased, the electron trajectories are altered less by encounters with ions, the effective distance between collisions is increased, and a decreased resistance to heat conduction by the electron gas results. This is a strong effect; the electron-ion mean free path is proportional to the fourth power of the average thermal speed of the electrons or the second power of the temperature. Also, because of their high thermal speed, the electrons are able to carry heat more rapidly. When both of these effects are considered, it is seen that the heat conduction varies as $T_e^{5/2} dT_e/dh$. Thus, the 10^6 K corona transfers heat 10^5 times more efficiently than the chromospheric gas at 10^4 K. Also, it is immediately apparent that over the range of heights in which the conductive flux is constant, dT_e/dh will become very steep at lower values of T_e. Numerically, the conductive flux of a gas at a pressure of 0.1 dyne/cm² and composed of hydrogen, 10% helium, and other elements at solar abundances is (Ulmschneider, 1969)

$$F_c = -1 \times 10^{-6} T_e^{5/2} dT_e/dh \qquad (5-50)$$

where F_c is in ergs/cm²-sec, T_e is in K, and h is in cm.

Space observations of XUV lines allow us to obtain estimates of F_c and $T_e(h)$. The emergent flux of radiation in the resonance line of a particular ion is

$$I = \frac{hc}{2\lambda} \int_{h_1}^{h_2} A_{\mu l} N_\mu \, dh \qquad (5-51)$$

where $A_{\mu l}$ is the transition probability from the upper to the lower level (sec. 4.8),

N_μ is the number density in the upper level, and h_1 and h_2 are the boundaries of the layer over which there is significant emission in the line. Assuming the spontaneous emission is balanced by collisional excitation,

$$I = \frac{hc}{2\lambda} \int_{h_1}^{h_2} N_e N_l C_{l\mu} \, dh \qquad (5\text{-}52)$$

Using an expression for $C_{l\mu}$ (Pottasch, 1964) the radiative flux can be expressed as (Athay, 1966a and 1971)

$$I = 0.55 \times 10^{-15} \, g_\lambda f A G(T_e) (N_e T_e)_{\text{tr}}^2 \left\langle \left(\frac{dT_e}{dh}\right)^{-1}\right\rangle \qquad (5\text{-}53)$$

where I is in ergs/cm²-sec, g_λ is a Gaunt factor of order unity, f is the oscillator strength for the transition, A is the abundance relative to hydrogen, $G(T_e)$ is a sharply peaked function of T_e and includes the effects of collisional excitation of N_μ and of ionization equilibrium in the corona, and $\langle (dT_e/dh)^{-1} \rangle$ is the value of $(dT_e/dh)^{-1}$ averaged over the height of the line-emitting layer. The value of $N_e T_e$ in the transition region $(N_e T_e)_{\text{tr}}$, which is proportional to electron pressure, has been assumed to be a constant in deriving equation (5-53). This is equivalent to assuming that the thickness of the transition region is much smaller than the mean atmospheric scale height. To an accuracy of about a factor of 2, $(N_e T_e)_{\text{tr}}$ is estimated to be 6×10^{14} K/cm³; $(2 \times 10^{10}$ cm$^{-3})(3 \times 10^4$ K) in the upper chromosphere where H I Lyman α is formed and $(4 \times 10^8$ cm$^{-3})(1.5 \times 10^6$ K) in the low corona. This corresponds to an electron pressure of 0.08 dyne/cm³. Using the observed strength of many XUV resonance lines formed at different T_e, calculated or estimated values of g_λ, f, $G(T_e)$, and A, the value of $\langle (dT_e/dh)^{-1} \rangle$ can be determined as a function of T_e. The resulting plots display nearly constant values of $T_e^{5/2} \, dT_e/dh$ between 10^5 and 10^6 K (fig. 5-32). Using these plots and radio data, which also have their origin in the corona, Athay (1971) concludes that F_c is approximately 5×10^5 ergs/cm²-sec.

Because the value of 5×10^5 ergs/cm²-sec estimated for F_c is comparable to the radiation emission from both the upper chromosphere or inner corona, the conductive flux can have an important and even locally dominant effect in the transition region. Because of the narrowness of this region, F_c is certainly much larger than the radiation emitted or the energy deposited locally. Although this explains the near constancy of F_c between 10^5 and 10^6 K, it creates a problem when we try to balance the energy fluxes on a local scale (eq. (5-47)). This can be illustrated by deriving $T(h)$, which is done by integrating equation (5-50) (Athay, 1971)

$$h_2 - h_1 = 2(T_{e_2}^{7/2} - T_{e_1}^{7/2}) \qquad (5\text{-}54)$$

where h is in km, T_e is in units of 10^5 K, and F_c has been set equal to 5×10^5 ergs/cm²-sec. This relation has been used to plot $T_e(h)$ for $T_e > 10^5$ K in figure 5-29 where it is seen that the temperature gradient becomes very steep at lower temperatures.

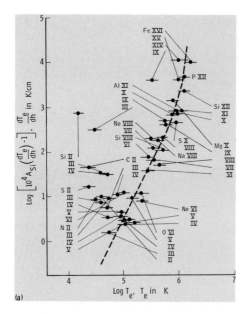
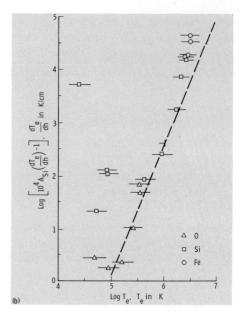

FIGURE 5–32.—Inverse of temperature gradient versus temperature in the transition region derived from XUV data. The straight dashed lines are a good representation of the data and imply a constant thermal conductive flux ($T_e^{5/2}\, dT_e/dh$ = constant) in the range of 10^5 to 10^6 K. Using a value of 3×10^{-5} for the abundance of silicon, the values of F_c for (a) and (b) are 3×10^5 and 1×10^6 ergs/cm²-sec, respectively (Athay, 1971). (a) Dielectric recombination not included. (From Athay, 1966a; copyright 1966, University of Chicago Press.) (b) Dielectric recombination included. (From Dupree and Goldberg, 1967; copyright 1967, D. Reidel.)

At $T_e = 10^5$ K, a change of 10^4 K is accomplished in only 0.7 km. Thus, a large amount of thermal energy is conducted into a very thin layer at approximately 10^5 K. On the other hand, the radiative losses are distributed over much thicker layers and cannot balance $\nabla \cdot \mathbf{F}_c$ on a local scale. It has been postulated that the upward flux of kinetic energy of spicules, which are observed to have their bases at approximately the transition region, could balance F_c (Kuperus and Athay, 1967). Although this is a plausible assumption, the physical situation is much more complicated than we have presented.

The presence of a nonuniform magnetic-field structure in the quiet chromosphere creates a nonuniform flow of thermal energy and gas kinetic energy. When the gas density is low, thermal energy is constrained to move along magnetic-field lines. This can be seen by tracing the path of a heat-carrying electron as it tries to move across magnetic-field lines. It will experience a force of $-e\mathbf{V}_e \times \mathbf{B}$, which is balanced by the centrifugal force of its curved trajectory, $m_e V_e^2 / r_e$. Thus, electrons of mean thermal speed V_e spiral around magnetic-field lines with a radius of

$$r_e = \frac{m_e V_e}{eB} \tag{5–55}$$

Collisions of an electron with other particles randomize its motion and reduce the tendency to spiral about B. The relative importance of the two effects can be determined by comparing r_e with the electron mean free path λ_e

$$1/\lambda_e = \sum_i N_i Q_{ei} \tag{5-56}$$

where the sum is taken over all species of particles with which an electron collides and Q_{ei} is the corresponding collision cross section. In the fully ionized gas of the upper chromosphere, collisions of electrons with other electrons are dominant so that $\lambda_e^{-1} \simeq N_e Q_{ee}$.

$$\frac{\lambda_e}{r_e} = \left(\frac{eB}{M_e V_e}\right)\left(\frac{1}{N_e Q_{ee}}\right) \tag{5-57}$$

The coefficient of thermal conductivity for conduction parallel to a magnetic field $K_{||}$ is unaltered by the presence of the field. On the other hand, the coefficient of thermal conductivity perpendicular to the field $K_\perp$ can be reduced significantly.

$$K_\perp = K_{||}\left[1 + \left(\frac{\lambda_e}{r_e}\right)^2\right]^{-1} = K_{||}[1 + (\omega\tau)^2]^{-1} \tag{5-58}$$

The latter expression is the one usually found in the literature (Chapman and Cowling, 1960) and is equivalent to the first expression; ω is the cyclotron frequency V_e/r_e, and τ is the mean free time, λ_e/V_e. For even very weak fields in the chromosphere, this effect is important. For $T_e = 10^4$ K, $N_e = 10^{11}$ cm^{-3} ($h \simeq 2000$ km), $Q_{ee} = 10^{-12}$ cm^2 and $B = 1$ gauss, both r_e and λ_e are approximately 10 cm. For stronger fields usually encountered in the quiet chromosphere, $B > 10$ gauss, $T_e = 10^5$ K, and $N_e = 6 \times 10^9$ cm^{-3} (transition region), $\lambda_e/r_e > 2 \times 10^2$ and $K_\perp < 3 \times 10^{-5} K_{||}$. Thus, heat from the corona flows back into the chromosphere along field lines and is deposited primarily in regions where the field is vertical. It will be seen that these regions coincide with the chromospheric network which is also the site from which the spicules arise that could carry away the deposited energy. This model is discussed further when spicules are considered (sec. 5.4).

In the intermediate corona there are two power outputs which are important. The temperature of the corona reaches a broad maximum at approximately $10^{-1}R_\odot$ and then slowly decreases outward. The outward thermal flux associated with this temperature gradient is estimated to be 4×10^4 ergs/cm^2-sec (Parker, 1963). Also, thermal, kinetic, and potential energy is carried away by the solar wind. This energy flux is estimated to be 4×10^4 ergs/cm^2-sec (Kuperus, 1969). The radiative loss per unit volume initially decreases as N_e^2 and is therefore negligible above the inner corona.

The above estimates of power output place constraints on theories of wave generation and dissipation which attempt to account for atmospheric heating. The total, on the order of 1×10^7 ergs/cm^2-sec, must be generated in the convection zone or low photosphere and most of it deposited in the photosphere and low chromosphere. However, even though relatively small, some of the wave energy must propagate all the way to, and be deposited in, the intermediate corona.

Generation of Nonradiative Energy

Similar to the situation we encountered in analyzing vertical oscillations, we are faced with the possibility of two different mechanisms for generating the upward flux of nonradiative energy; the power could be generated as either acoustic waves or gravity waves. We consider acoustic waves first.

In the convection zone, the buoyancy forces on a rising cell of fluid produce a conversion from thermal to mechanical energy. Some of this energy is immediately returned to the thermal form by viscous dissipation at the cell boundaries, but some is converted to sound waves. For simplicity, the turbulence is assumed to be locally isotropic, although the radial direction is clearly a preferred one. Under this assumption, the rate of generation of acoustical energy per unit volume is the product of kinetic energy density, characteristic frequency, and Mach number of the turbulence (Stein, 1968)

$$\nabla \cdot \mathbf{F}_w{}^a \simeq 10^2 (\rho V_t{}^2)(V_t/L) M_t{}^5 \qquad \text{ergs/cm}^2\text{-sec} \qquad (5\text{--}59)$$

where ρ is in grams/cm^3, V_t is the rms value of the local turbulent velocity in cm/sec, M_t is the local turbulent Mach number, L the characteristic size of the turbulence, and V_t/L is in sec^{-1}. In the convection zone, L is of the order of H. In figure 5–33, M_t is plotted versus height. Two features are of importance: M_t varies appreciably and there is a sharp peak immediately below the surface of the convection zone. Because the sonic velocity does not change rapidly in several hundred kilometers, $\nabla \cdot \mathbf{F}_w{}^a$ actually varies as $\rho V_t{}^8$. Thus, the power output is a very strong function of the magnitude and variation of the turbulent velocity. Figure 5–34 shows two estimates of $\nabla \cdot \mathbf{F}_w{}^a$, both indicating that almost all of the acoustic power is generated in a thin layer less than 100 km thick at the top of the convection zone. Assuming that one-half of the generated power is propagated upward, the flux of acoustical energy into the photosphere is

$$F_w = \underbrace{\frac{1}{2} \int \nabla \cdot \mathbf{F}_w{}^a \, dh}_{\text{convection zone}} \qquad (5\text{--}60)$$

Calculated fluxes are quoted in figure 5–30. Estimates for the peak in the frequency spectrum of generated power fall in the range of slightly greater than ω_a (Kato, 1966) to several octaves above ω_a (Stein, 1968). Thus, almost all of the acoustical energy flux emitted upward should penetrate the photosphere and be available for heating.

The existing estimates of the frequency spectrum and total acoustical power emitted by the convection zone are good to an order of magnitude only because of our inability to specify precisely both the functional dependence of $\nabla \cdot \mathbf{F}_w{}^a$ and $V_t(h, \omega)$. It has been suggested that during the conversion of convective motion into turbulent motion, the kinetic energy is distributed in all three directions, not just one. Hence, the turbulent velocities are overestimated by $1/\sqrt{3}$ which implies an overestimate of $\nabla \cdot \mathbf{F}_w{}^a$ by a factor of 81 (Dubov, 1966). Also, because of gravity the turbulence is not isotropic. Rising eddies expand and descending eddies con-

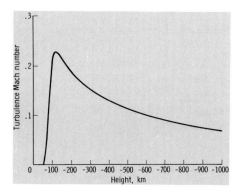

FIGURE 5–33.—Turbulence Mach number in the convection zone. (From Stein, 1968; copyright 1968, University of Chicago Press.)

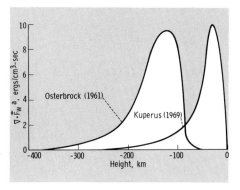

FIGURE 5–34.—Acoustical power generation in the convective zone.

tract, which creates an imbalance between upward and downward emission of flux (Kuperus, 1969). The presence of magnetic fields also creates locally preferred directions and possibly an amplification of acoustical power emission (Osterbrock, 1961).

Gravity waves and convection are similar in that both are driven by buoyancy forces. However, in the convection zone the Brunt-Väisälä frequency ω_B is imaginary and gravity waves cannot be generated. But, in the photosphere where ω_B is real and an appreciable convective overshoot exists (Frazier, 1968a, b), conditions are favorable for gravity wave emission. The power output per unit volume which results from gravity wave generation is (Stein, 1968)

$$\nabla \cdot \mathbf{F}_w{}^g \approx 10^2 (\rho V_t{}^2)(V_t/L)(L/H)^5 \qquad \text{ergs/cm}^2\text{-sec} \qquad (5\text{–}61)$$

where the terms are the same as in equation (5–59). We see that relative to acoustic waves, gravity wave generation in the solar atmosphere is very efficient. For acoustic waves, there is a mismatch between the turbulent velocity and the speed of sound. This results in a low efficiency for conversion of the turbulent power density, $\sim (\rho V_t{}^2)(V_t/L)$, into acoustical wave emission. The efficiency is essentially $M_t{}^5$ (eq. (5–59)). For gravity waves, however, the efficiency for converting the turbulent power density into gravity wave emission is $(L/H)^5$, which could be of the order of unity. Thus, the convective power overshoot is converted efficiently to gravity waves. Opposing this tendency are the effects of thermal relaxation in the low photosphere, as previously considered (fig. 5–24). However, above a few hundred kilometers, thermal relaxation should no longer have an appreciable effect. Estimates of the gravity wave flux, which excludes thermal relaxation, are relatively large. Based on observed photospheric velocities, $F_w{}^g$ at 500 km is estimated to be 4×10^7 ergs/cm²-sec (Whitaker, 1963), which is appreciably greater than that required from radiation power loss estimates (fig. 5–30). The calculated frequency spectrum of the generated gravity waves is very flat up to ω_B (Stein, 1967), hence the generated power is propagated to altitudes in the upper chromosphere when ω_B again decreases (fig. 5–26).

Estimates of $F_w{}^g$ suffer from the same order-of-magnitude inaccuracies as $F_w{}^a$, and for the same reasons. In addition, thermal relaxation effects must be included directly in the analysis of the generation mechanism. Also $V_t(h, \omega)$ is difficult to either predict or observe in the photosphere. Lastly, the dependence of the power generation rate on $V_t(h, \omega)$ for gravity waves is different than that for acoustic waves and a relative comparison is therefore difficult to make. Acoustic waves are generated primarily by the high-frequency portion of the turbulence spectrum in the convection zone, while gravity wave generation is dependent upon the low-frequency portion of the spectrum in the photosphere. The extent and manner that the turbulence of the convection zone extends into the photosphere is not well understood. The concept of "tongues of turbulence" that penetrate high into the photosphere and subsequently decay by the action of negative buoyancy forces has been proposed (Lighthill, 1967). This is analogous to the sometimes observed towering protrusions of terrestrial cumulus clouds through upper layers of stable air.

From this discussion, it must be concluded that the power generated in the form of either acoustic waves or gravity waves cannot be excluded from further consideration at this time as a source of the nonradiative atmospheric heating.

Propagation and Dissipation of Nonradiative Energy

Acoustical waves generated in the convection zone propagate outward as sound waves. The energy flux is

$$F_w{}^a = \tfrac{1}{2}\rho (V_w{}^{\text{rms}})^2 V_0 \tag{5-62}$$

where $V_w{}^{\text{rms}}$ is the root mean square of the gas velocity in the wavefront and V_0 is the local speed of sound. If this flux of energy is to remain nearly constant as the wave moves upward, $V_w{}^{\text{rms}}$ must increase with the decrease in ρ. An upward flux of 1×10^7 ergs/cm²-sec requires that $V_w{}^{\text{rms}}/V_0$ be approximately 10^{-2} at the top of the convection zone. Since V_0 changes only slightly in the photosphere and low chromosphere (fig. 5–27), the decrease in ρ of 10^{-4} that occurs in the first 1000 km requires an increase in $V_w{}^{\text{rms}}$ to sonic values. Thus, a shock front is formed in which the gas pressure, density, and temperature change abruptly with a few particle mean free paths. The changes experienced by the gas are no longer reversible, in a thermodynamic sense, and the passage of the front leaves the gas at a higher temperature. Some of the energy carried in the front is dissipated and the atmosphere is thereby heated. In figure 5–35 the transition of a sound wave to a shock front is shown. Nonlinear and unsteady gas-flow effects are included. The compression waves of the disturbance travel slightly faster than the rarefaction waves. These effects are cumulative and the sinusoidal waveform transitions to a shock front as shown. This illustrates the difficulty of using linearized theory to calculate the wave propagation because it assumes the waveform does not change in shape. In particular, our previous conclusion, arrived at by linear theory, that no acoustic waves with $\omega < \omega_a$ could propagate is incorrect whenever V_w^{rms} can increase to the order of V_0.

The objective of analyses of wave propagation and dissipation is to match the dissipation, $\nabla \cdot \mathbf{F}_w$, with the net power output per unit volume. In figure 5–36 the calculated shock heating in the atmosphere for several wave periods and energy fluxes is shown along with the calculated radiative energy loss, $\nabla \cdot \mathbf{F}_r$. It is seen that wave periods of approximately 10 sec are required for shock heating to balance the radiative output. These waves, if they exist, would not be directly observable with present resolution limitations since their wavelengths would be less than 100 km. Rather than line shifts, they would contribute to line broadening and in other ways appear as microturbulence (Ulmschneider, 1970).

In considering the propagation and dissipation of gravity waves, we must consider several factors. First, thermal relaxation strongly damps the waves in the photosphere. However, because the region of strong damping ($\Delta h \approx 200$ km) is small relative to the wavelength of the waves (≈ 2000 km) and because gravity waves can be generated above the low photosphere, thermal relaxation effects do not completely inhibit gravity wave propagation although they strongly attenuate it. Second, the thermal conductivity is high, which tends to smooth out the temperature perturbations of the waves. Third, ω_B decreases sharply in the upper chromosphere (fig. 5–26) and may inhibit propagation of all but very low frequency waves. However, the nonhomogeneous nature of the upper chromosphere prevents the calculation and interpretation of a meaningful single-stream value for ω_B. Last,

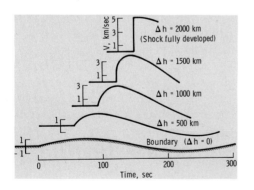

FIGURE 5–35.—Transition of an acoustic wave to a shock front. The flow velocity as a function of time for several heights above the convection zone is shown. The atmosphere is assumed to have $V_0 = 6$ km/sec, $T = 6000$ K, $\gamma = 5/3$, and $dT/dh = 33$ K/km at $\Delta h = 0$. (From Bird, 1964; copyright 1964, University of Chicago Press.)

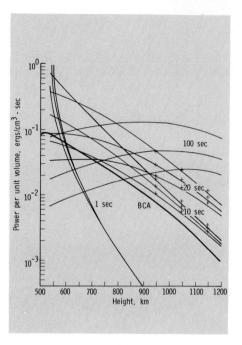

FIGURE 5–36.—Shock heating and radiative output of the solar atmosphere (BCA). The heating caused by shock waves having initial periods of 1, 10, 20, and 100 sec is shown for three different values of energy flux at 544 km: 1.6×10^6, 3.0×10^6, and 8.0×10^6 ergs/cm²-sec from top to bottom. The heavy dark line (BCA) is the calculated radiative power loss, $\nabla \cdot \mathbf{F}_r$. Periods of approximately 10 sec yield the best match. This result is unaltered when other model atmospheres are used. (From Ulmschneider, 1970; copyright 1970, D. Reidel.)

the propagation of gravity waves into a region of rapidly decreasing density could promote dissipation by cumulative nonlinear effects that distort the waveform, similar to the transition of acoustic waves to shock waves. In general, the dissipation of gravity waves in the solar atmosphere is not well analyzed; hence, its importance in heating the atmosphere is undetermined.

In addition to acoustic and gravity waves, a third type of wave, an Alfvén wave, can carry significant amounts of energy. Alfvén waves can propagate any time that a magnetic field is present in an electrical conducting fluid like the solar atmosphere.

Physically, sound waves and Alfvén waves are quite different. In sound waves, the gas displacement is longitudinal; that is, parallel to the direction of propagation of the wave. A pulse of pressure compresses the gas immediately surrounding it and the pulse thereby propagates. The speed of the propagation is approximately the same as the speed at which the atoms or molecules can communicate with one another, or the average thermal speed. On the other hand, the gas displacement in an Alfvén wave is transverse; that is, perpendicular to the direction of the wave propagation (fig. 5–37). An example of a wave with transverse material motion is the passage of a velocity pulse along a string under tension (fig. 5–38). In an Alfvén wave, the lines of magnetic force are analogous to the string (fig. 5–39). The forces are passed along by induced electrical currents and are not accompanied by changes in pressure or density to the first order. When the fluid element at the

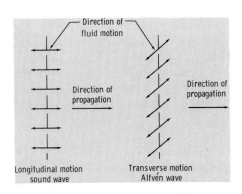

FIGURE 5–37.—Fluid motion in longitudinal and transverse wavefronts.

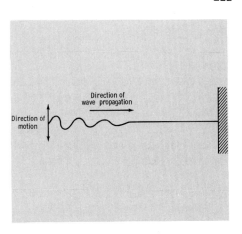

FIGURE 5–38.—Transverse wave propagation along a string.

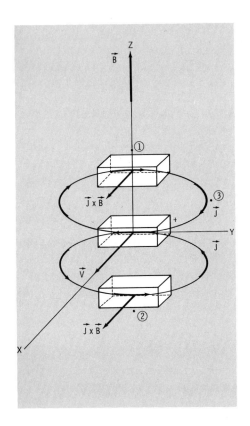

FIGURE 5–39.—Mechanism of Alfvén wave propagation.

origin is moved perpendicular to the magnetic field in the $+X$ direction, as shown in figure 5–39, it experiences a $\mathbf{V} \times \mathbf{B}$ electric field and a current in the $-Y$ direction is induced within it. This current closes upon itself by forming loops that run through the immediately adjacent elements along $\pm B$, as shown at points 1 and 2. The induced current flow is in the $-Y$ direction at these adjacent elements and a $\mathbf{J} \times \mathbf{B}$ force in the $+X$ direction results. The initial velocity of the element at the origin is therefore transferred to the adjacent elements where the process is repeated, thus propagating disturbances in the $\pm\mathbf{B}$ directions. The acceleration of the adjacent elements is proportional to the induced force divided by the mass, $\mathbf{J} \times \mathbf{B}/\rho$. The induced current is proportional to B; hence, the acceleration is proportional to B^2/ρ. Thus, it is not surprising that when the appropriate differential equations are derived, the velocity of propagation of the disturbance, the Alfvén velocity, is found to be

$$V_A = \left(\frac{B^2}{\mu_0\rho}\right)^{1/2} \tag{5–63}$$

where μ_0 is the magnetic permeability of a vacuum. We will see later that the quantity B^2/μ_0 exhibits the characteristics of a magnetic pressure, p_m. Thus, the square of the velocity of propagation along a magnetic field is equal to p_m/ρ and is analogous to the square of the velocity of propagation of acoustic waves, equal to $\gamma p/\rho$. An Alfvén wave has a strong tendency to propagate along the field lines rather than in other directions, as we have implied. For example, looking at point 3 in figure 5–39, we see that the induced current is parallel to the field; thus, no force or displacement results. Points in the YZ plane, other than along the Z-axis, always have a component of this induced current parallel to $\mathbf{B}$, and the tendency for motions at the origin to be transferred to these points is thereby decreased.

At locations in the solar atmosphere where the magnetic field is vertical and relatively strong, along the chromosphere network for example, Alfvén waves could propagate upward with the gas motion taking place primarily in the horizontal plane. It has been suggested that torsional oscillations of the magnetic lines of force could occur and rings of vorticity thereby propagate upward along the magnetic field (Lighthill, 1967). Oscillating closed loops of gas motion which are primarily in the horizontal plane and are comparable in diameter to granulation cells could be dragged clear of the convection zone by tongues of turbulence and propagate into the chromosphere (Howe, 1969).

We have seen that in order for an Alfvén wave to propagate, electrical current must flow (fig. 5–39). Thus, because of the nonzero resistivity of the gas, joule heating occurs and wave energy is dissipated. Electrons are accelerated by induced electric fields and the kinetic energy of their ordered motion is converted to the random motion of heat by collisions with ions and neutral particles. Alfvén waves are also dissipated by frictional damping which takes place via the ions. The magnetic-field oscillations tend to drag along the ions, but not the neutrals; and ion-neutral collisions convert the energy of the ion oscillations into heat.

In this section we have considered acoustic, gravity, and Alfvén waves and treated them as though they were independent. Actually, they are coupled to one another. This can be demonstrated by including magnetic effects in the previously used conservation equations. A $\mathbf{J} \times \mathbf{B}$ force term should be added to the right-hand side of the conservation of momentum equation (5–12), a corresponding energy term should be included in equation (5–14), and Maxwell's equations with appropriate material laws should be added to the total set. However, such an analysis is lengthy and, in order that we may continue to focus our attention on the effects in the solar atmosphere, only the results will be discussed.

We consider first the combination of magnetic pressure gradient and gas pressure gradient restoring forces which produce magnetohydrodynamic (MHD) waves. In a compressible and electrically conducting medium, three modes of wave propagation can exist. They are essentially combinations of the acoustic and Alfvén waves. The first mode of wave propagation, the "fast" mode, will be acoustical in character (longitudinal fluid motion) when $V_0 \gg V_A$, but becomes magnetic in character (transverse fluid motion) when $V_A \gg V_0$. The velocity of the fast mode is given by

$$V_{\text{fast}}^2 = \tfrac{1}{2} \{ V_0^2 + V_A^2 + [(V_0^2 + V_A^2)^2 - (2 V_0 V_A \cos \theta)^2]^{1/2} \} \qquad (5\text{–}64)$$

and is plotted in figure 5-40 for $V_A = 2 V_0$. Because V_0 and V_A enter into equation (5–64) in identical ways, the condition of $V_0 = 2 V_A$ is also covered by figure 5–40 by interchanging V_0 and V_A. The velocity of the fast mode becomes the faster of either V_0 or V_A for $\theta = 0$ and in the two limiting cases: for $V_0 \gg V_A$, $V_{\text{fast}} \simeq V_0$ and for $V_A \gg V_0$, $V_{\text{fast}} \simeq V_A$. Thus, the fast mode is essentially a sound wave in the convection zone, photosphere, and lower chromosphere, but it becomes an Alfvén wave in the upper chromosphere and corona (fig. 5–41). The second mode of propagation, the slow mode, assumes just the opposite character. That is, it assumes the velocity and type of wave structure of the slower of V_0 or V_A for $\theta = 0$ and in the two limiting cases: when $V_0 \gg V_A$, $V_{\text{slow}} \simeq V_A$ and the fluid motion is transverse and when $V_A \gg V_0$, $V_{\text{slow}} \simeq V_0$ and the fluid motion is longitudinal. The direction of propagation, however, is only in directions equal to or nearly parallel to the magnetic field for all cases of the slow mode. The third possible mode of propagation,

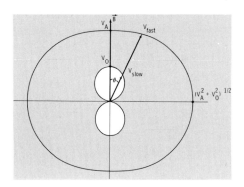

FIGURE 5–40.—V_{fast} and V_{slow} for $V_A = 2 V_0$ (from eq. (5–64)).

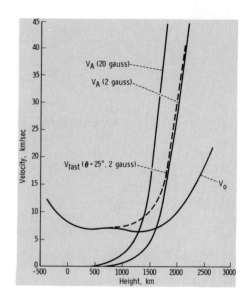

Figure 5–41.—Acoustic, Alfvén, and fast-mode wave propagation in the solar atmosphere. (Based on the BCA model.)

the Alfvén mode, is not combined with sound waves in any way. The direction of propagation is along the field and no changes in density or pressure occur.

The capability of the atmosphere to propagate MHD waves greatly increases the number of possible mechanisms by which nonradiative heating could be accomplished. Fast-mode waves, identical to acoustic waves, carry energy upward and tend to be accelerated by shocks. However, in regions where the field is vertical and relatively large, as on the chromospheric network, the waves become magnetic in character, V_{fast} increases rapidly, and $V_w{}^{\text{rms}}$ remains much less than V_0 to greater heights (energy flux$\sim(V_w{}^{\text{rms}})^2 V_{\text{fast}}$). Thus, the energy can be transported further into the chromosphere and corona before appreciable dissipation occurs. A similar result is obtained where the field is horizontal. When a magnetic field is parallel to a fast-mode wave shock front, the thickness of the front and the rate of dissipation can be reduced substantially, allowing the energy to propagate to greater heights (Mäckle, 1969). A second effect encountered when fast-mode waves are magnetic in character is their strong tendency to be refracted away from the local vertical. Because $V_A \sim \rho^{-1/2}$ and ρ decreases with height, the higher part of a wavefront will propagate faster and rotate the direction of propagation toward the horizontal. The magnitude of ρ decreases rapidly outward, thus this effect is a strong one for simple waves that follow the rules of geometrical optics.

A model of the propagation and dissipation of wave energy in the solar atmosphere has been provided by Osterbrock (1961). It is useful, not because it is correct in detail, but because it illustrates the type mechanisms that must be considered and serves as a focal point for further discussion and refinement. In his model, the noise generated in the convection zone propagates upward as soundlike fast-mode waves, presumably being observable as vertical oscillations (fig. 5–42). The slow-

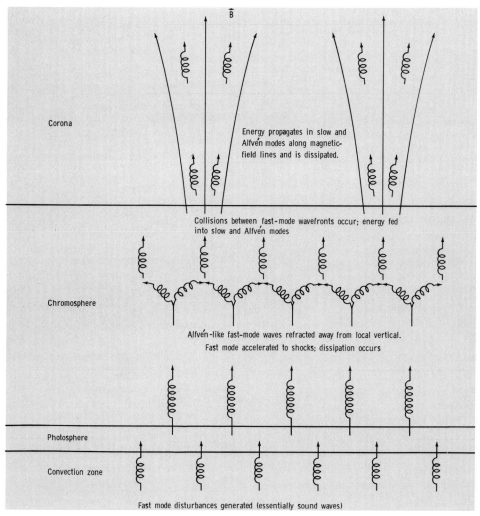

FIGURE 5–42.—The outward flow of nonradiative energy in the solar atmosphere. (After Osterbrock, 1961.)

mode waves that are generated are quickly damped. As the density decreases in the low chromosphere, the fast-mode waves are accelerated to shocks and much of the energy is dissipated. Higher in the chromosphere the fast-mode waves become Alfvén-like, tend to be refracted away from the local vertical, and collide with each other. These collisions feed energy into the slow and Alfvén modes, which then readily travel up along the magnetic field without refraction and dissipate in the upper chromosphere and corona. In figure 5–43 the calculated dissipation with

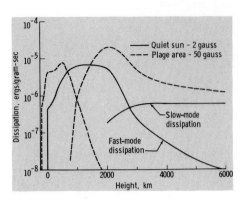

FIGURE 5–43.—Nonradiative energy dissipation in the solar atmosphere. The total acoustical wave flux entering the photosphere from below is 3×10^7 ergs/cm²-sec for the quiet sun and 3×10^8 ergs/cm²-sec for the magnetically enhanced areas. These values are appreciably larger than the estimates of the excess radiation flux.

height for the quiet sun and a magnetically enhanced area (plage) is illustrated. We see that most of the energy is dissipated as shocks in the low chromosphere where the steep temperature rise occurs. The effect of a strong magnetic field is to increase both the initial outward energy flux and the dissipation, accounting for the higher amount of radiation liberated by magnetically enhanced regions.

Osterbrock has used geometrical optics and treated each fundamental wave mode as a separate entity. Difficulty is encountered in transporting sufficient energy to the corona because of the large dissipation by fast-mode shocks in the low chromosphere and the strong refraction of the Alfvén-like fast-mode waves. In reality, however, geometrical optics is not a valid description of waves whose wavelength is of the same magnitude as the wavefront dimensions. Waves from different regions of generation intersect and allow the transformation of one type of wave into another type. It has been suggested that these transformations are very effective in the low chromosphere where $V_A \approx V_0$ (Pikel'ner and Livshits, 1965). Fast-mode waves can create Alfvén and slow-mode waves. The slow-mode waves are dissipated and heat the chromosphere. The Alfvén waves propagate directly to the corona where they produce slow-mode waves which subsequently dissipate and heat the gas. It is clear that the complexity of the MHD wave theory and the physical situation to which it is applied will require something more than a simple model to explain atmospheric heating.

The combination of magnetic pressure gradient and gravity-restoring forces could be of importance in atmospheric heating, but has received much less analysis than MHD waves. It has been shown that when a magnetic field and the gravity vector are not parallel, Alfvén waves and gravity waves can be coupled in such a way that no frequency limitations for propagation exist (Lighthill, 1967). When $\omega > \omega_B$, the wave is Alfvén-like and the energy is transported parallel to the field. Thus, wave energy generated in the form of gravity waves can be transformed into waves with a magnetic character and propagate above the region where gravity waves are normally reflected.

At this point in our discussion it is apparent that the most informative analysis of wave propagation must consider all three restoring forces simultaneously. That is, the conservation of momentum should be expressed as

$$\frac{D\mathbf{V}}{Dt} = -\nabla p + \rho\mathbf{g} + \mathbf{J} \times \mathbf{B} \qquad (5\text{-}65)$$

Because there are now three different vector forces that can interfere with or reinforce one another, the analysis is complicated greatly. Assuming a constant magnetic field, an exponentially varying isothermal atmosphere, and all wave perturbations to be small, the resulting dispersion relation yields three modes: a + mode, a − mode, and an Alfvén mode (McLellan and Winterberg, 1968). The + and − modes are strongly coupled to the acoustic, gravity, and magnetic types of wave motion and their characteristics are dependent upon the parameters of all three. However, the Alfvén mode is separable from the dispersion relation and therefore independent of compressibility and gravity. Further analysis of the coupling of the three restoring forces and application of the results to the real nonuniform solar atmosphere should yield considerable insight into the mechanisms which generate, propagate, and dissipate wave energy. This is an important, interesting, but not well-explored area that is open to future solar physics research.

5.3 THE CHROMOSPHERIC NETWORK

When we look at the photosphere in white light, we see a granulation pattern which appears as bright cells separated by a network of dark lanes (fig. 5-1). A larger, less well-defined network pattern is also visible in the chromosphere. The term "chromospheric granulation" has been used in connection with this network and, as we shall see later, can be identified with the structure of supergranulation flow.

The Network in Hα

Much chromospheric structure is visible when we look at the sun with a medium- or narrow-bandwidth Hα filter at line center (fig. 5-44). The observable features can be classified roughly into three groups, although there are no sharp lines of demarcation between them. The smallest detail observable, the fine mottling, appears as small dark fibrils. Fibrils usually are clustered together to form coarse mottles, which in turn are grouped so as to outline large adjacent polygonal areas approximately 25 000 to 50 000 km in size.

At what altitude are the features that we see in the center of Hα? We cannot specify any one altitude but rather must specify a range of altitudes. The height at which the optical depth is unity will vary greatly depending upon the feature we observe. The values specified in figure 4–30 are average values only. In general, however, it can be said that for Hα filter widths of 0.5 to 0.7 Å, we see to approximately 1500 km except at the mottles and active-sun features where τ_λ can be

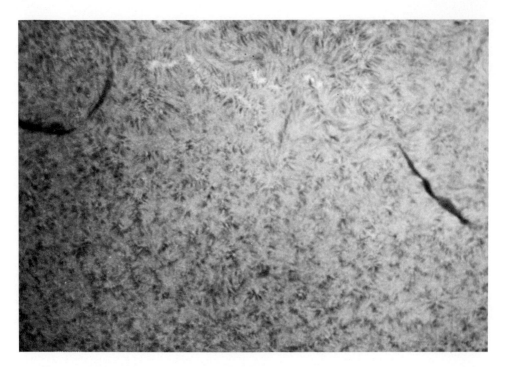

FIGURE 5–44.—Hα filtergram of the sun on February 17, 1968. This was made using an interference filter of 0.7-Å bandwidth of the type which has been designed for use on NASA's
solar Apollo telescope mount. It is a good compromise between a narrowband birefringent
Hα filter (<0.5 Å passband at line center) and one in the wings of Hα in that the primary
features from both can be seen (Hα fine structure, filaments, spots, and flare brightening
in the wings of Hα). The structure in the upper right, above a line between the two filaments,
is dominated by the magnetic fields of an active region. The region below the line between
the two filaments contains quiet-sun structure. The grouping of the coarse mottling provides
an excellent outline of the chromospheric network. (Courtesy of A. Title, Harvard College
Observatory.)

unity appreciably higher in the atmosphere. As we move offband, the character of
the observed structure changes (figs. 5–45 and 5–46). At ±0.7 Å, much of the
detailed fine structure is no longer observable and the mottling that remains clearly
outlines the chromospheric network. This is most evident in the red wing.

Near-limb high resolution Hα pictures in the red wing, such as the excellent
one in figure 5–47, clearly display the fine dark mottles or fibrils and the way in
which they are grouped to outline the network. The fibrils resemble blades of grass,
sprouting up in clumps and outlining nearly circular regions. These fibrils actually
are jets of gas which we will identify as spicules in the following section. Also
evident in figure 5–47 is the string of bright points at the bases of the fibrils which
outline the network. The greater contrast of the fibrils in the red wing of Hα, as
compared with the blue wing, is illustrated in the near-limb photos of figure 5–48.

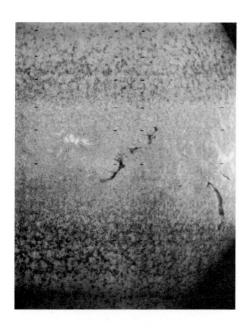

FIGURE 5-45.—An Hα spectrographic scan from −0.7 Å (top) to +0.7 Å (bottom) made on August 12, 1962. The structure of the coarse mottling becomes apparent in the regions of $\Delta\lambda \gtrsim |0.3$ Å$|$. (Courtesy of Mount Wilson and Palomar Observatories.)

The Network in Ca II K

The coarse mottling and chromospheric network is seen clearly in Ca II K (3934 Å) spectroheliograms (fig. 5–49). At the center of the absorption line, $K2R$ to $K2V$ (fig. 4–32), we see the network in emission. The bright mottling forms nearly continuous rings around cells, which in turn form the network. At $K3$, we see to approximately the same height as center Hα, 1000 km. At $K2$ we see to the base of the chromosphere, approximately 500 km. However, there is a close correspondence between the details seen in Hα and $K2$, which is revealed by a comparison of figures 5–46 and 5–49. We see the network in emission at $K2$ because the source function S_λ is locally higher than the photospheric radiation (eqs. (4–8) and (4–9)). This, in turn, is attributed to a locally higher temperature along the network. As we sweep across the Ca II K line (fig. 5–50), we see that outside $K2R$ to $K2V$, the network and mottling become much less pronounced. At $K1$ we are looking at lower altitudes where the atmospheric structure itself is less heterogeneous.

Magnetic-Field Correlation

The Ca II K network closely coincides with the network of locally strong, primarily vertical magnetic fields whose strength is at least 10 to 20 gauss (Simon and Leighton, 1964). Thus, a Ca II K picture accurately outlines the magnetic field. The bright points in Ca II K 232 at network intersections correspond to magnetic fields of several hundred gauss in areas extending over no more than 500 km (Sheeley, 1969). The continuum emission is often weakened at these points,

FIGURE 5–46.—Spectroheliograms taken on September 11, 1961. The structure in the equatorial band is dominated by solar activity. Above and below this band, a transition can be seen from detailed quiet-sun structure at line center to a sparse structure at +0.7 Å which outlines the chromospheric network. (a) Hα line center. (b) 0.35 Å to the red side of Hα line center. (c) 0.7 Å to the red side of Hα line center. (Courtesy of Mount Wilson and Palomar Observatories.)

suggesting they coincide with the dark lanes and pores of granulation. These areas of locally strong magnetic field also correspond to areas of weakened Fraunhofer lines. In fact, when spectroheliograms are made in lines that are formed low in the photosphere, not only do these magnetically enhanced areas appear brighter, but a very fine bright network pattern is evident (Chapman and Sheeley, 1968). This network, called the photospheric network, also closely coincides with the magnetic-field pattern but is finer in structure than the overlying chromospheric network. Both networks are manifestations of the magnetic-field structure which tends to spread out and become coarser with altitude. The photospheric network appears most readily in lines of ions with low ionization energies; that is, ions whose emission is most sensitive to temperature changes. The regions of the solar atmosphere where this network is formed are a few hundred degrees Kelvin hotter than their surroundings and the network of enhanced emission results. These hotter regions also appear at the limb in white light as photospheric faculae (Chapman and Sheeley, 1968).

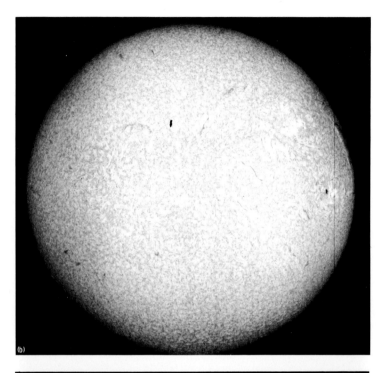

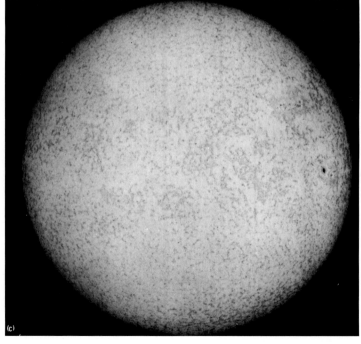

Figure 5–47.—Near-limb photograph in Hα−7/8 Å taken on February 13, 1971. This picture is an excellent illustration of the outlining of the chromospheric network by fine dark mottles (spicules). Also evident is the string of bright points at the bases of the mottles. (Courtesy of R. Dunn, Sacramento Peak Observatory, Air Force Cambridge Research Laboratories.)

Velocity-Field Correlation

A good correlation has been observed between the network of downward-flowing material (1 to 2 km/sec) observable in Doppler spectroheliograms taken in the wings of Hα or Hβ (fig. 5–51) and in the Ca II K network. This downward flow increases in cross-sectional area with height and is located at the edges of supergranular cells. Hence, the chromospheric network delineates supergranular cells in the same way as the network of downward-flowing, relatively dark material delineates the cells of white-light granulation. However, the downward flow tends to be concentrated at points rather than being spread out uniformly along the lineaments of the network. These regions of downward flow, which are evident as dark points in figure 5–51 (d), have been termed "funnels" by Leighton et al. (1962) and "downdrafts" by Frazier (1970). The correlation between velocity and magnetic fields is very strong in these regions as illustrated by figures 5–52 and 5–53.

Up to this point, the concept we have of flow in a supergranulation cell is one in which gas is buoyed at the center and sinks back down along its outside edges. Thus, we would expect to find isolated regions of upward flow and a network of downward flow. Instead, we find isolated regions of downward flow and we naturally ask, "How valid is the cell concept?" The answer to our question is well illustrated in figures 5–54 to 5–56 where averaged profiles of magnetic field, brightness, and flow velocity are shown. The excellent correlation between continuum brightness, Ca II K brightness, magnetic field, and velocity at a downdraft is shown in figure

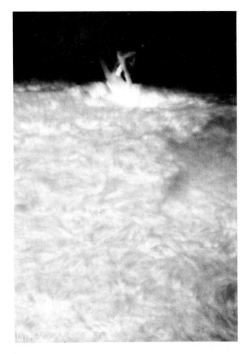

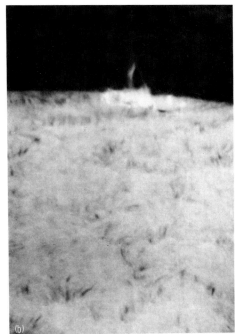

FIGURE 5-48.—Near-limb photographs in Hα
taken on December 3, 1970. The small dark
fibrils are most evident in the red wing. (a)
Center Hα. (b) Hα+1 Å. (c) Hα−Å.
(Courtesy of R. Dunn, Sacramento Peak
Observatory, Air Force Cambridge Research Laboratories.)

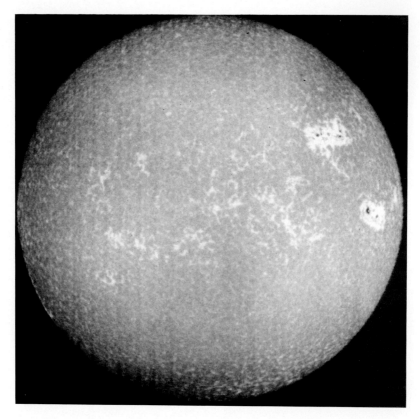

FIGURE 5–49.—Spectroheliograms taken on September 11, 1961. Note that the equatorial band
of solar activity appears as a band of plage regions. Both inside and outside this band, a bright
network of irregular ringlike structures can be seen, particularly at $K2V$ where the contrast
is more pronounced. A comparison of figures 5–46 and 5–49 reveals a correspondence between
the Hα dark network defined by coarse mottles and the Ca K bright network. (a) Red side
of Ca K line center ($K2R$). (Courtesy of Mount Wilson and Palomar Observatories.)

5–54. It is seen that the characteristic diameter of a downdraft is 10 000 km, about
1/3 of a supergranulation cell diameter. Profiles across a cell and the excellent correlation between observables are shown in figures 5–55 (a) and 5–55 (b). The scale
of each profile in these two figures is the same. Thus, even though the vertex-to-
vertex profiles are much more pronounced, the wall-to-wall profiles have the same
characteristics and are not random. This indicates that the concept of an array of
cells with enhancements in downward flow, magnetic field, and brightness at the
vertices is a valid representation. This is further illustrated in figure 5–56 where
the average profiles from vertex toward an adjacent vertex along a wall and vertex
toward cell center are shown. The elongation of vertex characteristics along the
direction of the walls, starting at approximately 4000 km, is evident. Thus, super-

FIGURE 5–49 (concluded).—Spectroheliograms taken on September 11, 1961. (b) Violet side of
Ca K line center (K2V). (Courtesy of Mount Wilson and Palomar Observatories.)

granulation cells are real entities even though the walls are weakly defined relative
to the vertices.

Network Lifetime

Like granulation cells, supergranulation cells have a lifetime which is of the
order of the depth of the cell divided by the upward velocity. Assuming the depth
of formation to be 10 000 km and the upward velocity to be 0.1 km/sec, a characteristic supergranulation lifetime of 28 hours results which, because of the close
correlation of the network with flow velocity, is also the characteristic lifetime of
the network. To obtain continuous monitoring of the network over a time greater
than the characteristic lifetime, observations have been made from above the
Arctic Circle for a period of 62 hours (Janssens, 1970, and Rogers, 1970). The
number of individual cells visible in $H\alpha + 0.65$ Å, which are also visible at either
earlier or later times, is shown in figure 5–57. The lifetime obtained in this manner

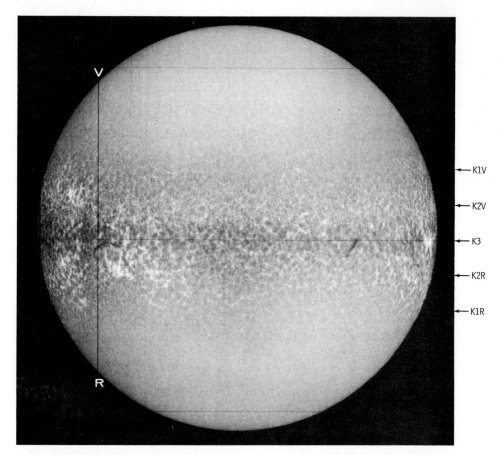

FIGURE 5–50.—Ca K spectroheliogram of the sun on August 11, 1962, made by scanning across
the line. Dark horizontal lines are at 0 and ± 1.0 Å. The features which are in emission or in
absorption in different parts of the K line are well illustrated here. The relatively dark band
at the center is caused by $K3$ absorption which originates at higher and not always hotter
layers than $K2$. Definition of the emission network is seen to be most pronounced at $K2R$ and
$K2V$. Outside of $K2R$ and $K2V$, the emission network disappears. (Courtesy of Mount
Wilson and Palomar Observatories.)

is 21 hours (Janssens, 1970) which compares well with the lifetime of 20 hours
obtained previously by Simon and Leighton (1964). Using the same Hα time-lapse
photographs as Janssens, Rogers made a cross-correlation analysis and determined
a value of 25.0 ± 1.6 hours for the mean $1/e$ lifetime and 38 ± 4.0 hours for twice
the half-life.

By following the history of a typical supergranulation cell in H$\alpha + 0.65$ Å,
three characteristic phases can be identified (Janssens, 1970). The development
and growth lasts approximately 5 hours, the mature stage is about 18-hour duration,

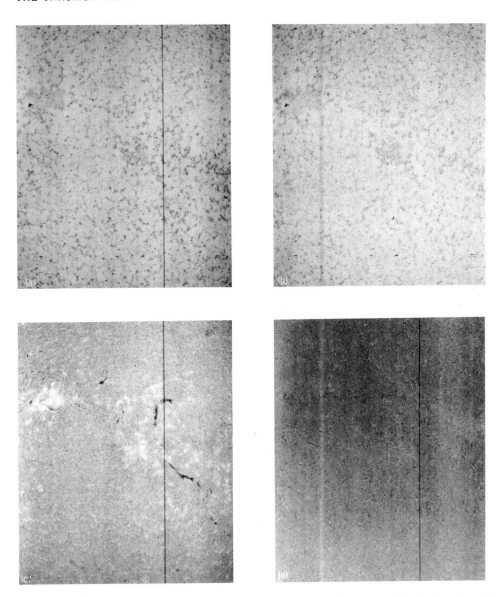

FIGURE 5–51.—Canceled-velocity spectroheliogram at the ±0.7-Å wings of Hα. This series of spectroheliograms was taken by N. Sheeley on August 19, 1963. Figure 5–51(a) was taken on the red wing (Hα+0.7 Å), (b) on the blue wing (Hα−0.7 Å), (c) at the line core, and (d) is the canceled-velocity spectroheliogram of (a) and (b) in which dark areas are moving away from the observer and light areas are approaching. Comparison of (a) and (b) reveals that the network is best seen on the side of line center, which implies that the material along the network is descending. The darker areas in (d) generally coincide with the network seen in the red wing; however, they appear as a string of points rather than a uniform grid outlining the supergranulation cells. (Courtesy of Mount Wilson and Palomar Observatories.)

FIGURE 5–52.—Line-of-sight velocities and magnetic fields in a quiet region at solar disk center. Many consecutive recordings were averaged to reduce the random effects of seeing and to eliminate the 5-min oscillations. A strong correlation between vertical velocity and magnetic field is evident. The maxima in downward velocity and field strength coincide exactly at values of 0.34 km/sec and 110 gauss, respectively. The zero velocity and 25-gauss contours coincide. (From Deubner, 1971; copyright 1971, D. Reidel.)

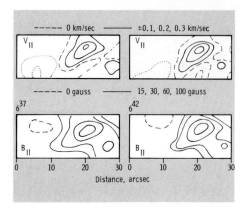

and the breakup takes place in about 12 hours. During the growth of a cell, rosettes and clumps of dark mottles link together into curved segments that outline a cell. Also, the cell is enlarged by the effect of "bubbling" which pushes back the boundaries of the cell. In the mature phase, the outline of the cell is well defined and of constant overall dimensions. It is characterized by overall roundness, indicating outward flow, even though it may change back and forth between circular and oval shapes. Also, the smaller details of the dark mottles may change appreciably but the gross outline remains well defined. This is also characteristic of the underlying photospheric network. The small details of the photospheric network change completely within 30 min by a lateral shifting of fragments, but the large-scale network pattern remains relatively unchanged after $2\frac{1}{2}$ hours (Sheeley, 1969). The breakup is evidenced by the cell walls becoming convex rather than concave as the components of the walls become parts of other adjacent newly forming cells. Eventually, this breakup proceeds to the point that the original cell has lost its identity.

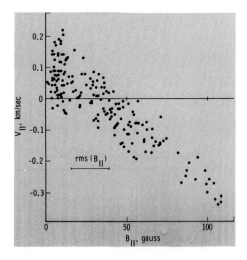

FIGURE 5–53.—Correlation between vertical velocity and magnetic field for the same region shown in figure 5–52. The horizontal bar represents the standard deviation of the averaged magnetic-field values. (From Deubner, 1971; copyright 1971, D. Reidel.)

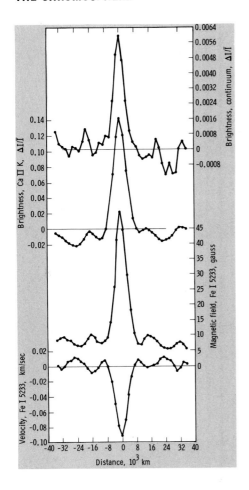

FIGURE 5–54.—Average downdraft profiles. Using the Kitt Peak multichannel magnetograph, Frazier (1970) made raster scans of 39 regions of downward flow centered at the local maxima in the brightness of the Fe I 5233 line. Scans were made 150 sec apart and averaged to eliminate the 300-sec oscillations. Subsequent scans were made over a 4-hour period to further reduce the effects of short-term nonperiodic flows. Scans across the points of maximum Fe I 5230 brightness in two perpendicular directions were then averaged to produce the above figure. (From Frazier, 1970; copyright 1970, D. Reidel.)

In summary, it has been seen that the chromospheric network is the site of enhanced vertical magnetic fields, downward-flowing material, and locally higher temperatures. The network itself coincides with the edges of supergranulation cells. The higher we observe above the photosphere, the wider the linear elements of the network appear. All of these seemingly diverse phenomena can be assembled into a coherent picture if we regard the dynamics of the photosphere as the primary driving mechanism and the solar magnetic field as a means of coupling these dynamics to the density and temperature nonuniformities; hence, to the emission nonuniformities of the chromosphere. In order to do this, we must first understand the concept of a magnetic field and an element of solar plasma being frozen together.

Frozen-in Magnetic Fields

The complete freezing together of a conducting fluid and a magnetic field is a limiting case that cannot be achieved in an absolute sense. There will always be

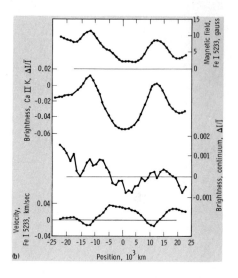

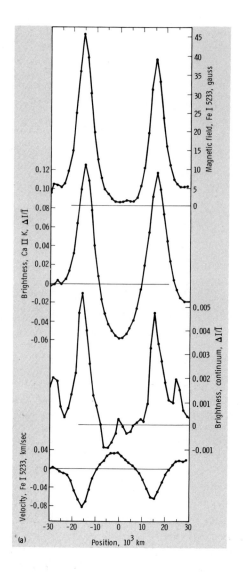

FIGURE 5–55.—Average profiles across supergranulation cells. The scans across 20 different supergranulation cells, made in the same way as in figure 5–54, were all normalized to the same diameter. Averages were then made of profiles from vertex to vertex; that is, downdraft to downdraft across cell center (a) and wall-to-wall across cell center (b). (From Frazier, 1970; copyright 1970, D. Reidel.)

some slipping of the field lines relative to the fluid. In figure 5–58 we show a simplified, one-dimensional case in which a conducting fluid moves across lines of force and tends to drag them along. The fluid moves with a velocity V across the magnetic field B whose strength will vary with x. The slippage of the field with respect to the fluid is given by $\delta(x)$. When a fluid element has moved a distance x, the fluid lines have been moved $x - \delta$; $\delta = 0$ if the field is completely frozen in and $\delta = x$ if the field is unaffected by the fluid motion. The ratio δ/x is thus a gage of the amount the

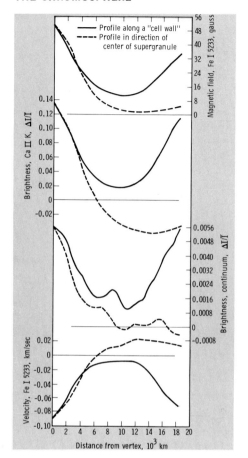

FIGURE 5-56.—Average semiprofiles at downdrafts in two directions. The raster scans
of downdrafts used in producing figure 5-54
were again used to produce average profiles
as a function of distance from downdraft
center. Two directions were chosen: the
direction along a cell wall to the adjacent
downdraft and the direction to cell center.
(From Frazier, 1970; copyright 1970,
D. Reidel.)

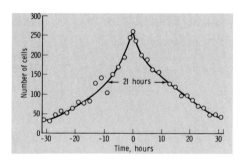

FIGURE 5-57.—Supergranulation cell lifetime. Using the cells visible at $t=0$, the
number of the same cells still identifiable
at earlier or later times is shown. The full
width at half maximum is 21 hours. (From
Janssens, 1970; copyright 1970, D. Reidel.)

field slips with respect to the fluid. The electric field generated in the fluid by the
relative motion of fluid and field is the product of the rate of slippage seen by the
fluid $\dot{\delta}$ and the field strength B. Thus, the current flow is

$$J = \sigma \dot{\delta} B \qquad (5\text{-}66)$$

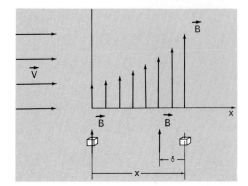

FIGURE   5–58.—Magnetic-field-line   slip
through a moving element of electrically
conducting fluid.

where σ is the electrical conductivity of the fluid. The current flow will produce a change in magnetic-field strength with x given by Ampere's law

$$\frac{\partial B}{\partial x} = \mu_0 J \tag{5-67}$$

Combining these two relations, we obtain

$$\frac{1}{B}\frac{\partial B}{\partial x} = \mu_0 \sigma \dot{\delta} \tag{5-68}$$

Thus, if σ is large, $\dot{\delta}$ will be correspondingly small. The characteristic length for a change in the magnetic field L is from equation (5–68)

$$L = \frac{1}{\mu_0 \sigma \dot{\delta}} \tag{5-69}$$

The parameter we are interested in is δ/L, the relative slip. Since

$$\dot{\delta} = \frac{V}{L}\,\delta(L) \tag{5-70}$$

then

$$\frac{\delta}{L} = \frac{1}{\mu_0 \sigma V L} \tag{5-71}$$

or

$$\frac{\delta}{L} = \frac{1}{R_m} \tag{5-72}$$

Thus, the degree to which the fluid and field are frozen together depends only upon the conductivity, the fluid velocity, and the characteristic size of the field changes under consideration. The dimensionless quantity $\mu_0 \sigma V L$ has been termed the magnetic Reynolds number R_m. If $R_m \gg 1$, the fluid and field are nearly frozen together, and one determines the dynamics of the other. If $R_m \ll 1$, the coupling is weak and the fluid dynamics and field configuration may be determined independently. In the quiet solar atmosphere, the lowest value of σ which is on the order of 10 (ohm-meter)$^{-1}$, occurs in the photosphere because of the low temperature and the corresponding low degree of hydrogen ionization. Assuming a characteristic velocity of 0.1 km/sec and a length L approximately equal to the limit of our resolution of solar features (700 km), we find $R_m \approx 10^3$. Thus, for all of the features we have observed so far, the approximation of field and fluid being frozen together is an extremely good one.

Knowing the value of R_m, however, does not tell us who pushes whom about. Are the dynamics and structure controlled by the fluid or by the magnetic field? Because of its motion, the fluid exerts forces by its dynamic pressure

$$p_d = \tfrac{1}{2}\rho V^2 \tag{5-73}$$

Likewise, the magnetic field exerts opposing forces by a pressure of its own. The magnetic force per unit volume is

$$F_m = JB \tag{5-74}$$

which from equation (5-67) is

$$F_m = B\,\frac{1}{\mu_0}\,\frac{\partial B}{\partial x}$$

$$\tag{5-75}$$

$$F_m = \frac{\partial p_m}{\partial x}$$

where

$$p_m = \frac{B^2}{2\mu_0} \tag{5-76}$$

The magnetic pressure p_m is also the energy density of the magnetic field; p_d is approximately the macroscopic kinetic energy density of the fluid. When $p_d \gg p_m$, the fluid dynamics define the magnetic-field structure. When $p_m \gg p_d$, the magnetic-field lines act as guides for the fluid flow; the fluid can flow only along the lines of force and will not displace them.

Both of these situations exist in the solar atmosphere. Equating the two pressures

$$\frac{1}{2}\,\rho V^2 = \frac{1}{2\mu_0}\,B^2 \tag{5-77}$$

we obtain

$$V = \left(\frac{B^2}{\mu_0 \rho}\right)^{1/2}$$

$$\tag{5-78}$$

$$V = V_A$$

TABLE 5–III.—Idealized Domains of Fluid and Magnetic Control

Height, km	Characteristic
<600	Complete control by the fluid.
600 to 1300	The mass motion is along the magnetic-field lines and the magnetic field can be confined by the fluid pressure.
>1300	Complete control by the magnetic field.

Thus, the dynamic and magnetic pressures are equal when the fluid velocity is equal to the Alfvén velocity. The dynamic pressure corresponding to 0.4 km/sec (the approximate horizontal velocity in a supergranulation cell) will equal the magnetic pressure of 20 gauss (the approximate field strength observed on the chromospheric network) at a height of approximately 600 km. Because $p_d \sim \rho$ and ρ drops off rapidly with height, the transition from fluid control to magnetic control will be a sharp one, and the height at which it occurs will not be a strong function of either B or V. Thus, in the photosphere and low chromosphere, the gas dynamics shape the magnetic field; but in the atmosphere above, up to the outer corona, the magnetic-field configuration determines the direction of gas motion.

In some instances, we will be concerned not with atmospheric dynamics but rather with the maintenance of a field configuration by a static atmosphere. In this case, the fluid's static pressure, rather than its dynamic pressure, opposes the magnetic pressure. Once $p_m \gg p$, the fluid will be unable to contain the field and the field will assume the configuration it would in a vacuum. The break-even point $p = p_m$ is again seen to be readily identifiable. From

$$p = p_m \tag{5–79}$$

we obtain

$$\gamma \frac{p}{\rho} = \frac{\gamma}{2} \frac{B^2}{\rho \mu_0} \quad \text{or} \quad V_0 = \left(\frac{\gamma}{2}\right)^{1/2} V_A \tag{5–80}$$

From figure 5–41, it is seen that $V_0 \simeq V_A$ at a height of 1300 km and a field of 20 gauss. Table 5–III summarizes the domains of fluid and magnetic control for the field strengths, material velocity, and model atmosphere we have considered here.

Formation of the Network

Returning now to the many interrelated phenomena of the chromospheric network, we begin by considering the photospheric fluid velocity field as the primary causal factor and the other observables as the resultants. In particular, the horizontal flow in each supergranular cell will cause a concentration of magnetic fields along the periphery (fig. 5–59). When opposing flows meet at the boundary of two cells and are turned downward, the shearing action that occurs produces nearly

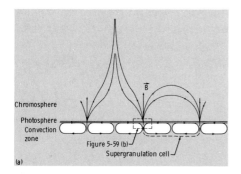 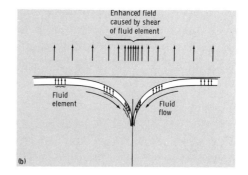

FIGURE 5–59.—Magnetic-field enhancement at supergranulation cell boundaries. (a) Large-scale structure. (b) Blowup of shear region.

vertical fields of enhanced strength. The field strength can be enhanced until $p_m \approx p_d$; that is, up to a height of approximately 600 km. Using a flow velocity of 0.4 km/sec and a cell radius of 16 000 km, it is seen that the magnetic-field configuration will be established in a time on the order of 11 hours, twice the Hα network growth time observed by Janssens (1970). In this way, a network of enhanced magnetic fields that extends well into the chromosphere is established. We should expect that the field is concentrated most in regions where the fluid flow is converging most strongly (Clark and Johnson, 1967). That is, the vertices of supergranulation cells (fig. 5–8) or downdrafts should be the sites of the strongest vertical magnetic fields. As we have seen, this is the case (figs. 5–52 to 5–56). The detailed structure of the chromospheric magnetic network depends quite strongly on the configuration of the velocity fields, especially the vertical extent of the vertical gas flows (Clark, 1968).

Because magnetic-field enhancements can occur where we have converging flow, is it not possible for other organized velocity patterns to create their own characteristic magnetic-field patterns?

Oscillations in the magnetic field are observed which roughly correlate with vertical oscillations (fig. 5–17). However, because the flow pattern is not strongly convergent, the accompanying magnetic-field structure is weak and not well ordered. On the other hand, we quite naturally expect a well-ordered but scaled-down network of magnetic fields to be created by the flow in granulation cells, analogous to the chromospheric network created by the flow in supergranulation cells. However, because the scale of granulation is small, what magnetic-field structure that does exist could not extend far into the chromosphere, if at all, and it would be extremely hard to observe because of atmospheric seeing limitations. Howard and Bhatnager (1969) observed field enhancements in intergranular regions of 20±15 gauss, while Livingston (1968) found these enhancements to be less than 2 gauss. Clearly, very high resolution observations of photospheric magnetic fields are required to discover the characteristics of any magnetic network resulting from granulation that does exist.

The enhancement of magnetic-field strength that occurs in converging flows is a result of the shearing that exists in the velocity field. Flow patterns, other than downdrafts, have velocity shear and can cause local enhancements in magnetic-field strength. In particular, if the horizontal velocity in a supergranulation cell increases with depth (fig. 5–8(b)), horizontal tubes of magnetic flux, perpendicular to the velocity, can be twisted and increased in strength. Weart (1970) calculates that for tubes with one complete twist and a thickness of 1000 to 2000 km, field strengths of approximately 100 gauss are energetically possible under a wide variety of assumptions. This mechanism may be responsible for some of the detailed quiet-sun structure observed in Hα, especially fibrils. It is noted that shearing action of this type, where the velocity and magnetic-field vectors are perpendicular, is similar to the creation of twisted flux tubes by differential rotation or by a more rapidly rotating solar interior, both of which have been considered in attempting to explain active-sun features.

The enhancement of the frozen-in magnetic fields, created by the converging flow in supergranulation cells, is in turn responsible for the network of enhanced emission observed in many Fraunhofer lines. In section 5.2 we have seen that enhanced magnetic fields can cause enhanced generation and propagation of non-radiative energy. This raises the temperature along the network, increases the source function in the lines and continuum, and creates the enhanced emission. The exact mechanisms, like nonradiative heating in general, are not well determined. Enhanced fast-mode generation and propagation, a greater conversion of gravity waves to Alfvén-like waves, or enhancement in other mechanisms with increasing magnetic-field strength could be responsible. In any case, it is evident that the heating at the network boundary completely overwhelms any convective heating at supergranulation cell centers, which Beckers (1968b) estimates to be less than 1 K.

The increasing coarseness of the network with altitude is directly related to the increases of p_m relative to p_d. As we move into the chromosphere, the dynamic pressure can no longer confine the magnetic field; the field lines diverge toward the configuration they would assume in a vacuum. Thus, the linear elements in the network become wider and more diffused. The fine-structured photospheric network undergoes a transition to the relatively coarse chromospheric network which is observed in Ca II K.

In Hα, especially in the red wing at about $+0.7$ Å, we have seen that the network is outlined by dark coarse mottles, even though there is some enhanced emission at their bases (figs. 5–44 to 5–48). We now turn our attention to the nature and detailed structure of these dark coarse mottles through a discussion of solar spicules.

5.4 SPICULES

Spicules are among the smallest observable features on the quiet sun. They are best displayed in limb observations (figs. 5–60 and 2–16), where they resemble

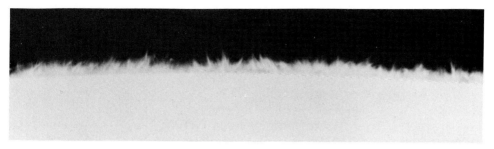

FIGURE 5-60.—Spicules observed 1 Å off Hα line center on October 14, 1970. (Courtesy of R. Dunn, Sacramento Peak Observatory, Air Force Cambridge Research Laboratories.)

a forest of flames reaching high up into the atmosphere. Because of high-number density along the line of sight on the limb, spicules overlap at their bases and a double limb often appears when observing at Hα line center without an occulting disk (fig. 5-61). The outer jagged limb is the top of the spicule forest, which will vary in height with the length of the film exposure. The inner smooth limb is the relatively intense white-light photosphere which arises from light outside the Hα passband that is not completely filtered out and reaches the film (White and Simon, 1968). The spicule forest is optically thick in Hα. Thus, when all of the light outside the Hα passband is sufficiently attenuated, the inner limb no longer appears.

From our mental picture of the vertical slice of the chromosphere, prompted by limb photography, we can define three atmospheric layers related to spicules. First, there is the low chromosphere which is essentially a continuation of the photosphere above the temperature minimum. Structural nonuniformities are not very pronounced here. The formation of the spicules is initiated in the middle chromosphere. Here we observe the change from the uniform low chromosphere to

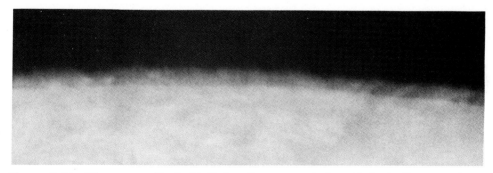

FIGURE 5-61.—The apparent Hα double limb at line center. The inner limb will disappear when a blocking filter is used to exclude all light outside the Hα passband (±0.8 Å). (Courtesy of S. Smith and B. Nolan, Lockheed Solar Observatory.)

the heterogeneous upper chromosphere which is clearly composed of two components, the spicules and the hot coronal gas reaching down between them. The boundaries of these two regions are not as well defined as the boundary with the photosphere, $dT/dh = 0$. The determination of the top of the low chromosphere is limited by our ability to observe spicules to their roots. Below approximately 5000 km they overlap and appear to merge into one uniform layer. A round number for the start of the middle chromosphere is 1500 km, a height where magnetic-field nonuniformities certainly control the structural nonuniformities (table 5–III) and which is slightly below the sharp rise in temperature. It is interesting that in the low chromosphere the temperature and degree of hydrogen ionization increase with height while the pressure decreases, so that a nearly uniform value of the electron density results (approximately 3×10^{10} cm^{-3}) as shown in figure 5–28. For lack of an observationally accurate value, the middle chromosphere will be assumed to be 1500 km thick. That is, the upper chromosphere where two distinct components are always visible is assumed to start at 3000 km, a height where the temperature has nearly reached coronal values (fig. 5–29). The height of the spicules is also subject to definition because spicule number and intensity slowly decrease with height. However, most observations of this height fall within the range of 7000 to 9000 km. Clearly, a smooth constant-radius boundary between the chromosphere and corona is not physically meaningful. The real boundary that separates coronal and chromospheric material is at the edges of the spicules themselves and at the height of rapid temperature rise for interspicule areas; that is, at the transition region. Because the magnetic field of a spicule most likely lies along its axis, heat flow in a direction perpendicular to this vertical axis is inhibited, the temperature gradient can be large, and the transition region at the edge of the spicule could be correspondingly very thin.

The observational properties of spicules, almost all of which have been determined in Hα (table 5–IV), have been thoroughly studied and well summarized by Beckers (1968a). The number of spicules per supergranular cell as a function of height is shown in figure 5–62. It is seen that there are approximately 30 spicules

TABLE 5–IV.—Properties of Hα Chromospheric Fine Structure

[Beckers, 1968a]

Property	Spicules	Fine dark mottles	Fine bright mottles
Diameter, km	825	700	3000
Length, km	4000	5000	6500
Number per supergranular cell	33	50	13
Lifetime, min	8	10	
Birth rate per supergranular cell, min^{-1}	4	5	
Average inclination to vertical, deg	20	21	
S_λ/I continuum	0.08 to 0.50	0.123	>0.16

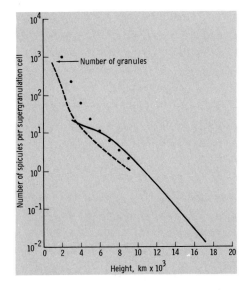

FIGURE 5–62.—Observed number of spicules per supergranulation cell above a height versus the height. The average supergranulation cell has been assumed to be circular with a diameter of 32 000 km. The full line is from Athay. The dashed line originates from Hiei's measurements as reduced by Beckers. Filled circles refer to Konnor's interpretation of Hiei's results. (From Beckers, 1968a; copyright 1968, D. Reidel.)

per supergranular cell at 3000 km. This decreases to one per cell at about 10 000 km. The orientation of most spicules is close to the vertical, 15° to 20° being typical deviations. The observed diameters are roughly 400 to 1500 km (0.5 to 2 arcsec). These measurements are near the limits of resolution of earthbound instruments and are hard to determine accurately. A distribution of spicule diameters determined by Dunn (1965) is shown in figure 5–63 where the diameter is defined as the total width at half intensity and is determined using a microphotometer. The average value of this distribution is 815 km. A correlation between size and brightness has been observed; the higher central intensities correspond to slightly larger diameters.

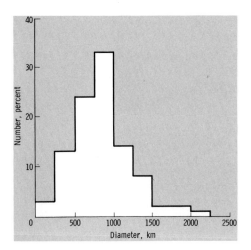

FIGURE 5–63.—Distribution of spicule diameters according to Dunn (1965). (From Beckers, 1968a; copyright 1968, D. Reidel.)

Spicules, like convection cells, are dynamic rather than static features. Mouradian (1967) has observed velocities of expansion ranging from 0 to 70 km/sec and averaging 22 km/sec. A spicule tends to first increase in intensity and then undergo an expansion lasting approximately 1.5 min, the brighter spicules expanding over a longer period of time. The overall lifetime of a spicule is usually within the range of 8 to 15 min (Beckers, 1968a). The rms vertical velocity of the mass motion in a spicule has been measured using Doppler shifts and is found to be 26 km/sec (Pasachoff et al., 1968). The distribution over velocity is seen in figure 5–64 where the correction for distribution of spicules over all inclinations to the local vertical has not been made. The dependence of velocity on height is very weak, and the motion can be regarded as uniform to the first approximation. However, a relatively small number of spicules have been observed to have velocities that increase with height (Pasachoff et al., 1968). On the average, spicules tend to accelerate upward, decelerate, and then come to a standstill as a function of time. Occasionally, the velocity of some spicules will reverse. However, most spicules exhibit a velocity in only one direction.

A confirmation of the magnetic character of spicules is found from the fact that changes in velocity at different heights occur almost simultaneously. Observations imply that the velocity of the accelerating force along the axis of the spicule can be as high as 400 km/sec (Beckers, 1968a) which is at least an order of magnitude greater than the local sound speed. However, the local Alfvén velocity can occasionally be this large; 10^{11} electrons/cm^3, an approximate value for N_e from present spicule models, corresponds to a gas density of 2×10^{-13} gram/cm^3 and a high but possible chromospheric network field strength of 63 gauss for $V_A = 400$ km/sec.

Other mass motions of spicules also have been observed. Oscillations parallel to the limb appear to be an inherent spicule property (Pasachoff et al., 1968). The amplitudes of these oscillations are of the order of a spicule diameter, the period is approximately 1 min, and the velocities are 10 to 15 km/sec (Nikolsky and Platova, 1971). Second, from the inclination of the spectra of spicules relative to the axis of dispersion, it is concluded that spicules often rotate about their long axes

FIGURE 5–64.—Distribution of spicule velocities. (From Athay and Bessey, 1964; copyright 1964, University of Chicago Press.)

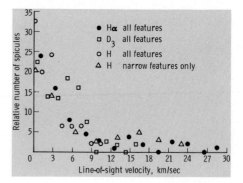

(Michard, 1956; Beckers et al., 1966; and Pasachoff et al., 1968). Assuming an upper limit of 30 km/sec for the rotational speed at the outer edge of a 1000-km-diameter spicule, a period of about 2 min and a centripetal acceleration of about six times solar gravity results (Pasachoff et al., 1968). Thus, the rotational motion could be quite violent and significantly influence the structure of a spicule.

Because spicules are optically thick in Hα and other Fraunhofer lines, they can be viewed as absorption features against the solar disk. Certainly, there is much chromospheric detail visible at the limit of our resolution (roughly 1 arcsec or one spicule diameter); but identifying which features correspond to spicules is a difficult task. We shall first discuss what organization can be made of the chromospheric fine structure and then attempt to relate this organization to spicule characteristics.

In figures 5–65 and 5–66, we see photographs taken at various points across the Hα line and a sketch which serves to organize the types of features observed. The characteristics of these features are listed in table 5–IV. The smallest absorption features visible are the fine dark mottles, having a diameter of about 700 km and a length-to-diameter ratio averaging 7. The most rapid changes of chromospheric structure occur in these features. The lifetime of the fine dark mottles, also called fibrils, is only 10 min, which is comparable to that of normal granulation. There are approximately 50 fibrils per supergranulation cell, giving a birth rate of 5 per minute per cell. The fine dark mottles are best seen in the red wing of Hα+0.5 Å, implying that they are receding along our line of sight. They are seen in absorption because their source function is less than the intensity of the photospheric radiation; $dI_\lambda \sim (S_\lambda - I_\lambda)\, ds$. In a nonequilibrium situation, however, we should not conclude immediately that they are at a lower temperature than that of the radiation. Fine

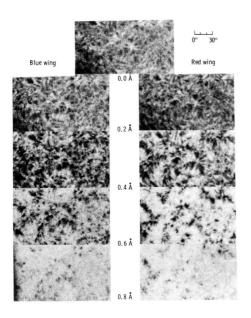

Blue wing   0'' 30''   Red wing

FIGURE 5–65.—A series of filtergrams taken across the Hα line using a 0.55-Å birefringent filter. Compare this series with the features identified in figure 5–66. Dark line mottles, rosettes (a bush at the limb), and the chromospheric network are best seen in the red wing at 0.4 to 0.6 Å from line center. Grains are best seen in the blue wing at 0.4 to 0.6 Å from line center. Bright fine and bright coarse mottles are more difficult to identify but are best seen at center line Hα or slightly in the blue wing. (Courtesy of J. Beckers, Sacramento Peak Observatory, Air Force Cambridge Research Laboratories.)

dark mottles cluster together to form coarse dark mottles or rosettes which appear as near-vertical structures or bushes when seen close to the limb (figs. 5–47, 5–67, and 5–68). Unfortunately, their lifetime is so short that, as solar rotation moves them across the limb, we cannot trace them to see if they really do appear as spicules. A coarse dark mottle has a diameter of roughly 10^4 km and a lifetime of 10 hours, which is surprisingly large compared to the lifetime of the fine mottles of which it is composed. Analogous to the fine dark mottles, fine bright mottles are also visible. However, they are fewer in number (13 per supergranulation cell), thicker (3000 km in diameter), and best seen slightly on the violet side of line center, indicating that they are rising structures. They are usually observed to lie close to the base of a rosette and between fine dark mottles. They, too, cluster together to form a bright coarse mottle whose characteristic size is 5000 km, one-half the size of a coarse dark mottle. Thus, one could tentatively draw a picture of a rosette having rising material at its center which then descends as it moves outward along fibrils. The location of mottles is not random but is observed to fall along the boundaries of supergranular cells. This is the best seen in the red wing of Hα where the dark mottles clearly outline the chromospheric network (figs. 5–47, 5–65, 5–67, and 5–68). Hence, the mottles are to be associated with regions of enhanced magnetic strength. Lastly, features called grains, small dark points observed best at Hα−0.5 Å, fall on the chromospheric network. Their full nature and their relation to other features is unknown.

Chromospheric structure is also visible in Ca II K, but it takes on a different appearance. With good resolution, bright/dark fine mottles seen at Hα line center correspond to bright/dark features seen in Ca K. That is, the gross relative intensities of detailed features seen at Hα line center and in Ca K are the same. When observing with low resolution, however, bright features are dominant in Ca K and dark features are dominant in Hα. Thus, it is quite easy to make the inverse identification (Ca K bright with Hα dark). In the blue wing of calcium ($K2V$) numerous small bright points are observed and it has been speculated that they correspond to the dark grains seen in Hα. If this is true, it is an exception to the general trend of the correspondence.

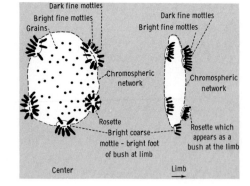

FIGURE 5–66.—Definition of chromospheric features. (From Beckers, 1968a; copyright 1968, D. Reidel.)

Would spicules appear bright or dark as seen against the solar disk and do they correspond to any of the features so far discussed? First, from our knowledge of spicules to date, it can be said that they could appear either bright or dark, depending upon where on the disk and where in the Hα line they were observed. If the source function is greater than the background intensity, a spicule will appear in emission. It will appear in absorption if the reverse is true. Both of these situations are possible since the conditions in the chromosphere are highly non-equilibrium and the source function can vary over a wide range with only modest changes in the local values of density and temperature. Second, the identification of fine mottles as spicules seen against the disk appears certain. Usually, the identi-

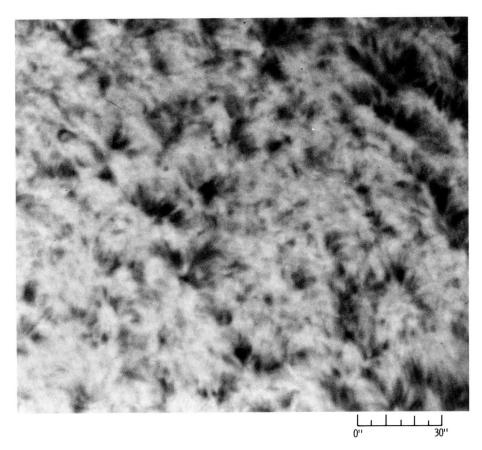

FIGURE 5–67.—Dark mottling and bushes at Hα+0.65 Å. As we move toward the limb (upper right) the dark coarse mottles which have clustered to form rosettes begin to take on the appearance of bushes. (Courtesy of J. Beckers, Sacramento Peak Observatory, Air Force Cambridge Research Laboratories.)

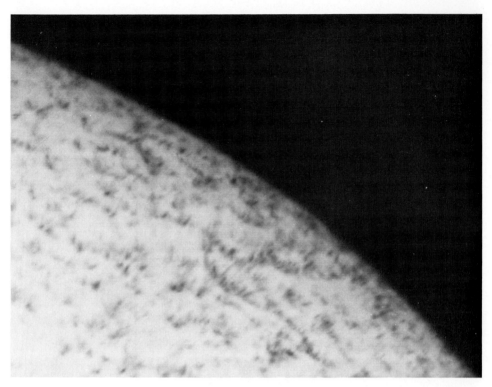

FIGURE 5-68.—Hα structures at the limb. In addition to the bushlike appearance of the dark mottling, the foreshortened outline of supergranular cells can be seen in this spectrohelio-gram made at Hα+0.74 Å. (Courtesy of J. Beckers, Sacramento Peak Observatory, Air Force Cambridge Research Laboratories.)

fication has been made only with the dark fine mottles; however, this is too restrictive since bright and dark fine mottles can be part of the same structure. High-resolution observations at Hα line center made immediately above the limb reveal small bright features with properties very similar to fine bright mottles on the disk, and have been identified as these mottles seen above the limb (Loughhead, 1969). It has been speculated, but not demonstrated, that the bright fine mottles (best seen at the slightly blue side of Hα) are the rising portions of spicules and that the dark fine mottles (best seen at the slightly red side of Hα) are the descending portions. Opposing this is the observation that the fine dark mottles are usually slightly displaced toward the limb relative to fine bright mottles. From this it is concluded that the bright mottles are phenomena of the lower and middle chromosphere ($\lesssim 3300$ km) and that the dark mottles are characteristic of the upper chromosphere (≈ 5000–7600 km) (Bray, 1969). We are forced to conclude that higher resolution observations than achieved to date are required to significantly increase our understanding of how spicules appear against the disk.

It is not surprising that we cannot predict how spicules should appear against the disk since we do not have a good spicule model nor do we understand the reasons for their existence. The model of Beckers (1968a), obtained by a study of spicule line spectra, shows the electron temperature to be approximately 16 000 K and roughly independent of height above 2000 km. In this model, spicules are about the same temperature as their environment in the middle chromosphere, but are cooler in the upper chromosphere. Other models are in disagreement with this. However, theories which attempt to explain how spicules are formed all have one feature in common: relatively strong magnetic fields are always a key element. It has been observed that fields of 25 gauss or greater are required for spicules to exist (Beckers, 1968a). We have seen how the flow pattern of supergranulation concentrates magnetic fields on cell boundaries. It is consistent with observation that spicules form there and outline supergranulation cells as fine dark mottles in Hα and bright mottles in Ca K. However, the dynamics of the interaction between the solar plasma and the magnetic fields in the formation of spicules is very much an open question.

One theory of spicule formation builds upon the theory of nonradiative energy propagation (Parker, 1964). In section 5.2, we saw how sound waves generated in the convection zone could be transformed into shock waves as they move into the relatively thin atmosphere above. These waves become Alfvén-like fast-mode waves in the low chromosphere and travel upward along the enhanced magnetic fields at the supergranulation boundaries. The upward-moving gas of a spicule is thus assumed to be the columnar structure of shocked gas behind the wavefront. This gas will continue to move upward until its direction of motion is reversed by gravity. It will then fall back down along the magnetic-field lines. Hence, the nonradiative energy flux moving into the corona would be concentrated in the spicules. This fails to explain why the spicules are colder than the corona and why they have a nearly uniform vertical temperature distribution.

A second attempt to explain spicules also utilizes nonradiative energy propagation but in the form of tongues of turbulence (Howe, 1969). Torsional oscillations, which consist of fluid motion in the horizontal plane perpendicular to the magnetic field, propagate upward along the field lines (sec. 5.2). These fluid motions form closed loops and are initiated by overshooting granulation cells, as in the previously mentioned protruding tongues of turbulence (Lighthill, 1967). Although this is a possible form of nonradiative energy propagation, it does not explain adequately the observed vertical movement of the relatively high density fluid in spicules.

Another theory attributes the formation of spicules to the energy flux conducted back into the chromosphere from the relatively hot corona (Kuperus and Athay, 1967; Kuperus, 1969; and Kopp and Kuperus, 1968). Because of the high-temperature gradient in the middle and upper chromosphere, the average backward conduction of heat can be as high as 5×10^5 ergs/cm^2-sec. This flow is channeled along, and concentrated in, regions of high magnetic-field strength (sec. 5.2). The result is a large flux of energy that flows into the regions at the base of the chromospheric network and which is much too large to be balanced locally by radiation emission. It is speculated that this flux can be balanced by a correspondingly large outward flux of kinetic energy of upward-flowing spicule material along magnetic-field lines. Where the field is horizontal, the large downward conduction of heat and upward flow of kinetic energy would be inhibited. In this theory no detailed mechanism has been proposed which would accelerate the material upward. In general, however, the heat flowing into a relatively small region at the base of the chromospheric network heats the gas and increases the vertical pressure gradient which in turn accelerates the overlying vertical column of gas upward. The model of the chromosphere that was qualitatively used in considering this theory is shown in figure 5–69. It is seen that the values of the temperature and its gradient are much higher in spicules than those proposed by Beckers. Unlike the previous theories, this one assumes the existence of a hot corona and the spicules are a response to it, not a contributing factor. It has the advantage of directly relating spicule formation to the observed sharp temperature rise of the middle chromosphere, the region from which spicules emerge.

Last, one theory of spicule formation attributes the origin of spicule material to condensing plasma from the corona (Krat and Krat, 1971). This gas falls down along magnetic-field lines and is channeled in the same manner as the heat flow. If the original mass of gas had a net angular momentum, its rotation rate would increase as it falls to heights where it is concentrated into a smaller horizontal cross-sectional area. This theory could explain the observed rotation of spicules, but it has not been tested in quantitative detail with respect to this and other observed spicule characteristics.

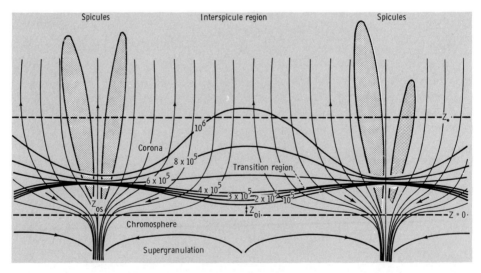

FIGURE 5–69.—A model of chromospheric structures. (From Kopp and Kuperus, 1968; copyright 1968, D. Reidel.)

We are thus led to the conclusion that spicules, in contrast to most of the phenomena so far considered, have fundamental causes and effects which are not understood. The mechanisms by which they are produced, their role in the outward fluxes of nonradiative energy and solar material, and their exact correlation with disk features are still open questions. Also, because of the lack of a reliable spicule model, the task of interpreting the high-energy radiation emitted by the solar atmosphere correspondingly becomes more difficult. We shall consider this problem in our discussion of the corona in the next chapter.

REFERENCES

APPENZELLER, I.; AND SCHRÖTER, E. H.: 1968, A Statistical Analysis of Large-Scale Brightness and Velocity Fluctuations in the Solar Atmosphere. Solar Phys. 4, 131–141.

ATHAY, R. G.: 1966a, Theoretical Line Intensities. V. Solar U.V. Emission Lines of Heavy Elements. Astrophys. J. 145, 784–795.

ATHAY, R. G.: 1966b, Radiative Energy Loss From the Solar Chromosphere and Corona. Astrophys. J. 146, 223–240.

ATHAY, R. G.: 1970, A Non-LTE Line-Blanketed Solar Model. Astrophys. J. 161, 713–735.

ATHAY, R. G.: 1971, Proc. Cavory Conf. (1970), C. Macris (ed.), Dordrecht, Holland: D. Reidel.

ATHAY, R. G.; AND BESSEY, J. J.: 1964, Doppler Shifts and Line Broadening in Spicules. Astrophys. J. 140, 1174–1181.

AVRETT, E. H.: 1970, Studies of the Upper Chromosphere and Low Transition Region. Working paper presented at OSO Work Shop at GSFC, Dec. 2, 1970.

BAHNG, J. D. R.; AND SCHWARZSCHILD, M.: 1961, Lifetime of Solar Granules. Astrophys. J. 134, 312–322.

BECKERS, J. M.: 1968a, Solar Spicules. Solar Phys. 3, 367–433.

BECKERS, J. M.: 1968b, Photospheric Brightness Differences Associated With the Solar Supergranulation. Solar Phys. 5, 309–322.

BECKERS, J. M.; AND PARNELL, R. L.: 1969, The Interpretation of Velocity Filtergrams. II. The Velocity and Intensity Field of the Solar Disk. Solar Phys. 9, 39–50.

BECKERS, J. M.; NOYES, R. W.; AND PASACHOFF, J. M.: 1966, New Observations of Solar Chromospheric Spicules. Astron. J. 71, 155–163.

BIRD, G. A.: 1964, The Propagation of Acoustic Waves Through the Solar Chromosphere. Astrophys. J. 140, 288–291.

BRAY, R. J.: 1969, High Resolution of the Solar Chromosphere. VI. Properties of the Bright Mottles. Solar Phys. 10, 63–70.

BRAY, R. J.; AND LOUGHHEAD, R. E.: 1967, The Solar Granulation. London: Chapman & Hall.

BUMBA, V.: 1967, Plasma Astrophysics. P. A. Sturrock (ed.), London: Academic Press.

BUMBA, V.; AND HOWARD, R. F.: 1965, Large-Scale Distribution of Solar Magnetic Fields. Astrophys. J. 141, 1502–1512.

CHAPMAN, G. A.; AND SHEELEY, N. R., JR.: 1968, The Photospheric Network. Solar Phys. 5, 442–461.

CHAPMAN, S.; AND COWLING, T. G.: 1960, The Mathematical Theory of Non-Uniform Gases. London: Cambridge University Press.

CLARK, A., JR.: 1968, Chromospheric Magnetic Fields Associated With Supergranulation. Solar Phys. 4, 386–400.

CLARK, A., JR.; AND JOHNSON, H. K.: 1967, Magnetic-Field Accumulation in Supergranules. Solar Phys. 2, 433–440.

CLARK, A., JR.; CLARK, P. A.; AND THOMAS, J. H.: 1971, Astrophysical Fluid Dynamics Rept. No. 14, Univ. of Rochester.

DEFOUW, R. J.: 1970a, Thermal-Convective Instability. Astrophys. J. 160, 659–669.

DEFOUW, R. J.: 1970b, Convective Instability of a Model Chromosphere. Solar Phys. 14, 42–61.

DEUBNER, F.-L.: 1967, Some Properties of Velocity Fields in the Solar Photosphere. I. Carbon, Nitrogen, and Oxygen. Solar Phys. 2, 133–149.

DEUBNER, F.-L.: 1969, Some Properties of Velocity Fields in the Solar Photosphere. II. The Spatial Distribution of the Oscillatory Field. Solar Phys. 9, 343–346.

DEUBNER, F.-L.: 1971, Some Properties of Velocity Fields in the Solar Photosphere. Solar Phys. 17, 6–20.

DUBOV, E. E.: 1966, Cooling of the Lower Chromosphere. Sov. Astron. AJ 9, 782–783.

DUNN, R. B.: 1965, Photometry of the Solar Chromosphere. AFCRL Environmental Res. Paper No. 109.

DUPREE, A. K.; AND GOLDBERG, L.: 1967, Solar Abundance Determination From Ultraviolet Emission Lines. Solar Phys. 1, 229–241.

EDMONDS, F. N., JR.: 1962, A Statistical Photometric Analysis of Granulation Across the Solar Disk. Astrophys. J. Suppl. 6, 357–406.

EDMONDS, F. N.; MICHARD, R.; AND SERVAJEAN, R.: 1965, Observational Study of Macroscopic Inhomogeneities in the Solar Atmosphere. VII. A Statistical Analysis of Photometric and Kinematic Inhomogeneities in the Deep Photosphere. Ann. Astrophys. 28, 534–555.

ELLIOTT, I.: 1969, Power Spectra of Hα Doppler Shifts. Solar Phys. 6, 28–40.

EVANS, J.; AND MICHARD, R.: 1962a, Observational Study of Macroscopic Inhomogeneities in the Solar Atmosphere, Pt. 1, Velocity Displacements of Fraunhofer Lines as a Function of Line Strength and Position on Disk. Astrophys. J. 135, 812–821.

EVANS, J.; AND MICHARD, R.: 1962b, Observational Study of Macroscopic Inhomogeneities in the Solar Atmosphere, Pt. 2, Brightness Fluctuations in Fraunhofer Lines and the Continuum. Astrophys. J. 136, 487–492.

EVANS, J.; AND MICHARD, R.: 1962c, Observational Study of Macroscopic Inhomogeneities in the Solar Atmosphere, Pt. 3, Vertical Oscillatory Motions in the Solar Photosphere. Astrophys. J. 136, 493–506.

EVANS, J. W.; MICHARD, R.; AND SERVAJEAN, R.: 1963, Observational Study of Macroscopic Inhomogeneities in the Solar Atmosphere, Pt. 5, Statistical Study of the Time Variations of Solar Inhomogeneities. Ann. Astrophys. 26, 368–382.

FIELD, G. B.: 1965, Thermal Instability. Astrophys. J. 142, 531–567.

FRAZIER, E. N.: 1968a, An Observational Study of the Hydrodynamics of the Lower Solar Photosphere. Astrophys. J. 152, 557–576.

FRAZIER, E. N.: 1968b, A Spatio-Temporal Analysis of Velocity Fields in the Solar Photosphere. Z. Astrophys. 68, 345–356.

FRAZIER, E. N.: 1970, Multi-Channel Magnetograph Observations. II. Supergranulation. Solar Phys. 14, 89–111.

GOLDBERG, L.; NOYES, R. W.; PARKINSON, W. H.; REEVES, E. M.; AND WITHBROE, G. L.: 1968, Ultraviolet Solar Images From Space. Science 162, 95–99.

GONCZI, G.; AND RODDIER, F.: 1969, A Fourier Spectrum Analysis of Long Samples of Solar Line Oscillations. Solar Phys. 8, 255–259.

HART, A. B.: 1956, Motions in the Sun at the Photospheric Level—VI. Large Scale Motions in the Equatorial Region. Mon. Notic. Roy. Astron. Soc. 116, 38–55.

HINES, C. O.: 1960, Internal Atmospheric Gravity Waves at Ionospheric Heights. Can. J. Phys. 38, 1441–1481.

HINTEREGGER, H. E.: 1963, Rocket Spectra of the Chromosphere. The Solar Spectrum, C. de Jager (ed.), Dordrecht, Holland: D. Reidel, 178–205.

HOWARD, R.: 1962, Preliminary Solar Magnetograph Observations With Small Apertures. Astrophys. J. 136, 211–222.

HOWARD, R.: 1967, Velocity Fields in the Solar Atmosphere. Solar Phys. 2, 3–33.

HOWARD, R.: 1971, The Large-Scale Velocity Fields of the Solar Atmosphere. Solar Phys. 16, 21–36.

HOWARD, R.; AND BHATNAGAR, A.: 1969, On the Spectrum of Granular and Intergranular Regions. Solar Phys. *10*, 245–253.

HOWARD, R.; TANENBAUM, A. S.; AND WILCOX, J. M.: 1968, A New Method of Magnetograph Observation of the Photospheric Brightness, Velocity, and Magnetic Fields. Solar Phys. *4*, 286–299.

HOWE, M. S.: 1969, On Gravity-Coupled Magnetohydrodynamic Waves in the Sun's Atmosphere. Astrophys. J. *156*, 27–41.

DE JAGER, C.; AND NEVEN, L.: 1968, On the Occurrence of Convective Motions in the Upper Photosphere. Solar Phys. *4*, 379–385.

JANSSENS, T. J.: 1970, Long Term Observations of the Hα Chromospheric Network. Solar Phys. *11*, 222–242.

JENNISON, R. C.: 1961, Fourier Transforms and Convolutions for the Experimentalist. New York: Pergamon, 82.

JENSEN, E.; AND ORRALL, F. Q.: 1963, Observational Study of Macroscopic Inhomogeneities in the Solar Atmosphere. IV. Velocity and Intensity Fluctuations Observed in the K Line. Astrophys. J. *138*, 252–270.

KAHN, F. D.: 1961, Sound Waves Trapped in Solar Atmosphere. Pt. 1. Astrophys. J. *134*, 343–346.

KAHN, F. D.: 1962, Sound Waves Trapped in Solar Atmosphere. Pt. 2. Astrophys. J. *135*, 547–551.

KATO, S.: 1966, On the Atmosphere Oscillations Excited by Turbulence. Astrophys. J. *143*, 372–378.

KIRK, J. G.; AND LIVINGSTON, W. C.: 1968, A Solar Granulation Spectrogram. Solar Phys. *3*, 510–512.

KOPP, R. A.; AND KUPERUS, M.: 1968, Magnetic Fields and the Temperature Structure of the Chromosphere-Corona Interface. Solar Phys. *4*, 212–223.

KRAT, V. A.; AND KRAT, T. V.: 1971, On Physical Properties of Solar Spicules. Solar Phys. *17*, 355–368.

KUPERUS, M.: 1969, The Heating of the Solar Corona. Space Sci. Rev. *9*, 713–739.

KUPERUS, M.; AND ATHAY, R.: 1967, On the Origin of Spicules in the Chromosphere-Corona Transition Region. Solar Phys. *1*, 361–370.

LAMBERT, D. L.; AND MALLIA, E. A.: 1968, Absolute Wavelength of Fraunhofer Lines: Convective Motions in the Solar Photosphere and the Gravitational Red Shift. Solar Phys. *3*, 499–504.

LEIGHTON, R. B.: 1961, Int. Astron. Union Symp. 12th, 321.

LEIGHTON, R. B.: 1963, The Solar Granulation. Ann. Rev. Astron. Astrophys. *1*, 19–40.

LEIGHTON, R. B.; NOYES, R. W.; AND SIMON, G. W.: 1962, Velocity Fields in the Solar Atmosphere, Pt. 1, Preliminary Report. Astrophys. J. *135*, 474–499.

LIGHTHILL, M. J.: 1967, D. Predictions on the Velocity Field Coming From Acoustic Noise and a Generalized Turbulence in a Layer Overlaying a Convectively Unstable Atmospheric Region. Int. Astron. Union Symp. 28th, 429–469.

LIVINGSTON, W. C.: 1968, Magnetograph Observations of the Quiet Sun. I. Spatial Description of the Background Fields. Astrophys. J. *153*, 929–942.

LOUGHHEAD, R. E.: 1969, High-Resolution Photography of the Solar Chromosphere. VII. Structure of the Low Chromosphere. Solar Phys. *10*, 71–78.

MÄCKLE, R.: 1969, On the Energy Dissipation of Fast Hydromagnetic Shock Waves in the Solar Chromosphere. Solar Phys. *10*, 348–356.

MCLELLAN, A., IV; AND WINTERBERG, F.: 1968, Magneto-Gravity Waves and the Heating of the Solar Corona. Solar Phys. *4*, 401–408.

MATTIG, W.; MEHLTRETTER, J. P.; AND NESIS, A.: 1969, Studies of Granular Velocities. I. Granular Doppler Shifts and Convective Motion. Solar Phys. *10*, 254–261.

MICHARD, R.: 1956, Spectrophotometry of Strong Emission Lines in the Chromosphere. II. The Hα Line in Spicules. Ann. Astrophys. *19*, 1.

MOORE, D. W.; AND SPIEGEL, E. A.: 1964, The Generation and Propagation of Waves in a Compressible Atmosphere. Astrophys. J. *139*, 48–71.

MOURADIAN, Z.: 1967, Diffusion of Spicules in the Solar Corona. Solar Phys. *2*, 258–266.

Musman, S.: 1969, The Effect of Finite Resolution on Solar Granulation. Solar Phys. *7*, 178–186.

Musman, S.; and Rust, D. M.: 1970, Vertical Velocities and Horizontal Wave Propagation in the Solar Photosphere. Solar Phys. *13*, 261–286.

Namba, O.; and Diemel, W. E.: 1969, A Morphological Study of the Solar Granulation. Solar Phys. *7*, 167–177.

Nikolsky, G. M.; and Platova, A. G.: 1971, Motions of Hα Spicules Along the Solar Limb. Solar Phys. *18*, 403–409.

Noyes, R. W.: 1967, A. Observational Studies of Velocity Fields in the Solar Photosphere and Chromosphere. Int. Astron. Union Symp. 28th, 293–344.

Noyes, R. W.; and Leighton, R. B.: 1963, Velocity Fields in the Solar Atmosphere. II. The Oscillatory Field. Astrophys. J. *138*, 631–647.

Noyes, R. W.; and Kalkofen, W.: 1970, Solar Phys. *15*, 120.

Orrall, F. Q.: 1965, Observational Study of Macroscopic Inhomogeneities in the Solar Atmosphere. VI. Photospheric Oscillations and Chromospheric Structure. Astrophys. J. *141*, 1131–1138.

Orrall, F. Q.: 1966, Observational Study of Macroscopic Inhomogeneities in the Solar Atmosphere. Pt. 8, Vertical Chromospheric Oscillations Measured in K_3. Astrophys. J. *143*, 917–927.

Osterbrock, D. E.: 1961, The Heating of the Solar Chromosphere, Plages, and Corona by Magnetohydrodynamic Waves. Astrophys. J. *134*, 347–388.

Parker, E. N.: 1963, Interplanetary Dynamical Processes. New York: Interscience.

Parker, E. N.: 1964, A Mechanism for Magnetic Enhancement of Sound-Wave Generation and the Dynamical Origin of Spicules. Astrophys. J. *140*, 1170–1173.

Pasachoff, J. M.; Noyes, R. W.; and Beckers, J. M.: 1968, Spectral Observations of Spicules at Two Heights in the Solar Chromosphere. Solar Phys. *5*, 131–158.

Phillips, O. M.: 1966, The Dynamics of the Upper Ocean. New York: Cambridge Univ. Press, 71.

Pikel'ner, S. B.; and Livshits, M. A.: 1965, Theory of Heating the Active and Undisturbed Chromosphere. Sov. Astron. AJ *8*, 808–818.

Pottasch, S. R.: 1964, On the Interpretation of the Solar Ultraviolet Emission Line Spectrum. Space Sci. Rev. *3*, 816–855.

Roddier, F.: 1966, High-Resolution Studies of Fraunhofer Lines by Observation of Optical Resonance of an Atomic Beam. III. Periodic Oscillations of the Lines. Ann. Astrophys. *29*, 639–644.

Roddier, F.: 1967, Observation of the Solar Line Oscillations With an Atomic-Beam Spectrometer. Astrophys. J. *147*, 1113–1116.

Rogers, E. H.: 1970, Lifetime of the Hα Chromospheric Network. Solar Phys. *13*, 57–77.

Severnyi, A. B.: 1967, Preliminary Communication on Short-Term Oscillations of Solar Magnetic Fields. Sov. Astron. AJ *11*, 383–388.

Sheeley, N. R., Jr.: 1969, The Evolution of the Photospheric Network. Solar Phys. *9*, 347–357.

Simon, G. W.: 1967, Observations of Horizontal Motions in Solar Granulation: Their Relation to Supergranulation. Z. Astrophys. *65*, 345–363.

Simon, G. W.; and Leighton, R. B.: 1964, Velocity Fields in Solar Atmosphere. III. Large-Scale Motions, the Chromospheric Network, and Magnetic Fields. Astrophys. J. *140*, 1120–1147.

Simon, G. W.; and Weiss, N. O.: 1968, Supergranules and the Hydrogen Convection Zone. Z. Astrophys. *69*, 435–450.

Simon, G. W.; and Weiss, N. O.: 1970, On the Magnetic Field in Pores. Solar Phys. *13*, 85–103.

Souffrin, P.: 1966, Hydrodynamics of an Atmosphere Disturbed by a Subjacent Turbulent Convective Zone. Ann. Astrophys. *29*, 55–101.

Souffrin, P.: 1967, Int. Astron. Union Symp. 28th, 459.

Spiegel, E. A.: 1957, The Smoothing of Temperature Fluctuations by Radiative Transfer. Astrophys. J. *126*, 202–207.

Stein, R. F.: 1967, Generation of Acoustic and Gravity Waves by Turbulence in an Isothermal Stratified Atmosphere. Solar Phys. *2*, 385–432.

STEIN, R. F.: 1968, Waves in the Solar Atmosphere. I. The Acoustic Energy Flux. Astrophys. J. *154*, 297–306.

STIX, M.: 1970, On Radiative Relaxation of Chromospheric Oscillations. Astron. Astrophys. *4*, 189–201.

TANENBAUM, A. S.; WILCOX, J. M.; FRAZIER, E. N.; AND HOWARD, R.: 1969, Solar Velocity Fields: 5-min Oscillations and Supergranulation. Solar Phys. *9*, 328–342.

THOMAS, J. H.; CLARK, P. A.; AND CLARK, A., JR.: 1971, Trapped Gravity Waves and the Five-Minute Oscillations of the Solar Atmosphere. Solar Phys. *16*, 51–66.

THOMAS, R. N.; AND ATHAY, R. G.: 1961, Physics of the Solar Chromosphere. New York: Interscience.

UCHIDA, Y.: 1965, Standing Mode of Compressional-Body Gravity Wave in the Solar Chromosphere. Astrophys. J. *142*, 335–350.

UCHIDA, Y.: 1967, Resonant Responses of the Solar Atmosphere to the Gravitational-Hydrodynamic Waves. Astrophys. J. *147*, 181–192.

ULMSCHNEIDER, P. H.: 1969, Proc. Conf. Chromosphere-Corona Transition Region, High Altitude Observatory, Aug. 1969, 9.

ULMSCHNEIDER, P.: 1970, On Frequency and Strength of Shock Waves in the Solar Atmosphere. Solar Phys. *12*, 403–415.

ULRICH, R. K.: 1970, The Five-Minute Oscillations on the Solar Surface. Astrophys. J. *162*, 993–1002.

WEART, S. R.: 1970, Production of Solar Magnetic Fine-Structure by Convection. Solar Phys. *14*, 274–279.

WHITAKER, W. A.: 1963, Heating of the Solar Corona by Gravity Waves. Astrophys. J. *137*, 914–930.

WHITE, O. R.; AND SIMON, G. W.: 1968, Resolution of the Hα Double-Limb Controversy. Solar Phys. *3*, 269–281.

WILSON, P. R.: 1969a, Temperature Fluctuations in the Solar Photosphere. Solar Phys. *6*, 364–380.

WILSON, P. R.: 1969b, Temperature Fluctuations in the Solar Photosphere. II. The Mean Limb-Darkening and the Second Maximum. Solar Phys. *9*, 303–314.

ZIRIN, H.: 1966, The Solar Atmosphere. Waltham, Mass.: Blaisdell.

The Corona

6.1 THE VARIETY OF OBSERVATIONS

The corona, the sun's very tenuous outer atmosphere, can be observed throughout the entire range of the electromagnetic spectrum from X-ray to radio wavelengths. It can also be directly sampled by space probes. Although this exposes the corona to a wide variety of observational techniques, most of them are difficult to apply and their results are often difficult to interpret. Most corona observations must be made either from above the earth's atmosphere where the X-ray and UV emissions are not absorbed, in interplanetary space where the solar wind can be sampled, or at times of eclipse only when the strong photospheric emission is blocked and the faint white light of the corona out to many solar radii can be detected. Only in the radio range of the spectrum, where several windows exist in the earth's atmosphere, are we able to make routine but low-resolution observations of the corona. It will be seen that the elusive nature of the corona can be traced back to its extremely low density.

The nonradiative energy that travels outward past the chromosphere in the form of Alfvén and slow-mode MHD waves is dissipated in the relatively low-density atmosphere above and raises the gas temperature to over 10^6 K. This high temperature is responsible for the great extent of the corona as seen during an eclipse (figs. 6–1 to 6–5) because it produces a large atmospheric scale height. It also greatly enhances the thermal conductivity of the gas, which in turn tends to create a condition of nearly uniform high temperature. It was previously shown that the conductive flow of heat varies as $T^{5/2} \, dT/dh$ (sec. 5.2). Thus the 10^6 K corona transfers heat 10^5 times more efficiently than the chromospheric gas at 10^4 K, and a temperature results that is far more uniform than in the atmosphere below.

Even though the temperature is high, the low density of the corona precludes much radiation emission in the visible range of the spectrum relative to the emission from the photosphere. The white light coming from the corona during an eclipse is primarily white light emitted by the 6000 K photosphere and subsequently scattered toward us by coronal material. Widely spaced emission lines extending above the photospheric continuum are also seen in the coronal visible spectrum during an eclipse. However, their combined energy is small relative to the scattered radiation.

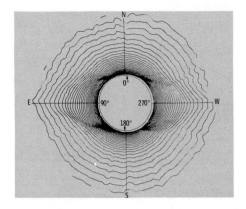

FIGURE 6–1.—The corona at solar minimum. (*a*) Photograph taken June 30, 1954. (*b*) Isophotes of the corona at solar minimum. Contours of equal intensity, spaced every 0.2 magnitude, are shown for the photograph appearing in (*a*). The solar axis of rotation is marked by arrows. (Courtesy of A. Wallenquist, Uppsala Observatory.)

In the XUV and X-ray range the corona replaces the atmosphere below as the prime source of emission. This occurs, despite the low coronal densities, because of the high coronal temperature and the tendency for the radiation to peak at shorter wavelengths. Many closely spaced emission lines are observed in the XUV and X-ray ranges which provide information on the abundances of the elements. However, these lines are often difficult to interpret because they arise from non-LTE sources. One advantage of making observations in the XUV and X-ray ranges is that the corona can be seen against the disk of the sun and it is not necessary to eclipse the photospheric light. As we move to shorter wavelengths, radiation comes from higher layers in the atmosphere, the observable edge of the sun becomes

FIGURE 6–2.—The intermediate corona. (Courtesy of L. Hobbs, Yerkes Observatory.)

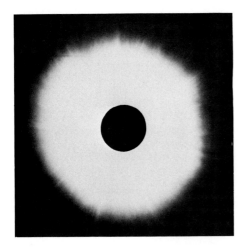

FIGURE 6–3.—The corona at solar maximum. (Courtesy of L. Hobbs, Yerkes Observatory.)

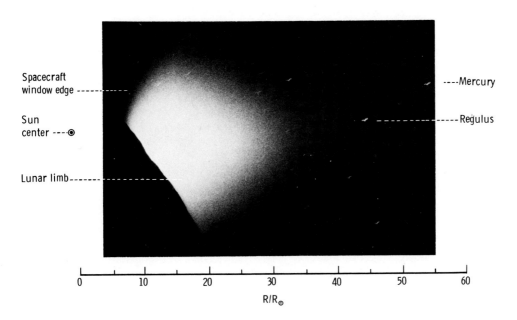

Spacecraft window edge

Sun center

Lunar limb

----Mercury

----Regulus

R/R$_\odot$

FIGURE 6–4.—The east solar corona photographed from Apollo 15 on July 31, 1971. This photograph was made by Astronaut Alfred Worden 1 min before sunrise through the window of the Apollo Command Module. The image of the lunar horizon was held in a fixed position on the film during the exposure by the spacecraft attitude-control jets. Thus, orbital motion caused a smearing of the background stars. This excellent photograph shows the F corona out to approximately $32R_\odot$. An exposure of approximately 10 sec was made using Kodak 2485 film. (NASA, MSC, AS15–98–13311.)

FIGURE 6–5.—The corona seen during the eclipse on March 7, 1970. (*a*) With radial density gradient filter. This photograph was made using a radial density gradient filter in the same manner as figure 2–42. It was taken from a point about 30 miles southwest of San Carlos Yautepec, Mexico, at 8800-foot altitude. Features can be traced out to $4.5R_\odot$ on the original negative. The number of streamers at high latitude is larger than expected. (Courtesy of G. Newkirk, High Altitude Observatory.) (*b*) Superposition of figure (*a*) and the X-ray photograph of figure 2–34. It is seen that there is a good correspondence between the coronal X-ray activity and the relatively bright streamers. (Courtesy of Solar Physics Group, American Science & Engineering, Inc.)

less well defined and moves outward from the photospheric disk, and limb brightening becomes very pronounced.

At the other end of the spectrum the corona is also observable. At radio wavelengths the corona is optically thick and the emission and absorption of radiation is primarily caused by electrons. This radiation is characteristic of the long-wavelength tail of a million-degree-Kelvin equilibrium radiation distribution. As in the XUV and X-ray ranges, limb brightening is observed, the size of the sun is larger than the photospheric disk, and various atmospheric heights can be studied by varying the wavelength of the observation. However, the much larger wavelengths in the radio range require much larger apertures for the observing instruments to obtain the same resolution as that at shorter wavelengths.

The last type of coronal observations to be considered are those which have been made by space probes. A very hot, tenuous, high-velocity outward flux of particles, termed the "solar wind," has been observed. This wind has been seen to be quite variable and contains a complex frozen-in magnetic-field structure. The energy supply for the solar wind, as well as the radiation emitted by the corona, is the nonradiative energy carried up from the underlying convection zone.

6.2 THE SCATTERED CORONA

Much of our knowledge of the large-scale structure of the corona has come from white-light eclipse photographs (figs. 6–1 to 6–5). Several points become evident from a study of these photographs. First, the corona has structure which is a function of solar latitude, longitude, radius, and progression of the solar cycle. Also, it is difficult to separate the quiet corona, which we here assume to be associated with spicules and the chromospheric network but which has not been shown to exist, from the active corona, which is associated with active regions. Finally, the full three-dimensional structure of coronal features cannot be determined from a single set of photographs made during an eclipse because there is no way to determine the distribution of scattering particles along our line of sight. Thus, in the interpretation of results, it is usually assumed that the coronal structure is a function only of radius and an angle about our line of sight to sun center. Coronal properties are often stated as a function of radius only, with a distinction made between equatorial and polar values. This assumption is probably valid at the equator during solar minimum, but is not valid at the poles where we would expect a variation with latitude always to exist. If symmetry is not assumed, there is no one unique electron density distribution which will match any one observation. It is apparent that there is a significant advantage to be gained from monitoring the corona for at least a solar rotation from an orbiting observatory to determine structural variations in longitude.

In figure 2–19, it is seen that the white-light corona has three components. Photospheric light scattered by electrons, termed the K corona, is the dominant component inside approximately $2.3R_\odot$. Outside this region the dominant component is the F corona which arises from photospheric light scattered by small dust particles. Because the electrons originate from the sun and the dust particles do not, the K corona will be considered more basic in our discussion. Using somewhat arbitrary criteria, the corona can be divided into three regions: the inner, the intermediate, and the outer coronas (fig. 6–6). The inner region extends from the top of the chromosphere out to about $1.3R_\odot$. The chromosphere has essentially disappeared at a height of 12 000 km where the spicules are less than one per supergranular cell

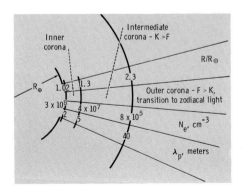

FIGURE 6–6.—Coronal regions.

(fig. 5–62) and the Ca II and H Balmer lines have faded into the coronal background. The intensity of the inner corona is great enough that under ideal conditions an eclipse is not required for its observation. The intermediate corona extends from $1.3R_\odot$ to approximately $2.3R_\odot$. In the outer corona above $2.3R_\odot$, the F corona dominates and a transition to the zodiacal light occurs.

Figure 2–19 also shows that the intensity of the scattered light is no larger than 10^{-5} that of the photospheric light. Thus, the small amount of photospheric light which is scattered has an extremely small chance of being scattered a second time. Because each coronal electron scatters light in proportion to its illumination by the photosphere, the K corona will give an indication of the total electron content along the line of sight on which it is viewed. Therefore, in order to study the electron-density distribution, which is our end objective here, the F corona must be separated from the K corona. To accomplish this, the differences in either the spectroscopic or polarization properties of the K and F coronas can be used. (See Billings, 1966.)

Spectroscopic Separation of K and F Coronas

Because both the K and F coronas arise from scattered photospheric light, it is natural to expect them to contain the Fraunhofer lines. However, because the random thermal motion of the coronal electrons is very rapid, because of their low mass and high temperature (eq. (4–56)), the scattered Fraunhofer lines are broadened to several hundred times their original width and are no longer distinguishable. The Hα line is broadened to 120 Å by a million-degree-Kelvin electron gas. On the other hand, the relatively heavy, slow-moving dust particles do not appreciably change a Fraunhofer line shape when they scatter light and the F corona mimics the Fraunhofer line profiles of the photosphere. Because of the presence of the continuous K corona, the observed corona has line depths relative to the continuum that are not as great as in the photosphere. Setting l_c equal to the intensity at line center relative to the continuum for the observed coronal spectrum (fig. 6–7)

$$l_c = \left(\frac{I_{\lambda_o}}{I_{continuum}}\right)_{corona} \tag{6–1}$$

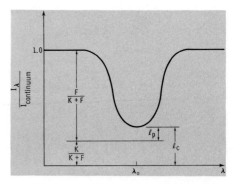

Figure 6–7.—Depth of photospheric and coronal lines.

and l_p equal to the corresponding value for the photospheric spectrum

$$l_p = \left(\frac{I_{\lambda_o}}{I_{continuum}}\right)_{photosphere} \tag{6-2}$$

it is seen that

$$l_c = \frac{Fl_p + K}{F + K} \tag{6-3}$$

where K and F are the radiation intensities of the two coronas, F corresponding to the continuum far away from the line center. Thus, the fraction of the corona which is attributable to the K component, k, is $K/(K+F)$, or

$$k = \frac{l_c - l_p}{1 - l_p} \tag{6-4}$$

Polarization Separation of K and F Coronas

Because the above method of separating the K and F coronas requires a spectrographic slit that can admit only a very narrow strip of the faint coronal radiation at one time, only a small number of locations in the inner and intermediate coronas can be sampled during an eclipse. The polarization method of separation does not share this limitation. However, it must be assumed that the K corona is the sole source of polarization, which is a valid assumption out to only approximately $5R_\odot$. Beyond $5R_\odot$ the ratio of F/K is so large that only a minute polarization of F causes significant errors in the calculation of K.

The manner in which coronal electrons scatter photospheric radiation is of fundamental importance to the interpretation of the K corona and the polarization method of separation. Whenever an electromagnetic wave encounters an electron, the electron is accelerated by the electric field of the wave. Basic electromagnetic theory states that whenever a charge is accelerated, radiation is emitted. This type of radiation production is the cause not only of radiation scattering by electrons in the corona, but also of the following radiation:

(1) Cyclotron radiation produced by charged particles moving across magnetic-field lines.
(2) Electron thermal bremsstrahlung (German for braking radiation) produced when free electrons in random thermal motion are accelerated during encounters with ions and the other electrons. (In each encounter, the free electron gives up a small amount of kinetic energy to radiation and the term "free-free" is often applied.)
(3) Antenna radiation produced by the vibration of a collection of charges confined by the geometry of a conducting antenna.

Figure 6–8 illustrates geometry of the scattering of an electromagnetic wave by a coronal electron. In figure 6–8 (a), the direction of propagation of the incident wave, which is parallel to $\mathbf{E}_i \times \mathbf{B}_i$, and the electric field of the incident wave $\mathbf{E}_i$ lie

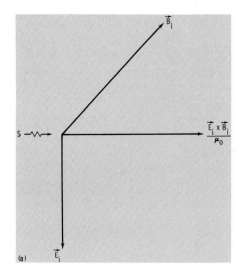
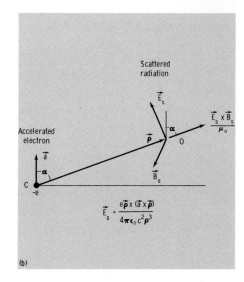

FIGURE 6–8.—Electromagnetic wave scattering. (a) Incident electromagnetic wave. The wave originates at the source (point S) and has electric and magnetic fields which are perpendicular to each other and the direction of the wave propagation. The energy per unit area and unit time carried by the wave is $\mathbf{E}_i \times \mathbf{B}_i/\mu_0$. (b) Scattered electromagnetic wave. The incident wave of figure (a) is scattered by the electron charge at point C. The charge is accelerated in the direction **a**. The observer at point O, specified by the vector ϱ relative to the scattering electron, sees the scattered wave which has electric and magnetic fields $\mathbf{E}_s$ and $\mathbf{B}_s$.

in the plane of the figure. In figure 6–8 (b), the observer is at point O and the plane of the figure contains both **a** and ϱ. The electric field in the scattered wave is given by

$$\mathbf{E}_s = \frac{e\varrho \times (\mathbf{a} \times \varrho)}{4\pi\epsilon_0 c^2 \rho^3} \qquad (6\text{–}5)$$

where ϱ is the radius vector and **a** is the acceleration at the earlier time $t-\rho/c$. Because the acceleration of the electron is $-e\mathbf{E}_i/m_e$,

$$\mathbf{E}_s = \frac{e^2 (\mathbf{E}_i \times \varrho) \times \varrho}{4\pi\epsilon_0 m_e c^2 \rho^3} \qquad (6\text{–}6)$$

The corresponding magnetic field is

$$\mathbf{B}_s = \frac{\mu_0 e^2 \mathbf{E}_i \times \varrho}{4\pi m_e c \rho^2} \qquad (6\text{–}7)$$

The direction of propagation of the scattered radiant power is along ϱ and its magnitude per steradian ψ is

$$\psi(\alpha) = \rho^2 \left| \frac{\mathbf{E}_s \times \mathbf{B}_s}{\mu_0} \right|$$

or

$$\psi(\alpha) = \frac{e^4 E_i^2 \sin^2 \alpha}{16\pi\epsilon_0 m_e^2 c^3} \qquad (6\text{-}8)$$

where α is the angle between $\mathbf{E}_i$ and $\boldsymbol{\rho}$. Thus, no energy is scattered along a direction parallel to $\mathbf{E}_i$ but is a maximum at right angles to it (fig. 6–9). Because the power in an electromagnetic wave is proportional to the square of the electric field ($\psi \approx E^2$), the ratio of scattered to incident power is easily calculated using equation (6–6).

$$\left(\frac{E_s}{E_i}\right)^2 = \left(\frac{e^2}{4\pi\epsilon_0 m_e c^2}\right)^2 \left(\frac{\sin \alpha}{\rho}\right)^2 \qquad (6\text{-}9)$$

Integrating this ratio over the total surface of a sphere of radius ρ yields the ratio of the total scattered power to the incident power per unit area.

$$\sigma_T \equiv 2\pi\rho^2 \int_{-\pi}^{+\pi} \left(\frac{E_s}{E_i}\right)^2 \sin \alpha \, d\alpha \qquad (6\text{-}10)$$

$$\sigma_T = \frac{1}{6\pi}\left(\frac{e^2}{\epsilon_0 m_e c^2}\right)^2 \qquad (6\text{-}11)$$

$$\sigma_T = 6.6 \times 10^{-25} \text{ cm}^2$$

The Thomson cross section σ_T, whose value we have just derived, is a measure of the scattering power of an electron. It has the units of area and is determined by fundamental constants only. It can be classically pictured as the size of an electron as seen by incident radiation. Thus, as photospheric light travels out through the corona, its probability of being scattered is only one part in 10^{24} times the number of electrons encountered per unit area. Because the maximum intensity of the inner corona is 10^{-5} that of the photosphere (fig. 2–19), there are approximately 10^{19} electrons per square centimeter along a line-of-sight tangent to the top of the chromosphere. This is the same number of particles contained in only 1 cm³ of the earth's atmosphere at sea level, but, in the very tenuous corona, this number of electrons is distributed all the way along our line of sight. The major portion of the scattered light that we see coming from the inner corona originates in a volume having an approximate thickness of H, the atmospheric scale height, and an approximate length of $(2HR_\odot)^{1/2}$ for $H \ll R_\odot$ (fig. 6–10). For a temperature of 10^6 K,

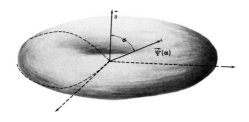

FIGURE 6–9.—Radiation from an accelerated charge. The three-dimensional radiation pattern, a picture of the surface defined by constant $\Psi(\alpha)$, is "doughnut shaped" as shown above. The cross section, shown by the curved dotted line, is a plot of $\sin^2 \alpha$. It is seen that the radiated energy is zero along the direction of acceleration but a maximum at right angles to it.

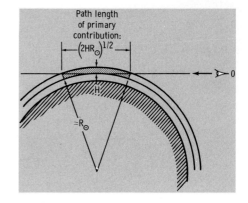

FIGURE 6–10.—Path length of primary contribution of scattered light. Since the electrons outside of this path length but along the line of sight also scatter light toward the observer, the electron density estimated using this length will be slightly large.

$H = 5 \times 10^9$ cm (eq. (3–27)) and the length of this volume is roughly 10^{10} cm. Thus, the electron density at the base of the corona must be slightly less than 10^9 cm^{-3}, a value in agreement with the results of the more detailed calculations that we now consider.

The three-dimensional character of the origin of the K corona is shown in figure 6–11(a). An element of the coronal plasma at point C is illuminated by the source at point S. Along the strip shown having a constant value of θ, the angle of S from sun center, the illumination at C is of constant intensity but varying direction. As we move the source point by varying θ, the intensity at C also changes because of the limb-darkening effect which is a function of wavelength. The assumption of spherical symmetry is introduced when the density of scattering electrons is assumed to be a function of r only. The radiation incident at C is unpolarized; that is, the electric-field vector of the radiation $\mathbf{E}_i$ has equal probability of lying in any direction in the plane perpendicular to its propagation. However, when the scattered radiation leaves C and moves toward the observer at O, $\mathbf{E}_s$ does not have equal probability of being in any direction perpendicular to ϱ. The polarization directions are most naturally taken along the directions of the unit vector $\mathbf{e}_t$ and $\mathbf{e}_r$, which are tangent and perpendicular to the limb of the sun, respectively, as seen by the observer at O (fig. 6–11(b)). The predominant direction of $\mathbf{E}_s$ is easily determined by assuming the sun to be a point source, which becomes more valid as r increases, and taking C to be on a radius vector perpendicular to ϱ, which is where the density of scattering electrons is a maximum along ϱ. In this case $\mathbf{E}_i$ is always in a plane perpendicular to ϱ, and from equation (6–6), it is seen that $\mathbf{E}_s$ must be in the direction of $\mathbf{e}_t$. Therefore, when the angle of scattering is 90°, the light is completely polarized in the direction perpendicular to the plane defined by the incident and scattered directions; that is, parallel to $\mathbf{e}_t$. Because angles of scattering other than 90° occur in the real case, there is always scattered radiation in which $\mathbf{E}_s$ has a component along $\mathbf{e}_r$.

Relations for the intensities of the K corona polarized along the tangential and radial directions have been stated by van de Hulst (1953).

$$K_t(R) = C \int_R^{\infty} N_e(r) A(r) \frac{r \, dr}{(r^2 - R^2)^{1/2}} \tag{6-12}$$

$$K_r(R) = C \int_R^{\infty} N_e(r) \left[\left(1 - \frac{R^2}{r^2}\right) A(r) + \frac{R^2}{r^2} B(r) \right] \frac{r \, dr}{(r^2 - R^2)^{1/2}} \tag{6-13}$$

where R is the projected distance from the line of observation to sun center (fig. 6–11(b)), C is a constant proportional to the intensity of the photospheric radiation and the Thomson cross section, and $A(r)$ and $B(r)$ are functions which account for the limb darkening. The sum of K_t and K_r is $K(R)$, which is plotted in figure 2–19. The electron-density distribution was determined by van de Hulst by a series of successive approximations in which $N_e(r)$ was adjusted to fit both the observed K_t and K_r. By definition, the degree of polarization of the K corona is

$$p = \frac{K_t - K_r}{K_t + K_r} \tag{6-14}$$

An equivalent quantity can be defined for the total corona $K+F$. Assuming the F component is unpolarized, all of the observed coronal polarization must come from the K component. Thus, pk is the degree of polarization of the sum of both

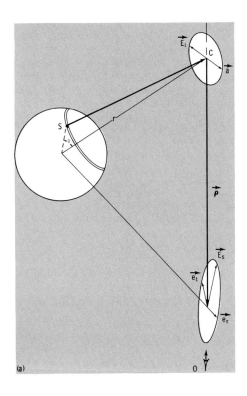

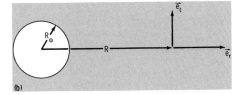

FIGURE 6–11.—Light scattering by the corona. (a) Three-dimensional geometry of light scattering. This is a composite of figures 6–8(a) and 6–8(b). Light originates at point S, is scattered at point C, and observed at point O. The observer divides the scattered light into two components by placing a polarizing filter in front of the observing instrument. The axis of polarization can be placed tangent to the limb (e_t) or parallel to the radial direction (e_r). (b) Definition of the projected radius of observation, the radial direction, and the tangential direction.

components, $K+F$. As used in equation (6–4), k is the fraction of the corona attributed to K, $K/(K+F)$. The separation of K and F can therefore be accomplished by calculating p (eqs. (6–12) to (6–14)), measuring pk, and computing k.

In figure 6–12, the values calculated by van de Hulst (1953) for $p(R)$ and $k(R)$ and the observed pk are shown for both the equator and poles at solar maximum and minimum. These values are representative of the range of observed values that are possible. In figure 6–12 (a), it is seen that as R increases, the polarization of the K corona, p, also increases as we would expect. That is, the sun becomes more of a point source and the average scattering angle moves toward 90°. The strong dependence of the K corona on solar activity is seen in the plot of $k(R)$ (fig. 6–12 (b)). At maximum, the electron density is enhanced and its distribution approaches spherical symmetry (fig. 6–3); thus, k is relatively large and approx-

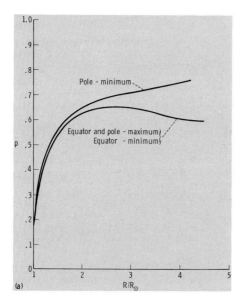

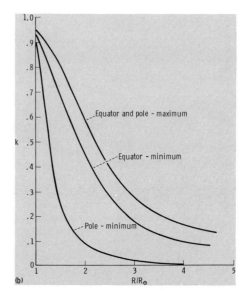

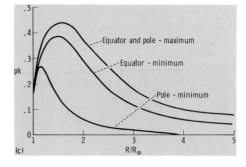

FIGURE 6–12.—The K corona. (a) Degree of polarization of the K corona. (b) Fraction of the corona attributable to the K component. (c) Polarization of the total corona. (Data from van de Hulst, 1953.)

imately the same at the equator and pole. At solar minimum, the intensity of the K corona drops but F remains the same, thus K is lower. The large drop in the electron density at the pole is evidenced by the low polar values of k. The problem encountered in the polarization method of separation of the F and K coronas is illustrated by the low values of k at large R. Only slight amounts of polarization of F can produce a polarized component of the same magnitude as that of K. The observed polarization of $F+K$, pk, is shown in figure 6–12(c). The characteristics of pk follow directly from the individual characteristics of $p(R)$ and $k(R)$. An important fact to the experimenter is that as pk becomes very small, there is an accompanying increase in the chance of error caused by light scattering and polarization within the observing instrument. The physically meaningful result of all these observations, the electron-density distribution, is shown in figure 6–13. The distributions calculated by van de Hulst display large differences between the densities at solar maximum and minimum. These densities are lower than those found by most subsequent investigators (fig. 2–20).

To determine what data are required to arrive at $N_e(R)$, it is noted that at any given point in the projected corona, the three quantities K_t, K_r, and F must be determined. Alternately, the sum $K+F$, k, and p must be found. Thus, at least three independent measurements must be made at each point. This can be done by using polarizing filters oriented at three different directions, most simply at 120° intervals (fig. 6–14). When this is done, specification of the state of polarization of the coronal light is possible. This can conveniently be put in terms of the Stokes parameters which are used to specify the state of polarization of partially polarized light (Papas, 1965). Note that the information from the coronal light reaching an observer on earth is not easily converted into an electron-density distribution. After the observer exposes his photographic film during an eclipse, he must determine the radiation intensity from the photographic density point by point over each of three different pictures. Then the iterative computations of

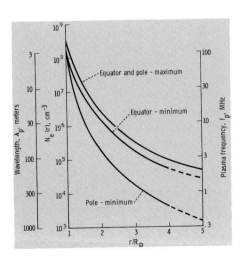

FIGURE 6–13.—Electron density. Also shown are the corresponding values of plasma frequency f_p and plasma wavelength in a vacuum λ_p, which are both functions of N_e only. (Data from van de Hulst, 1953.)

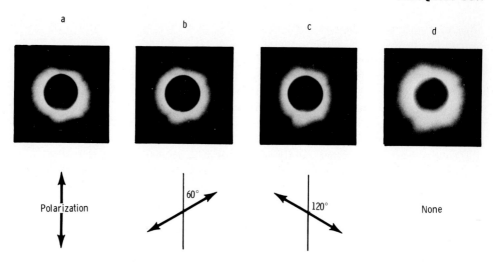

FIGURE 6–14.—The corona seen through polaroids at three different orientations. These photographs of the corona, as seen during the eclipse of March 7, 1970, were made using a hand-held 70-mm Hasselblad camera, a 250-mm lens, Kodak 2485 film, $f/5.6$, and exposure times of 1/500 sec. They were taken by K. Henize and the author from a T–38 aircraft at 47 000 feet over the Gulf of Mexico. Figures (a), (b), and (c) were made using a polaroid oriented in the directions indicated. Figure 6–14(d) was made with the polaroid removed. Some small differences can be noted between (a), (b), and (c) and can be explained by the general rule of scattering: When the angle of scattering is 90°, the scattered light will be completely polarized in the direction perpendicular to the plane defined by the incident and scattered directions. Assuming the predominate scattering to be close to 90°, the observed corona should be slightly extended in the direction perpendicular to the arrow indicating the direction of polarization. This effect can be seen, especially between (a) and (b) and between (a) and (c).

$N_e(R)$, $k(R)$, and $p(R)$ must be initiated by assuming a coronal model. The iteration procedure is continued until the model does not undergo significant changes over one cycle of computation. When this labor is completed, questions remain concerning the validity of the assumption of spherical symmetry and its effect on the results. It is obvious that the number of solar observers present at an eclipse will far outnumber the resulting plots of $N_e(R)$.

Coronal Kinetic Temperature

From the radial gradient in the electron density, it is possible to obtain an estimate of the kinetic temperature of the ions, most of which are protons. There is a very strong tendency for the gas to remain electrically neutral; that is, for the electron-charge density to equal the ion-charge density. Thus, because gravity acts primarily on the ions, the total mass density distribution is the same as the electron distribution scaled by a constant factor. Using this fact and equations (3–3), (3–13), and (3–14) to balance the pressure gradient with the gravity force, we obtain

$$\frac{dN_e}{N_e} = -\frac{\mu m_H g_\odot}{kT}\left(\frac{R_\odot}{r}\right)^2 dr - \frac{dT}{T} \tag{6-15}$$

where $g_\odot$ is the value of solar gravity at $r = R_\odot$. Assuming the gas to be isothermal

$$\frac{N_e(r)}{N_e(R_\odot)} = \exp\left[-\frac{\mu m_H g_\odot R_\odot}{kT}\left(1 - \frac{R_\odot}{r}\right)\right] \tag{6-16}$$

As in previous analysis, a scale height can be defined, but it is a function of radius

$$H \equiv \frac{N_e}{\left|\dfrac{dN_e}{dr}\right|} \tag{6-17}$$

$$H = \frac{kT}{\mu m_H g_\odot}\left(\frac{r}{R_\odot}\right)^2 \tag{6-18}$$

If the corona were isothermal, a plot of $\log N_e$ versus $1/r$ should yield a straight line whose slope defines T. Numerically, the relation for T is

$$T = 6.20 \times 10^6 \left[\frac{d \log_{10} N_e}{d\left(\dfrac{R_\odot}{r}\right)}\right]^{-1} \quad \text{K} \tag{6-19}$$

where μ has been set equal to 0.619, the value for a fully ionized mixture having a hydrogen-to-helium number density ratio of 9 to 1. In figure 6–15, where $\log_{10} N_e$ is plotted as a function of $R_\odot/r$, it is seen that straight lines are obtained for values of r less than approximately $2.5R_\odot$. For larger values of r, the slope gradually increases, indicating a slow decrease in T. The temperatures corresponding to these curves are approximately 1.45×10^6 K for the equator and poles at maximum and the equator at minimum and 1.03×10^6 K for the poles at minimum.

Determination of the coronal temperatures in this way rests on two assumptions which have not been stated. Equation (6–15) has been derived from the expression for a complete momentum balance on the gas.

$$\rho\left(\frac{\partial \mathbf{V}}{\partial t} + \mathbf{V} \cdot \nabla \mathbf{V}\right) = -\nabla p + \rho\mathbf{g} + \mathbf{J} \times \mathbf{B} \tag{6-20}$$

Here, ρ is the mass density, $\mathbf{V}$ is the macroscopic velocity, and $\mathbf{J}$ is the electric current density. We have first assumed that $\mathbf{V}$ is zero, an assumption which will not be made in discussing the solar wind and which makes our derived values of temperature a lower bound. We have also neglected the $\mathbf{J} \times \mathbf{B}$ force, which is valid in the outer corona except near the high magnetic fields of the active-sun features (rays, fans, arches, etc.). When $\mathbf{J} \times \mathbf{B}$ is not negligible, equation (6–15) is still

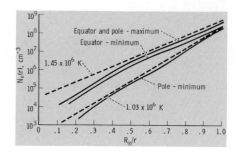

Figure 6–15.—Determination of coronal temperature. (Data from van de Hulst, 1953.)

valid, but only for the component parallel to **B**. For $\mathbf{V}=0$, $(0=-\nabla p+\rho\mathbf{g}+\mathbf{J}\times\mathbf{B})\cdot\mathbf{B}$ yields

$$\left(\frac{\partial p}{\partial s}\right)_{\parallel} = -\rho g_{\parallel} \tag{6–21}$$

where the subscript $\parallel$ denotes the direction parallel to **B**.

The F Corona

The second component of the scattered corona, the F corona, arises from an interplanetary dust cloud rather than from material originating from the sun. The cloud is shaped like a large flat lens which is concentrated in the equatorial plane (fig. 6–4) and extends out past the orbit of the earth. Because particles close to the sun evaporate, the cloud has a large spherical void in the center, extending out to approximately $4R_{\odot}$. The dust particles themselves are small (on the order of 10 μm) and electrically nonconducting. Most of the F corona close to the sun comes from the diffraction of photospheric light in which the probability of scattering in directions other than the forward direction is relatively low. For large elongations $R\gg R_{\odot}$, most of the F corona comes from the direct reflection of light. In fact, the faint glow that can barely be seen in the night sky close to the antisolar point (the point in the night sky opposite the location of the sun) is attributed to the reflection of sunlight by dust particles outside the earth's orbit. This glow is called the "gegenschein," German for counterglow.

The F corona can also be seen in the night sky but usually only from the lower earth latitudes against a very dark background. It appears as a cone of light extending upward from the horizon where the sun has just set or is about to rise. Because it appears against the circle of constellations called the zodiac, the outer F corona is termed the zodiacal light. In figure 6–16, the smooth transition from the outer corona, almost all caused by the F component, to the zodiacal light is illustrated. The predominance of the F over the K corona from a few $R_{\odot}$ outward is primarily due to the rapid decrease of the electron density relative to the particle density.

Unlike the electrons, the particles are in orbit about the sun and rely upon centrifugal force rather than a pressure gradient to balance the pull of solar gravity.

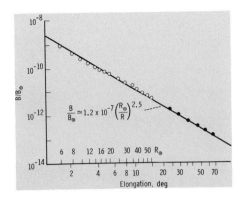

FIGURE 6–16.—Transition from the outer corona to the zodiacal light. Data are from Blackwell and Chacaltaya as given by Zirin (1966). (From Zirin, 1966; copyright 1966, Blaisdell Publishing Co.)

The F and K coronas are alike, however, in that both suffer a decrease in strength with increasing radius because of the decrease in solar illumination. Also, because the solar illumination and the dust-particle distribution are not noticeably affected by solar activity, the properties of the F corona are not functions of the solar cycle.

Effects of Solar Activity

Our discussion has implied that in the corona, unlike the interior, photosphere, or chromosphere, the effects of solar activity cannot be ignored. It would be convenient to describe the quiet corona as a function of radius only, ignoring the variations that occur with latitude, longitude, and time in the solar cycle. However, it is not clear if a corona caused only by quiet-sun phenomena is ever observable, even at the poles during solar minimum. Active-sun phenomena are not as highly localized in the corona as they are in the photosphere and chromosphere. The observed K corona must be assumed to be affected, if only slightly, by what activity does exist.

A gross measure of the effect of the solar cycle is obtained by following coronal deviations from spherical symmetry (figs. 6–1 to 6–3). Using any one isophote (fig. 6–1(b)), the flattening of the corona can be defined by

$$\epsilon = \frac{D_e}{D_p} - 1 \tag{6-22}$$

where D_e is the average of the three equatorial diameters of the isophote at latitudes of $\pm 22.5°$ and $0°$, and D_p is similarly defined for the polar direction. In figure 6–17, ϵ first increases with increasing distance from the sun as a result of the increasing concentration of the K corona near the equator. The subsequent decrease to a minimum at about $4R_\odot$ is attributed to the decrease of the K corona relative to the nearly spherically symmetric F corona. The F corona itself then becomes elliptical for large values of R.

If we restrict our attention to the range from $1R_\odot$ out to almost $2R_\odot$, we can

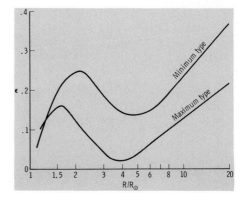

FIGURE 6–17.—Variation of the flattening index with radius. It is seen that the corona is never completely symmetric but it is nearly so at the solar maximum and $R \simeq 4R_\odot$. (Courtesy of G. Newkirk, High Altitude Observatory.)

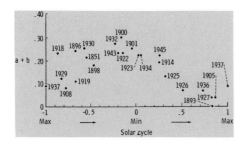

FIGURE 6–18.—Variation of flattening index parameters with solar cycle. (From van de Hulst, 1953; copyright 1953, University of Chicago Press.)

approximate the initial rise of ϵ by a straight line given by

$$\epsilon = a + b \left(\frac{R}{R_\odot} - 1 \right) \tag{6–23}$$

where a and b are parameters easily determined from plots of $\epsilon(R)$ such as figure 6–17. The sum of $a+b$ is thus a measure of the flattening of the K corona. In figure 6–18, where the variations of $a+b$ with the solar cycle are shown, it is seen that the K corona tends toward sphericity at maximum and appreciable ellipticity at minimum. The change in the equatorial electron density throughout the cycle is relatively small. The increase from minimum to maximum in figure 6–13 is only about a factor of 2. However, at the poles, the change is relatively large. In figure 6–13 an increase by a factor slightly greater than 10 occurs at $2R_\odot$ from minimum to maximum. Thus, the electron-density distribution resulting from solar activity at minimum is concentrated at the equatorial regions; but at maximum, the activity tends to create a spherically symmetric corona.

6.3 THE EMISSION CORONA

The emission of radiation from the corona arises under highly non-local-thermodynamic-equilibrium (NLTE) conditions and our task of interpretation is more complex. The corona is composed of low-density, high-kinetic-temperature particles immersed in the low-temperature radiation field of the photosphere. The rates of encounters of the atoms and ions with either the energetic electrons or the low-energy photons are not sufficient to bring about any generalized form of equilibrium. These conditions are not reproducible in the laboratory and the emissions by ions in high stages of ionization produce coronal spectra in the visible range unlike the Fraunhofer spectrum. This led early investigators to erroneously assume that a new element existed in the corona which they called "coronium." As mentioned previously, we also experience difficulty in separating quiet- and active-sun phenomena. Figure 6–19 illustrates the tendency for an active region to be widespread in the high-temperature coronal emission relative to the localization that we have seen to exist in the photosphere and chromosphere.

The coronal emissions contain much detailed but significant information. Many stages of ionization of each element contribute to the absorption-emission spectrum from visible to X-ray wavelengths. Each stage of ionization corresponds to the location where conditions are just right for its maintenance, a fact which assists in defining temperature and density nonuniformities with good spatial resolution. Also, the abundances of many elements can be determined from the strengths or equivalent widths of the lines. The wide range in the stages of ionization that can exist for each element and the presence of nonuniform conditions complicate the task, however. The most abundant elements, in addition to hydrogen, are almost all of low and even atomic number. Fe, which is of relatively high abundance, exhibits a wide range in its stages of ionization and is an exceptionally prolific generator of emission lines.

Coronal Line Emission

To determine the strength of emission in a line originating from an excited level of an ion, the number density in that excited level must be determined by considering the rates of the detailed processes involved. That is, the rates of production and removal of a level are equated. The processes that lead to a balance of transitions between two levels of an ion in the corona are shown in figure 6–20. Here R_{12} is the rate at which an ion in lower level 1 absorbs radiation and undergoes transitions to level 2, and $N_e C_{12}$ is the corresponding rate for collisions (eq. (4–98)). Only collisions with electrons are considered important because of their relatively high thermal speed and correspondingly high collision frequency. The rate of downward transitions of level 2 to level 1 by spontaneous emission per ion in level 2 is A_{21}. The UV, XUV, or X-ray emissions are rarely of sufficient strength that induced emissions must be considered. Lastly, the rate of downward transitions by collisions per ion in level 2 is $N_e C_{21}$. In this balance of detailed processes we have assumed that the rate of emission by the transition of $2\rightarrow1$ is proportional to the rate of transition $1\rightarrow2$, neglecting population of level 2 by transitions from above. Because of the relatively low density of excited levels of an ion, this is usually a good assumption.

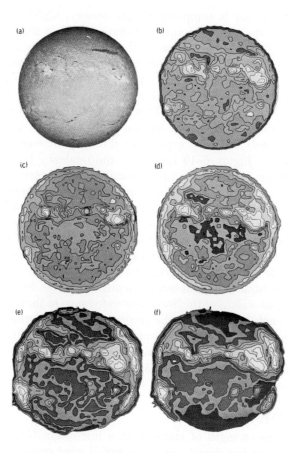

FIGURE 6–19.—Solar UV images made by OSO 4. The Hα photograph in (a) was made by the Sacramento Peak Observatory on the same day as the UV images (b) to (f). As has been typical of recent solar cycles, the activity in the northern hemisphere is significantly greater than in the southern hemisphere. This asymmetry is evident in all the UV images. These images have been arranged in order of increasing temperature of line formation, hence, of increasing height in the solar atmosphere. The lighter regions are hotter; darker ones are cooler. The image in (b) is formed in the Lyman continuum of hydrogen in the chromosphere and corresponds to a temperature of approximately 10^4 K. Generally, the features observable in Hα also appear here: filaments, plages, and limb darkening. The image in (c) was made in the light of N III (corresponding to a temperature of approximately 10^5 K) and begins to show features which become more pronounced at greater heights; increased contrast between active regions and quiet sun, limb brightening, enhanced emission along belts of activity, especially in the northern hemisphere, and polar darkening. Figure (d) was made in the light of O VI (3.25×10^5 K) and (e) in Si XII (2.25×10^6 K). Evident at the limb is the fact that as we observe at greater temperatures and heights, the contours of equal line radiation intensity become very jagged and protrude appreciably into the corona because of solar activity. Hence, the effects of activity can no longer be considered localized in the corona as was the case in the photosphere and chromosphere. (Courtesy of L. Goldberg and E. Reeves, Harvard College Observatory. Used with permission of *Scientific American*.)

At very high densities, the balance between the levels are dominated by collisions

$$N_1 C_{12} \simeq N_2 C_{21} \tag{6-24}$$

For the conditions in the inner corona, the radiation intensity is low enough that $R_{12} \ll N_e C_{12}$ and the gas density is low enough that $N_e C_{21} \ll A_{21}$. Hence

$$N_e N_1 C_{12} \simeq N_2 A_{21} \tag{6-25}$$

Because the number density in all levels, including N_1, is proportional to the total gas density which itself is proportional to N_e, the rate of spontaneous emission per unit volume is proportional to N_e^2, not just N_e. Moving outward in the corona, a point is reached at which $N_e C_{12} \ll R_{12}$, where the radiation causing R_{12} is usually that generated low in the solar atmosphere. Thus,

$$N_1 R_{12} \simeq N_2 A_{21} \tag{6-26}$$

and the emission will vary as N_e/r^2, as does the scattered light that produces the K corona.

Although we must consider each process individually in NLTE, the rate coefficients themselves are related, as can be seen by comparison with the TE situation. In TE (fig. 6–20), not only does the total rate of downward transitions balance the total rate of upward transitions, but the collision and radiation rates balance individually. That is,

$$\frac{R_{12}}{A_{21}} = \frac{N_2}{N_1} \tag{6-27}$$

and

$$\frac{C_{12}}{C_{21}} = \frac{N_2}{N_1} \tag{6-28}$$

where the radiation intensity in R_{12} and the density ratios are equilibrium values corresponding to a single temperature (eqs. (4–11) and (4–17)).

Also simplifying the situation in NLTE is the overpopulation of the ground state N_1. Because of the low gas density and low radiation intensity, the rate at which an ion in level 1 undergoes the transition to level 2 ($N_e C_{12} + R_{12}$) is much less than the equilibrium rate corresponding to the kinetic temperature. However, the rate of downward transition of an ion in level 2, A_{21}, is independent of density and radiation present. Hence, relative to the TE situation, the ground level is overpopulated with respect to the upper levels. This effect is more pronounced higher

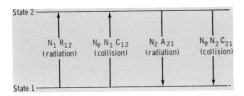

FIGURE 6–20.—Radiation and collisional balance between two energy levels of an ion.

in the atmosphere and is responsible for the formation of Fraunhofer lines in layers above the temperature minimum. The ground levels are present to absorb the radiation at discrete lines, but there is not a sufficient density of excited states to emit the corresponding amount of radiation.

Coronal Ionization

The extreme departure from TE conditions in the corona is evident when ionization recombination is considered. Ionization occurs by electron impact rather than by photoionization because of the low radiation intensity. In equilibrium (fig. 6–21), this is balanced by the recombination of an electron and ion with a second electron carrying away the ionization energy, a process in which the rate per unit volume is proportional to the cube of the density. The low density makes this process ineffective and recombination occurs with the excess energy radiated away by photo recombination. The corona is optically thin to the XUV and X-ray radiation present, most of which is produced in the corona itself. Thus, for both excitation and ionization, there is a direct uninhibited flow of energy from the electrons to the high-energy radiation which is immediately lost to space. In this sense, the deviation from TE is not slight but is complete.

The emission from the corona and chromosphere-corona transition region will be discussed in two separate steps. First, the production of the high stages of ionization of the elements is considered, followed by the general character of the radiation from the ions.

The fact that the ionization energies of the many possible coronal ions can be much less than, comparable with, or much greater than the average thermal energy of a coronal electron indicates that a wide range in the stages of ionization is to be expected. The average thermal energy $3/2kT$ is approximately 260 eV at 2×10^6 K, whereas the ionization energies for coronal elements vary from 5 to 10^3 eV. The ionization energies for H I and He II are 13.6 and 54.5 eV, respectively, and they are completely ionized in the corona.

In the general case, the calculation of the degree of ionization of an element proceeds by equating the ionization and recombination rates that relate successive stages of ionization (fig. 6–21).

$$N_e N_s C_{1\infty}{}^s = N_e N_{s+1} A_{\infty 1}{}^s \qquad (6\text{--}29)$$

FIGURE 6–21.—Ionization and recombination for TE and the NLTE corona. In TE, ionization by electron impact is balanced by three-body recombination and photo-ionization is balanced by photo recombination. In the corona, however, because of low particle and radiation densities, ionization by electron impact must balance photo recombination.

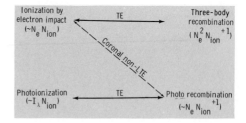

or

$$\frac{N_{s+1}}{N_s} = \frac{C_{1\infty}{}^s}{A_{\infty 1}{}^s} \tag{6-30}$$

Here N_s is the number density of atoms in the sth stage of ionization, $C_{1\infty}{}^s$ is the rate coefficient for transitions from the ground level 1 to an ionized level (∞) by electron impact for an ion at the sth stage of ionization, $A_{\infty 1}{}^s$ is the corresponding rate coefficient for photo recombination which includes not only the straight transition from ionized to ground level but also the cascading down through the possible levels of excitation. Normally, the ionization from excited levels of an ion can be neglected with respect to ionization from the ground level. The overpopulation of ground levels in the corona makes this an even more valid assumption. From equation (6-30), it is seen that the ratio of number densities in successive stages of ionization of an element is independent of density. However, the actual density of a given stage is proportional to the total density and therefore proportional to N_e. In the TE case, equation (6-30) is replaced by the Saha equation (eq. (3-15)). For a given stage of ionization, the density can be determined by relating it to a density which is known or the total of all stages set equal to the known total density of the element. Relations of the type

$$\frac{N_{s+4}}{N_s} = \frac{N_{s+1}}{N_s} \frac{N_{s+2}}{N_{s+1}} \frac{N_{s+3}}{N_{s+2}} \frac{N_{s+4}}{N_{s+3}} \tag{6-31}$$

are employed. Each factor is calculated by equation (6-30) so that systematic errors made in the method of calculation of the rate constants $C_{1\infty}{}^s$ and $A_{\infty 1}{}^s$ are compounded. It is difficult to calculate $C_{1\infty}{}^s$ because of the complexities of the many electron ions, but it can be measured for many of the low-temperature ions that can be produced in the laboratory. However, the major source of calculation error introduced in the past has not been in $C_{1\infty}{}^s$ but in the concept underlying the calculation of $A_{\infty 1}{}^s$.

Up to this point, we have pictured recombination as occurring in one step; that is, an incoming electron combines with an ion and simultaneously one or more photons are emitted which drops the total energy of the ion to that of a bound level (fig. 6-22(a)). The kinetic energy of the incoming electron plus the ionization energy of the ion is radiated away by the photons. However, it is also possible for the incoming electron to be captured and raise the ion to a condition of excitation in which two electrons are in energy levels above the ground level (fig. 6-22(b)). The ion then undergoes transitions to the ground level in two or more radiative steps. This process is called "dielectronic recombination" because two electrons, the incoming one and an initially bound one, participate in the emission of radiation. The probability of occurrence of dielectronic recombination at high temperatures is at least a factor of 20 higher than for normal recombination. For He II above 3×10^5 K, the dielectronic recombination coefficient is approximately 100 times larger than the radiative recombination coefficient (fig. 6-23). The inclusion of dielectronic recombination results in an increase by a factor of 2 for the estimate of

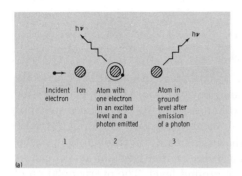

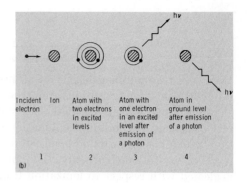

FIGURE 6–22.—Normal and dielectronic recombination. In normal recombination shown in (a), step 2 is often not present and the incident electron plus the ion undergo a direct transition to the ground level. This gives rise to the bound-free continuum. Dielectronic recombination shown in (b) is unlike normal recombination in that two electrons rather than one are involved in the change of the atomic configuration.

electron kinetic temperature required to produce the observed coronal ionization. As a result, this method of determining the coronal kinetic temperature is in agreement with other methods, including the measurement of the Doppler width of emission lines. Doppler widths yield an ion kinetic temperature of approximately 2×10^6 K which is an upper limit because of possible microturbulence. In equilibrium conditions, the process that balances dielectronic recombination is autoionization. An ion is excited to a configuration in which two electrons are in excited levels, their combined energy being greater than the ionization energy of the ion. The ion subsequently emits an electron and drops to its ground level. In the corona, however, autoionization is very unlikely because of the low densities of electrons and high-energy radiation. An ion in an excited level will drop back to its ground level by emission of radiation before it can be put into a doubly excited state by either electron impact or radiation absorption. In figure 6–24, the results of calculations for oxygen are shown. The stages of ionization having maximum number density

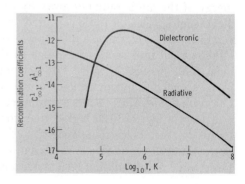

FIGURE 6–23.—Recombination coefficients of He II by radiative and dielectronic recombination. (From Burgess, 1964; copyright 1964, University of Chicago Press.)

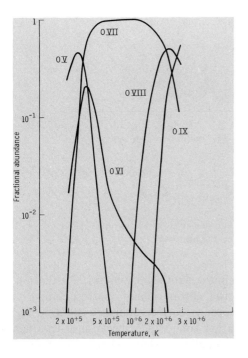

FIGURE 6–24.—Stages of ionization of oxygen. Note the broad peak of heliumlike O VII and the high-temperature tail of lithium-like O VI. (From Kozlovsky and Zirin, 1968; copyright 1968, D. Reidel.)

will be at $N_{s+1}/N_s = 1$. Because the coronal conditions are not uniform, however, the observed spread around this peak will be broader than shown in this figure.

The Emission Spectrum

As we move from the UV toward X-ray wavelengths, the general trend of the emission spectrum is that lines become more pronounced with respect to the continuum background, their intensities are more sensitive to the kinetic temperature of the gas, and the emission comes from higher layers in the solar atmosphere. Assuming the photospheric emission to be described by blackbody radiation at 5600 K, which varies as $\lambda^{-5} \exp\left(-hc/\lambda kT\right)$ at short wavelengths, the photospheric continuum will decrease by a factor of 10^{-80} in going from 1000 to 100 Å. Hence, the solar XUV and X-ray emission receives negligible contribution from the photosphere and the emission produced in the hot NLTE corona is dominant. The obvious advantage for the observer is that the corona can be seen in the XUV and X-ray wavelengths over a whole hemisphere at one time. In figure 6–25, the XUV solar image dispersed in wavelength is seen. The enhancement at various wavelengths, active region locations, and the limb are apparent. Another characteristic of the emission spectrum is that lines arising from the middle stages of ionization are very weak or absent. Stages of ionization with ionization energies between 100 and 200 eV are not easily observed. Because the energies of excitation of an ion are usually comparable to the ionization energy required to produce the ion,

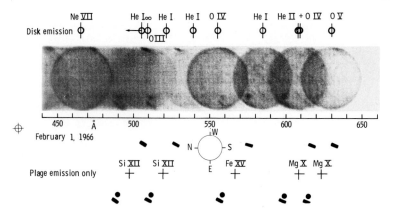

FIGURE 6–25.—A negative XUV photograph of the sun dispersed in wavelength. (Courtesy of R. Tousey, Naval Research Laboratory.)

a stage of ionization that is present should emit a significant amount of radiation. Low stages of ionization are observed in the chromosphere (corresponding to 5000 to 10 000 K) and high stages in the corona (corresponding to 10^6 K). The intermediate stages correspond to the transition zone which, because of the high temperature gradient, is very thin. Figure 6–26 indicates that a change in temperature of 5×10^5 K occurs in a distance of approximately 300 km. Thus, the volume

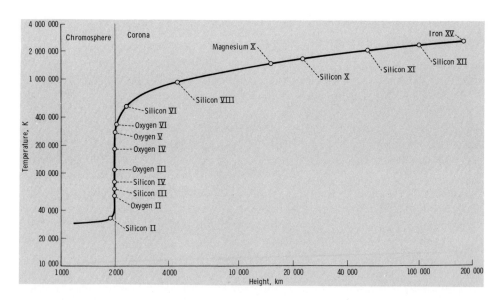

FIGURE 6–26.—Temperature distribution in the chromosphere-corona interface and location of various stages of ionization. (From Goldberg, 1969; copyright, W. H. Freeman.)

occupied by each intermediate stage of ionization is very small and only the strongest lines are observable.

Figures 6–27 to 6–32 show the UV, XUV, and X-ray solar spectra. Some of the lines and their sources are given in appendixes B and C. Some of the coronal emission lines in the visible spectrum, called the E corona, are included. The majority of this information is relatively new and only a portion of it has been analyzed and fully understood. It is to be expected that, as the capabilities of space observations are improved in the near future, much of this information will be substantially improved by instruments with higher spectral and spatial resolution.

Isoelectronic Series

In order to organize the complex data from the spectra and make significant generalizations about the emission characteristics, an attempt has been made to classify the lines according to their relations to solar activity, as illustrated by

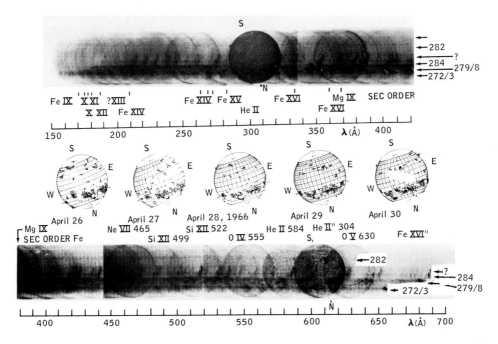

FIGURE 6–27.—The XUV spectroheliograms dispersed in wavelength, photographed on April 28, 1966. The negatives of the photographs have been spliced together and are reproduced here. The maps are from the Fraunhofer Institute and the McMath plage numbers have been added. Limb brightening for all images from 150 to 700 Å is evident. The strongest emissions evident include He II (304 Å) (which has a relatively strong second-order image at 608 Å), Mg IX (368 Å), and Ne VIII (465 Å). The ambiguity that exists in the intensity of disk features where images overlap can be reduced or eliminated by dispersing the image in a direction at right angles to the original. (Courtesy of R. Tousey, Naval Research Laboratory.)

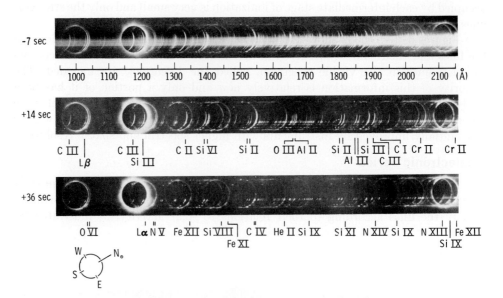

FIGURE 6–28.—The solar spectrum between 950 and 1050 Å. These spectra were made from a sounding rocket 7 sec before and 14 and 36 sec after totality during the March 7, 1970, eclipse. (Courtesy of E. Reeves, Harvard College Observatory.)

tabulation of lines in the visible spectrum in table 6–I. Lines often used to represent the three groups and to follow the level of coronal excitation or its kinetic temperature are the red line of Fe X at 6374 Å, the green line of Fe XIV at 5303 Å, and the yellow line of Ca XV at 5694 Å.

A more inclusive and useful approach is to make use of the organization which already exists in atomic structure itself. First, we investigate the spectrum emitted by a neutral atom which we can readily observe in the laboratory. By then increasing the charge on the nucleus but keeping the electron configuration unchanged, we predict, if we are not able to directly observe, the spectra of successively higher states of ionization of elements with successively higher atomic numbers. For example, H I, He II, Li III, etc., all have one bound electron; and He I, Li II, Be III, etc., all have two bound electrons. A series of ions with the same number of bound electrons but differing nuclear charge is called an isoelectronic series. When studied in this manner, the spectra of all members of such a series are found to be very similar in character but shifted to shorter wavelengths as the nuclear charge is increased. The spectra of ions with ionization energies less than a few hundred electron volts are observed in the laboratory and correlate well with the spectra of the neutral atoms at the beginning of their isoelectronic series. The properties of ions of higher ionization energies are extrapolated. Using this approach significantly reduces the additional conceptual complexity resulting from the occurrence of many stages of ionization of the many solar elements.

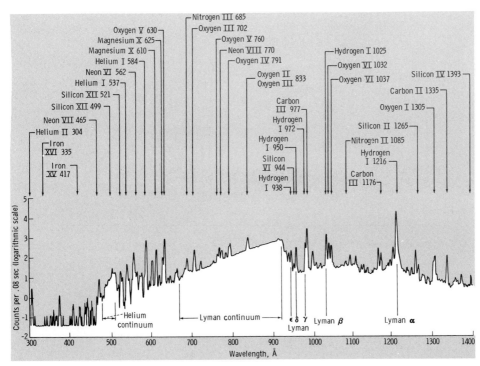

FIGURE 6–29.—An overview of the spectrum from 1400 to 300 Å recorded by OSO 4. Prominent features include the strongest emission line (Lyman α), the other members of the Lyman series leading up to the edge of the Lyman continuum, the helium continuum, and the general shift to higher stages of ionization at shorter wavelengths. (Courtesy of L. Goldberg and E. Reeves, Harvard College Observatory.)

The organization within a bound electron configuration and the nomenclature used to describe it are displayed in table 6–II. For the purposes of this discussion, the table extends up to only 30 bound electrons to include the elements abundant in the solar atmosphere. If the elements above 30 were included, the table would extend up to seven major divisions, K to Q, to describe the ground-state electron configurations.

The description of the one-electron atom in section 4.5 is now extended to investigate the underlying principles and associated nomenclature of the many electron atoms. The major divisions within a bound electron configuration are made by principal or total quantum number which corresponds to the successively higher energies and larger dimensions of the one-electron orbit. In table 6–II, the letters K, L, M, and N specify the total quantum number; $K \widehat{=} 1$, $L \widehat{=} 2$, $M \widehat{=} 3$, and $N \widehat{=} 4$. The lowercase letters s, p, d, and f specify the azimuthal angular momentum quantum numbers of the electron about the nucleus; $s \widehat{=} 0$, $p \widehat{=} 1$, $d \widehat{=} 2$, and $f \widehat{=} 3$. Thus, the ground state of H I has one $1s$ electron; that is, one electron in the

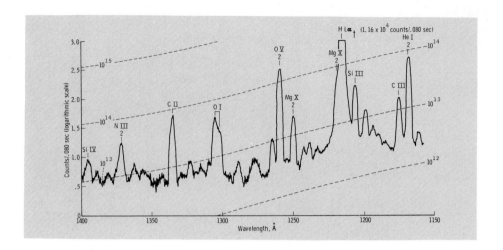

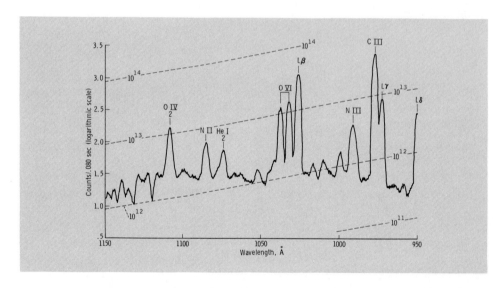

FIGURE 6–30.—A detailed view of the spectrum from 1400 to 300 Å recorded by OSO 4. This spectrum results from the average of approximately 20 spectral scans made at the center of the solar disk over a 1-arcmin-square field of view. These scans were made in regions remote from solar activity during October 1970. Not only does the relatively high spectral resolution permit the identification of many weak lines, but the small field of view allows the spectrum to be measured essentially at a point rather than over the whole disk. Thus, center-to-limb effects do not have to be approximated to interpret the data but can be explicitly measured. The dashed lines running across the figures give the photometric calibration averaged over a 1-arcmin-square region at disk center in units of photons/sec-cm²-sr. The line of maximum peak emission, Lyman α (1216 Å), had a corresponding peak intensity of 3×10^{15} photons/sec-cm²-sr. (Courtesy of L. Goldberg and E. Reeves, Harvard College Observatory.)

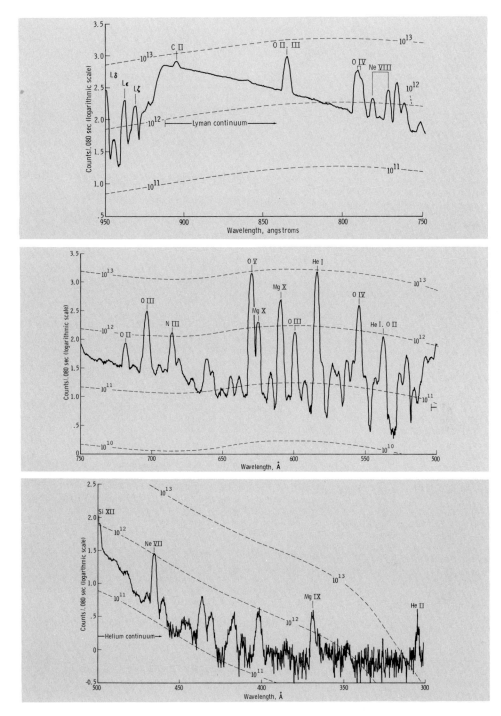

FIGURE 6–30 (concluded).—A detailed view of the spectrum from 1400 to 300 Å recorded by OSO 4.

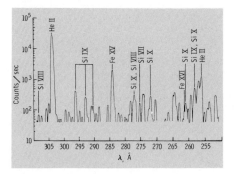
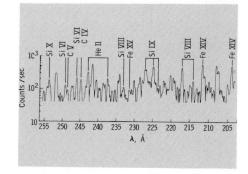
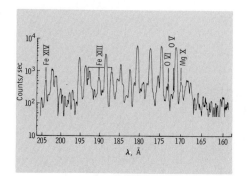
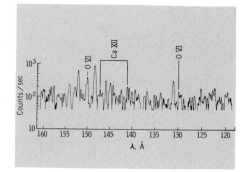
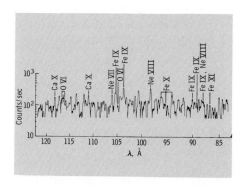
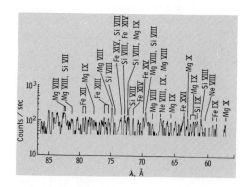

FIGURE 6–31.—The detailed spectrum from 310 to 55 Å obtained on May 2, 1963, 1007 hours MST, 230 km over White Sands, N. Mex. The spectrum is dominated by the ions of many electron atoms at high stages of ionization: Fe, Si, Mg, Ca, and O. Fe is seen to be a most prolific generator of lines. (Data from Hinteregger et al., 1964, and additional line identification by Zirin, 1966; copyright 1966, D. Reidel.)

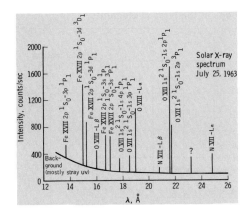

FIGURE 6–32.—The spectrum from 26 to 12 Å. The transitions giving rise to these lines are indicated. To be noted are the Lyman series lines of hydrogenlike N VII and O VIII. (From Blake et al., 1965; copyright 1965, University of Chicago Press.)

smallest orbit with zero angular momentum. The ground configuration of He I has two $1s$ electrons, the only difference between them being their electron spins, which are in opposite directions. In analogy to the one-electron atom, the net properties

TABLE 6–I.—Representative Line Grouping by Relation to Solar Activity

Group	Characteristic	Wavelength, Å	Ion	Ionization energy, eV
I	Prominent during solar minimum and in quiet regions	3533	V X	206
		3987	Fe XI	262
		6374 (red line)	Fe X	235
		7892	Fe XI	262
II	Prominent during solar maximum and in active regions	3388	Fe XIII	330
		3643	Ni XIII	350
		4232	Ni XII	321
		5303 (green line)	Fe XIV	355
		7060	Fe XV	390
		8024	Ni XV	430
		10 747	Fe XIII	330
		10 798	Fe XIII	330
III	Prominent in regions of very high excitation; e.g., during flares or above large spots	3327	Ca XII	592
		3601	Ni XVI	455
		4086	Ca XIII	655
		4351	Co XV	412
		4412	A XIV	687
		5446	Ca XV	820
		5694 (yellow line)	Ca XV	820
		6740	K XIV	717

TABLE 6–II.—Electron Configurations of the First 30 Elements

Element	z	K	L		M			N				Ground term
		$1s$	$2s$	$2p$	$3s$	$3p$	$3d$	$4s$	$4p$	$4d$	$4f$	
H	1	1										$^2S_{1/2}$
He	2	2										$^1S_0$
Li	3	2	1									$^2S_{1/2}$
Be	4	2	2									$^1S_0$
B	5	2	2	1								$^2P_{1/2}$
C	6	2	2	2								$^3P_0$
N	7	2	2	3								$^4S_{3/2}$
O	8	2	2	4								$^3P_2$
F	9	2	2	5								$^2P_{3/2}$
Ne	10	2	2	6								$^1S_0$
Na	11	2	2	6	1							$^2S_{1/2}$
Mg	12	2	2	6	2							$^1S_0$
Al	13	2	2	6	2	1						$^2P_{1/2}$
Si	14	2	2	6	2	2						$^3P_0$
P	15	2	2	6	2	3						$^4S_{3/2}$
S	16	2	2	6	2	4						$^3P_2$
Cl	17	2	2	6	2	5						$^2P_{2/3}$
A	18	2	2	6	2	6						$^1S_0$
K	19	2	2	6	2	6		1				$^2S_{1/2}$
Ca	20	2	2	6	2	6		2				$^1S_0$
Sc	21	2	2	6	2	6	1	2				$^2D_{3/2}$
Ti	22	2	2	6	2	6	2	2				$^3F_2$
V	23	2	2	6	2	6	3	2				$^4F_{3/2}$
Cr	24	2	2	6	2	6	5	1				$^7S_3$
Mn	25	2	2	6	2	6	5	2				$^6S_{3/2}$
Fe	26	2	2	6	2	6	6	2				$^5D_4$
Co	27	2	2	6	2	6	7	2				$^4F_{9/2}$
Ni	28	2	2	6	2	6	8	2				$^3F_4$
Cu	29	2	2	6	2	6	10	1				$^2S_{1/2}$
Zn	30	2	2	6	2	6	10	2				$^1S_0$

of an electron configuration can be specified by the total orbital angular momentum L rather than l, the total electron spin S rather than s, and the total angular momentum J, which is determined by the way L and S combine. The total properties are summarized by the expression $^{(2S+1)}L_J$. (See the last column of table 6–II.) As was the case with the orbital angular momentum of an individual electron l, the total angular momentum of an atom is also denoted by letters $S \hat{=} 0$, $P \hat{=} 1$, $D \hat{=} 2$, and $F \hat{=} 3$. This choice of letters does not immediately appear to be systematic but it evolved from the observations of the different character of series of atomic lines. Some series were observed to be sharp (S series), some were the strong or principal series of an element (P series), some were diffuse (D series), and some fundamental

(*F* series). Later it was found that these series corresponded to a division by total angular momentum of the atom, but the terminology remained. The ground term of Fe, $^5D_4$, therefore corresponds to $L \widehat{=} 2$, $S \widehat{=} 2$, and $J \widehat{=} 4$. The significance of $2S+1$, rather than just S, is that it equals the number of different configurations of the electron spin which lead to the same value of S and J. This is what we previously called multiplicity or number of different terms within a configuration (states within a state). However, if $L < S$, then $2L+1$ is actually the correct value of the multiplicity of the electron configuration.

The systematic order in which the electronic states are filled with an increasing number of electrons is displayed in table 6–II and can be explained by two principles. First, the Pauli exclusion principle, applied to the atom, states that no two electrons can be in the same electronic state; or each electron must differ from all other electrons in at least one of the values of n, l, m_l, and m_s, where m_l and m_s are the projection of l and s on an arbitrarily chosen axis. For the one-electron atom, each value of n corresponded to $2n^2$ different values of l, m_l, and m_s (sec. 4.5). This is still applicable to determining the number of available electronic states for the many-electron atom. The second principle is that states of lowest energy are filled first. Hence, the K shell is filled first by two electrons of opposite spin and we arrive at the configuration of helium. Next, the L shell is filled by eight electrons and we arrive at neon. The next subshell to be filled is only part of the M shell, $3s+3p$, to obtain argon (table 6–III). The first 18 electrons up to argon are added as we would expect; states of successively higher energy are filled in order. However, the next electron becomes a $4s$ rather than a $3d$ electron. This occurs because a $4s$ electron, which has zero orbital angular momentum, penetrates the inner electronic shells that normally shield the outer electron from the high field of the nucleus. Therefore, a $4s$ electron has a lower energy and is more tightly bound than a $3d$ electron.

The objective of this discussion is to illustrate the similarity between ions having the same number of bound electrons but differing in nuclear charge. The similarity in ionization energies is illustrated in figure 6–33. It is seen that the plots of ionization energy versus the number of bound electrons are very similar for each increase in stage of ionization, but the energies are shifted to higher values. Also

TABLE 6–III.—Inert Gases

Element	Total number of electrons	Number of electrons per subshell	Subshell filled
He_____	2	2	$1s$
Ne_____	10	8	$2s+2p$
A_____	18	8	$3s+3p$
Kr_____	36	18	$3s+3p+4p$

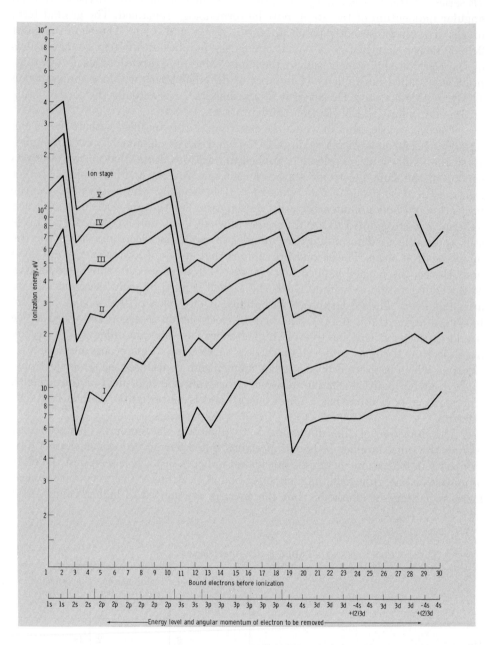

FIGURE 6–33.—Similarities in ionization energies for families of equal stages of ionization. As the nuclear charge is increased (holding the number of bound electrons constant and increasing the stage of ionization), the ionization energies vary in an identical manner but at higher levels.

evident are the relatively high values of the inert-gas-like electron configurations (completely closed subshells, some of which are listed in table III) and the low values of the alkali metallike configurations (one electron outside a completely closed subshell). Electrons all having the same angular momentum (the six $3p$ electrons of argon, for example) all experience the same strong nuclear field because they are all approximately the same distance from the nucleus. The corresponding ionization energy is therefore high. However, a single electron outside a closed shell, like the $4s$ electron of potassium, is very effectively shielded from the nuclear field by all the inner electrons and therefore is easily removed. Some of the ions that have been observed to contribute to the solar spectrum are summarized in figure 6–34. This list is not complete and is used for illustrative purposes only.

The electronic transitions of ions with the same number of bound electrons but different nuclear charges are also similar. The simplest series to explore includes

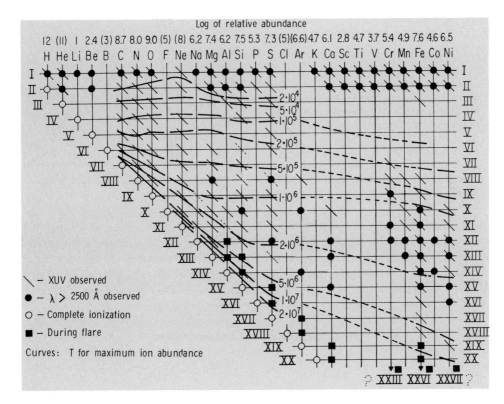

Figure 6–34.—Summary of atoms and ions that have been observed in solar spectra. Isoelectronic sequences run at 45° diagonals from the upper left to the lower right. Many of the sequences are well filled out with gaps occurring only at elements of low relative abundance. Sequences with rarely observed members include the inert gas neonlike sequence and the complex spectra of the fluorinelike sequence. (Courtesy of R. Tousey, Naval Research Laboratory.)

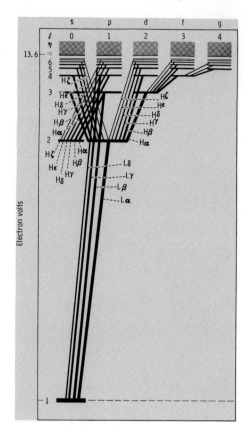

FIGURE 6–35.—Energy level diagram for hydrogen. Quantum mechanics states that an allowed transition between states is one in which l can change by only ± 1. Thus, the Lyman series ($L\alpha$, $L\beta$, $\cdots$) arises only from transition of $P(l=1)$ to $S(l=0)$. The Balmer series (Hα, Hβ, $\cdots$) has three possibilities: P to S, S to P, and D to P.

the hydrogenlike or one-electron ions. The strongest emission line of hydrogen is the Lyman-α line, $L\alpha$ 1216 Å, which arises when a $2p$ electron drops to the ground $1s$ level (fig. 6–35). Because the energy levels of one-electron atoms vary as z^2, the $L\alpha$ lines for other hydrogenlike ions are located at wavelengths of $1216/z^2$ Å. Also, $L\beta$ lines are located at $1026/z^2$ Å and Balmer-α (Hα) lines are at $6563/z^2$ Å.

TABLE 6–IV.—Observed $L\alpha$ and $L\beta$ Lines

F	Ion	$L\alpha$ $(1s-2p)$ $1215.7/z^2$, Å	$L\beta$ $(1s-3p)$ $1025.7/z^2$, Å
1	H I	1215.7	1025.7
2	He II	303.9	256.3
6	C VI	33.8	28.5
7	N VII	24.8	20.9
8	O VIII	19.0	16.0

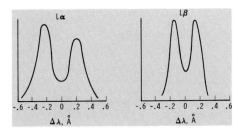

Figure 6–36.—Lyman-α and Lyman-β line profiles integrated over the full solar disk on August 22, 1962. (Courtesy of R. Tousey, Naval Research Laboratory.)

The $L\alpha$ and $L\beta$ series of lines are illustrated in table 6–IV where only a few of total number of observed lines are included. The observed line profiles of hydrogen $L\alpha$ and $L\beta$ integrated over the whole sun are shown in figure 6–36. These lines are produced high in the chromosphere, and the central absorption evident in the profiles results from the absorption of cooler overlying spicules. In this case, the Doppler width of the absorbing gas is appreciably smaller than that of the emitting gas.

The series of two-electron heliumlike ions is not as easily related to the neutral atom by simple relations involving z because the second electron introduces quantum-mechanical considerations that were not previously important. However, similar transitions can be identified and are illustrated in table 6–V. A general characteristic of the solar spectrum is that the inert-gas-like ions, including the heliumlike ions, are barely observable even though they are very abundant. Their relatively high abundance results from their high ionization energy; that is, their stability against further ionization. However, they also require high energies for excitation; hence, they are not as readily observed. The more abundant inert-gas-like ions and the members of some of the other significant isoelectronic series of the solar atmosphere are listed in table 6–VI.

The three-electron lithiumlike ions have the opposite character of the helium-like ions. The one electron outside the closed K shell requires relatively little energy for excitation or ionization. Although this means that the lithiumlike ions are not abundant, what ions do exist are readily observable. Because the elements Li, Be,

TABLE 6–V.—Observed Lines of Heliumlike Ions

Transition	Ion	Wavelength, Å
$1s^2$–$1s2p$	He I	584.4
	O VII	21.7/21.6
$1s^2$–$1s3p$	He I	537.1
	O VII	18.6
$1s^2$–$1s4p$	He I	522.2
	N VI	23.2
	O VII	17.7

TABLE 6–VI.—Isoelectronic Series Observed in the Solar Atmosphere

Isoelectronic ions	Characteristics
One emission electron, easily excited and ionized, observable	
Hydrogenlike: H I, He II, C VI, N VII, Ne X, Mg XII, Si XIV	Relatively simple spectra of one-electron atom, $\lambda \sim z^{-2}$, strong resonance lines
Lithiumlike: Li I, C IV, N V, O VI, Ne VIII, Mg X, Si XII	One $2s$ electron—resonance lines from $2s$–$2p$ transition give strong doublet
Sodiumlike: Na I, Mg II, Si IV_ _ _ _ _ _ _ _ _ _ _ _ _ _	One $3s$ electron—resonance lines from $3s$–$3p$ transition give strong doublet
Potassiumlike: K I, Ca II_ _ _ _ _ _ _ _ _ _ _ _ _ _ _ _ _ _	One $4s$ electron—resonance lines from $4s$–$4p$ transition give strong doublet
Closed shell, stable ions, not easily observed	
Heliumlike: He I, C V, N VI, O VII, Ne IX, Mg XI, Si XIII	Closed K shell
Neonlike: Ne I, Na II, Mg III_ _ _ _ _ _ _ _ _ _ _ _ _ _	Closed L shell
Argonlike: A I, K II, Co III_ _ _ _ _ _ _ _ _ _ _ _ _ _ _	Closed $3s$–$3p$ subshell—next state filled is $4s$ (potassium) rather than $3d$

and B are not abundant, they are rarely observed and C IV, N V, and O VI are the first lithiumlike ions that produce significant emission. It is seen in figure 6–24 that there is an appreciable amount of O VI present over a wide range of temperatures. The long high-temperature tail in the distribution results because the dielectronic recombination of heliumlike O VII becomes very effective at high temperatures where sufficiently energetic electrons are available to produce excited states of O VII at 559 eV (Kozlovsky and Zirin, 1968). This leads us to believe that a long high-temperature tail should exist in the distribution of all alkali metallike ions. As expected, the strongest emission lines of the lithiumlike ions result from a transition from the ion's first excited level to its ground level. This transition $2s$–$2p$ is shown in figure 6–37, where the similarity to the energy-level diagram for hydrogen (fig. 6–35) is apparent. Unlike in the hydrogen case, however, the electron outside the closed K shell, called the optical or radiating electron, can penetrate the inner electron shell and experience a relatively high binding force. Hence, the $2p$ electronic configuration is appreciably higher in energy than the $2s$ configuration and the electronic transition $2s$–$2p$ yields the strongest line in the spectrum of all lithiumlike ions. In table 6–VII, where the wavelengths for these resonance lines are given, it is seen that each multiplet is composed of two lines and the splitting between them increases with increasing nuclear charge. The discussion of equation (4–81) pointed out that the amount of energy stored by magnetic moment in a magnetic field is a function of their relative orientation.

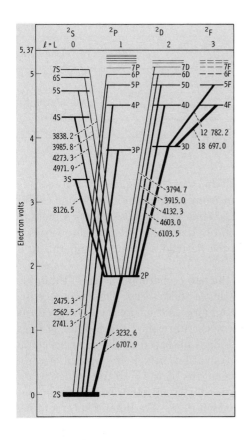

FIGURE 6–37.—Energy level diagram for lithium. Note the appreciable energy difference between configurations with the same principal quantum number: 2S–2P, 3S–3P, 4S–4P, etc.

The splitting of the $2p$ electronic term results from the difference in energy between the two possible orientations of the electron spin magnetic moment with respect to the magnetic field created by the orbital electron motion; that is, the two possible values of J. It has been found that there is a strong correlation between the XUV

TABLE 6–VII.—Observed Resonance Lines $(2s–2p)$ of Lithiumlike Ions

Ion	Wavelength, Å
Li I	6708.0/6707.8
C IV	$\approx 1548/\approx 1545$
N V	1242.8/1238.8
O VI	1037.6/1031.9
Ne VIII	780.3/770.4
Mg X	625.3/609.8
Si XII	521.1/499.4

TABLE 6–VIII.—Observed Resonance Lines ($3s$–$3p$) of Sodiumlike Ions

Ion	Wavelength, Å
Na I	5895.9/5890.0
Mg II	2802.7/2795.3
Fe XVI	360.8/335.3

emission of coronal ions and the intensity of the scattered light of the K corona. In particular, regions of high or low emission from lithiumlike ions do not exhibit appreciable temperature differences. Thus, the emission of those ions is a measure of N_e^2 along the line of sight (Withbroe, 1971). Using the relative intensities of Si XII (499 Å) and Mg X (625 Å), Withbroe derived a coronal temperature of 1.8×10^6 K.

The other alkali metallike ions exhibit the same character as the lithiumlike ions. Table 6–VI lists some of the characteristics of these series. The resonance line transition of Na I, where the optical electron undergoes the transition $3s$–$3p$, forms the very strong yellow doublet in the visible spectrum called the sodium D lines. These and other strong sodiumlike resonance lines observed in the solar spectrum are given in table 6–VIII. In the resonance transition of K I, the optical electron undergoes the transition $4s$–$4p$ and the wavelengths of the resulting emission are 7699.0 and 7644.9 Å. The corresponding lines for Ca II are the Ca H (3968 Å) and the Ca K (3934 Å) lines, the importance of which in the Fraunhofer spectrum has previously been discussed (figs. 4–32 and 4–33).

A study of the tables in appendixes B and C indicates that most of the emission comes from ions which have one to three emission electrons outside closed subshells and that the lines can be related in the same isoelectronic manner that we have just described. Because the degree of ionization and resulting emission from each element are sensitive to the ambient electron kinetic temperature and, to a lesser degree, the electron density, much can be learned about both quiet- and active-sun structure in the corona by future space observations of the type shown in figures 6–19 and 6–25 but with higher spectral and spatial resolution.

Continuum Emission

An obvious feature of the solar spectrum (fig. 6–29) that we have not discussed is the Lyman continuum which extends from 912 Å to approximately 600 or 700 Å. It is produced when an electron and a proton combine to form H I, referred to previously as bound-free emission. An electron with zero kinetic energy combining to form H I in the ground level results in a proton of energy 13.59 eV, which is equivalent to 912 Å. As the kinetic energy of the recombining electron is increased from zero, the emitted photon energy increases, the probability of recombination decreases, and a spectrum of the type shown in figure 6–29 is produced. When this emission is compared to the Planck curve (eq. (4–11)), it is found that the slope corresponds to a temperature between 8000 to 9000 K, but that the absolute intensity corresponds to a temperature of approximately 6500 K. A possible explanation is the overpopulation of the hydrogen ground level, relative to the excited and ionized levels, by a factor of 200 (Noyes and Kalkofen, 1970). This tends to increase the absorption relative to the emission. It is to be expected that each ion would have a continuum analogous to the hydrogen Lyman continuum but that because of their relatively low abundances, very few could be observed. The He I continuum is seen in figure 6–29 extending to shorter wavelengths from 505 Å (24.5 eV).

At shorter wavelengths, less than approximately 200 Å, free-free or thermal bremsstrahlung becomes of importance and is a significant mode of heat loss from the corona. The power emitted by thermal bremsstrahlung per unit volume, wavelength interval, and solid angle is

$$ j_\lambda = 1.7 \times 10^{-23} \left(\frac{10^6}{T_e} \right)^{1/2} \left(\frac{GF}{\lambda^2} \right) N_e N_i \, e^{-h^c / \lambda k T_e} \qquad \text{ergs/cm}^3\text{-sec-Å-sr} \qquad (6\text{–}32) $$

where N_e and N_i are in cm^{-3}, T_e in K, λ in Å, and GF is the Gaunt factor which is normally close to unity. Thus, the emission is proportional to exp $(-hc/\lambda k T_e)/\lambda^2$ which has a maximum at $\lambda = hc/2kT_e$ or 72 Å for 10^6 K. Figures 6–38 and 6–39 show the emission from the solar corona calculated by Elwert (1961). It is seen that a quiet corona of 10^6 K has a substantial total continuum emission in the 20- to 200-Å range. Also, in the very hot regions of 10^8 K of a flare, emission of the Lyman-α line of hydrogenlike Fe XXVI at 1.8 Å should be observable.

6.4 THE RADIO CORONA

The radio corona is in many ways similar to the X-ray corona at the other end of the spectrum. Both contain only a relatively small amount of the total emitted energy (fig. 6–40) but an appreciable amount of information. Also, bremsstrahlung radiation, which is a major contributor in the X-ray range, is also a major contributor in the radio spectrum. The spectrum between these two extremes is dominated by other processes. A third similarity is that the corona can be observed directly against the disk of the sun in both X-ray and radio wavelengths because the photosphere and low chromosphere do not emit a significant background in either wavelength range. Even if significant background radiation were emitted in the radio range, it would most likely not be observed because the corona is opaque to most radio waves emanating from below. Lastly, it is generally true that as we observe in the XUV and X-ray ranges at wavelengths progressively farther from the visible range, we see to higher layers. Correspondingly, as we observe in the radio range at longer wavelengths, we also see to higher layers.

Radio observations also differ from XUV and X-ray observations in several ways. At radio wavelengths, the index of refraction can be much less than unity

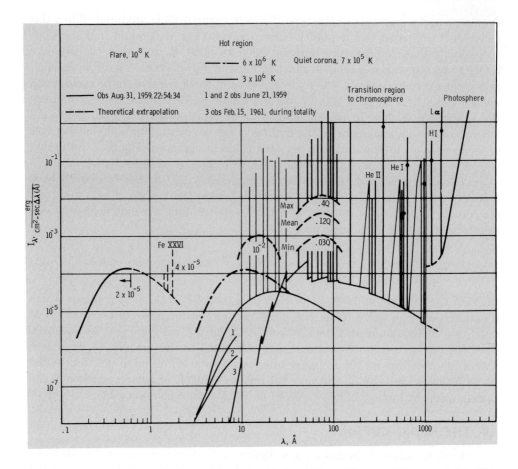

FIGURE 6–38.—Observed and calculated solar emission. (From Elwert, 1961; copyright 1961, American Geophysical Union.)

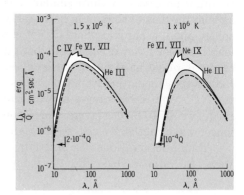

FIGURE 6–39.—Coronal continuum emission. (From Elwert, 1961; copyright 1961, American Geophysical Union.)

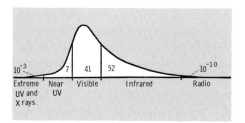

FigURE 6–40.—Energy distribution within the solar spectrum. The numbers refer to the percent of the total solar emission in that range. The number for the energy in the radio spectrum is for the band between 1 cm and 20 meters. (From Smith, 1967; by permission of Van Nostrand Reinhold Co.)

or can be imaginary. Thus, radio waves can undergo appreciable bending or refraction in the corona or not propagate at all. The second difference (and an important advantage to us) is that a large window exists in our atmosphere for wavelengths between approximately 1 cm and 10 meters. As in the visible spectrum, we can observe the sun directly from earth at these wavelengths. The third difference, the difficulty of achieving high spatial resolution, limits our ability to exploit this advantage. The smallest angle difference that can be resolved in an observation is limited by diffraction and is approximately λ/D radians, where D is the diameter of the instrument aperture. To resolve only the sun itself, an apparent angle of about 0.01 radian, an aperture of approximately 100λ is required; this is very easily accomplished at visible or shorter wavelengths. However, at a wavelength of 1 meter, for example, the instrument aperture must be 100 meters in diameter. To resolve individual solar features would require much larger apertures. Despite the development of several ingenious observing techniques, this restriction in resolution severely limits our interpretation of solar radio emissions.

Radio-Wave Emission

To describe the emission of solar radio waves, the relation for thermal bremsstrahlung (eq. (6–32)) is again applicable and can be simplified because $\exp(-hc/\lambda kT) \simeq 1$. When the gas is optically thick, the emitted radiation is that of a blackbody which in this wavelength range can be approximated by the Rayleigh-Jeans formula (sec. 4.1)

$$B_\lambda(T_e) \simeq \frac{2ckT_e}{\lambda^4} \qquad (4\text{–}16)$$

or

$$B_\nu(T_e) \simeq \frac{2kT_e}{\lambda^2} \qquad (6\text{–}33)$$

It has become customary to use equation (4–16) and define a brightness temperature of the emission T_b, even though the emission source may not be optically thick. That is

$$I_\lambda \equiv B_\lambda(T_b) \qquad (6\text{–}34)$$

or

$$T_b \equiv \frac{\lambda^4}{2ck} I_\lambda \qquad (6\text{–}35)$$

where T_b can be less but not greater than T_e.

A critical frequency f_p exists at radio wavelengths for the range of electron densities found in the corona. When the frequency of an electromagnetic wave is close to f_p, the wave's propagation will be appreciably altered. In the corona, f_p is the plasma frequency at which the electrons can collectively oscillate; that is, it is a natural frequency of the plasma. A simple one-dimensional derivation of the electron equation of motion and of f_p follows which uses figure 6–41. The element of electron gas is initially of length Δx, but a movement of the gas in the $+X$ direction of amount $\eta(x, t)$ changes the length to $(1+\partial\eta/\partial x)\,\Delta x$. The corresponding change in the electron density is $-N_e\,\partial\eta/\partial x$. The electrons can rapidly oscillate but, because of their relatively large mass, the ions cannot. Hence, a net electric charge is produced by the electron motion and is equal to $+eN_e\,\partial\eta/\partial x$. This charge, in turn, produces an electric field that attempts to reverse the electron motion and restore electrical neutrality. Using Gauss' law

$$\frac{\partial(\epsilon_0 E)}{\partial x} = +eN_e\frac{\partial\eta}{\partial x} \tag{6–36}$$

which is easily integrated to

$$E = +\frac{eN_e}{\epsilon_0}\eta \tag{6–37}$$

where E is the electric field and ϵ_0 is the permittivity of free space. A steady-state electric field $(\eta=0)$ has been excluded. The force on an electron, $-eE$, is equal to its mass times acceleration.

$$m_e\frac{\partial^2\eta}{\partial t^2} + \frac{e^2 N_e}{\epsilon_0}\eta = 0 \tag{6–38}$$

Thus, the natural frequency of oscillation is

$$f_p = \frac{1}{2\pi}\left(\frac{e^2 N_e}{\epsilon_0 m_e}\right)^{1/2} \tag{6–39}$$

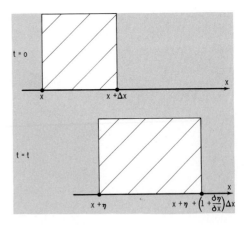

FIGURE 6–41.—One-dimensional variation of the volume of an element of electron gas with time and element displacement.

Numerically,

$$f_p = 9.0 N_e^{1/2} \quad \text{kHz} \tag{6-40}$$

and the corresponding wavelength

$$\lambda_p = \tfrac{1}{3} \times 10^7 \, N_e^{-1/2} \quad \text{cm} \tag{6-41}$$

where N_e is in cm^{-3} and it has been assumed that the velocity of propagation is that of light in a vacuum. In figure 6–13 the plasma frequency and corresponding wavelength are shown as a function of height in the corona. It is seen that the radio window in the earth's atmosphere (approximately 1 cm to 10 meters) corresponds to plasma frequencies in the chromosphere and inner and intermediate corona. Waves of frequency greater than f_p (light, for example) can propagate outward through the corona. However, waves of frequency less than f_p cannot propagate because the electron gas can respond rapidly to set up a space charge which opposes and nulls the electric field of the wave.

Two other frequencies affect wave propagation to a lesser degree and in a more complex manner. The collision frequency of the electrons determines the rate of thermal bremsstrahlung emission. It also determines the rate at which coherent electron motions produced by a propagating wave are randomized; that is, the rate at which the wave energy is absorbed and transformed into heat. The second frequency, called the gyrofrequency f_m, is the frequency at which an electron spirals around magnetic-field lines. The centripetal acceleration experienced by the electron causes the emission of cyclotron radiation. The gyrofrequency is derived by equating the centrifugal force of a spiraling electron $m_e \omega_e V$ to the centripetal force eVB where V is the component of velocity perpendicular to the magnetic field and ω_e is the rate of angular rotation about the field lines. Thus, the gyrofrequency is

$$f_m = \frac{1}{2\pi} \frac{eB}{m_e}$$

$$f_m = 2.8B \quad \text{MHz} \tag{6-42}$$

where B is in gauss. Normally, f_m is much less than both f_p and f and its effect on the index of refraction is small, except over strong sunspots.

Ray Trajectory

The trajectory of a radio wave is determined by the manner in which the electron gas alters the phase velocity of the wave. This velocity is given by

$$\frac{V}{c} = \left[1 - \left(\frac{f_p}{f} \right)^2 \right]^{-1/2} \tag{6-43}$$

and the index of refraction by

$$\mu \equiv \frac{c}{V}$$

$$\mu = \left[1 - \left(\frac{f_p}{f} \right)^2 \right]^{1/2} \tag{6-44}$$

For $f < f_p$, the velocity and index of refraction is imaginary and propagation cannot occur; for $f > f_p$, the velocity increases with increasing f_p, which corresponds to increasing N_e. Thus, the radio waves which can propagate in the corona are always bent away from the solar surface. Figure 6–42 shows the trajectories along which the parallel rays that we observe originate. The distance of a ray's closest approach to the sun is at sun center and equals the height at which $f = f_p$. Hence, unlike the other wavelength ranges considered, radio waves do not completely originate along our line of sight. Instead, we must take into account the emission and absorption along each point of a curved trajectory. Analogous to the transfer of radiation discussed in section 4.1 (specifically, eq. (4–7)), the governing relation is

$$\mu^2 d\,\frac{I_\lambda}{\mu^2} = (j_\lambda - \kappa_\lambda I_\lambda)\rho\,ds \qquad (6\text{–}45)$$

where κ_λ is related to j_λ by the equilibrium relation

$$\frac{j_\lambda}{\kappa_\lambda} = \mu^2 B_\lambda(T_e) \qquad (6\text{–}46)$$

This relation is valid, even though TE does not exist, because the emission and absorption of thermal bremsstrahlung depends only on the properties of the electron gas, which does have an equilibrium velocity distribution characterized by the kinetic temperature T_e. Written in terms of the optical depth along the ray trajectory, the transfer equation becomes

$$\mu^2\,\frac{d\,(I_\lambda/\mu^2)}{d\tau_\lambda} = -\left(\frac{j_\lambda}{\kappa_\lambda} - I_\lambda\right) \qquad (6\text{–}47)$$

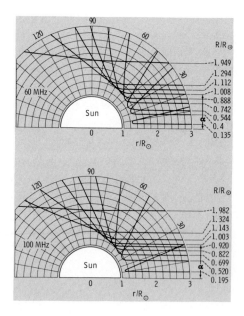

FIGURE 6–42.—Trajectories of parallel radio waves observed from the sun. (From Kundu, 1965; copyright 1965, John Wiley & Sons.)

where

$$\tau_\lambda = \int_s^\infty \rho \kappa_\lambda \, ds \qquad (6\text{--}48)$$

The limit of integration runs along a wave's trajectory from the furthermost source at s to the observer at ∞. These relations reduce to those previously derived in the case of $\mu = 1$. For the situation depicted in figure 6–42, where a wave of zero intensity originates at ∞ and ends up at the observer $(\tau = 0, \mu = 1)$, the solution to equation (6–47) is

$$I_\lambda = \int_0^{\tau_\lambda} B_\lambda (T_e) e^{-\tau_\lambda'} \, d\tau_\lambda' \qquad (6\text{--}49)$$

where equation (6–46) has been used. Hence, the emergent radiation is the sum of each contribution along the trajectory (B_λ) times the fraction which escapes $(\exp(-\tau_\lambda'))$. Because $B_\lambda(T_e)$ is proportional to T_e (eq. (4–16)), the brightness temperature of the emergent radiation is

$$T_b(\lambda) = \int_0^{\tau_\lambda} T_e(\tau_\lambda') e^{-\tau_\lambda'} \, d\tau_\lambda' \qquad (6\text{--}50)$$

If the region from which the major contribution is made is isothermal, then

$$T_b(\lambda) = (1 - e^{-\tau_\lambda}) T_e \qquad (6\text{--}51)$$

The fraction $(1 - e^{-\tau_\lambda})$ is the ratio of the emergent radiation to the blackbody value and is plotted in figure 6–43 for the ray trajectory at solar center. It is seen that in moving from 200 MHz (1.5 meters) to 100 MHz (3.0 meters), the optical depth is no longer large, and the radiation therefore becomes less than the blackbody value.

Disk Temperature

The brightness temperature of the whole sun averaged over the solar disk T_d is a useful and easily made observation

$$T_d = 2 \int_0^\infty T_b(\xi) \xi \, d\xi \qquad (6\text{--}52)$$

where $\xi = R/R_\odot$. In the plot of $T_d(\lambda)$ in figure 6–44(b), T_d is observed to increase with λ to a maximum of 2×10^6 K at 2 meters. The emission at 0.1 to 2 meters (150 MHz) originates in optically thick regions, and T_d therefore increases with T_e as we shift to higher atmospheric layers. For $\lambda > 2$ meters, the source of emission becomes optically thin (fig. 6–43) and T_d becomes less than T_e. The variation of T_d with sunspot cycle is shown in figure 6–45. The enhancement at maximum appears to be about a factor of 2, between 0.03 and 3 meters of wavelength. The start of a divergence between maximum and minimum temperatures is indicated for wavelengths above 3 meters. The correlation between T_d and solar activity, expressed by the projected sunspot area, is shown in figure 6–46 for a wavelength

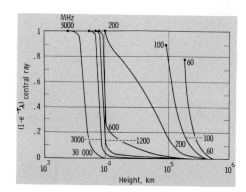

FIGURE 6-43.—Ratio of emergent radiation
to the blackbody value for the central ray.
(From Pawsey and Smerd, 1953; copyright 1953, University of Chicago Press.)

of 50 cm. A quiet-sun value of T_d is obtained by extrapolating back to zero sunspot
area. This procedure yields reasonable values except for wavelengths on the order
of 1 meter and greater where the total active-region emission becomes much greater
than the quiet-sun emission. Also, values obtained in this manner are upper limits
since some plage can exist on the sun without sunspots being evident. A second way
to obtain a value for the quiet-sun disk temperature is by superimposing one-
dimensional brightness temperature scans as shown in figure 6-47. The lower
envelope is equated to the quiet-sun value.

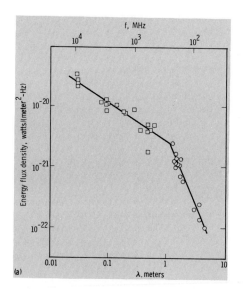

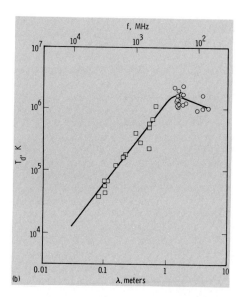

FIGURE 6-44.—Energy flux and solar brightness temperature as functions of wavelength. (a)
    Solar energy flux per frequency interval as a function of wavelength for the whole sun. (b)
    Brightness temperature of the whole sun averaged over the solar disk (disk temperature)
    as a function of wavelength. (From Kundu, 1965; copyright 1965, John Wiley & Sons.)

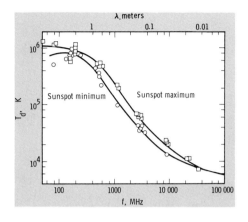

FIGURE 6–45.—Variation of disk temperature with frequency at sunspot minimum and maximum. (From Kundu, 1965; copyright 1965, John Wiley & Sons.)

Spatially Resolved Observations

A significantly greater amount of information is obtained from observations which resolve the solar disk. The brightness isophotes observed at 21 cm with a resolution of 4 arcmin are shown in figure 6–48(a). The variation of T_b with R and the angle from the pole of the sun are shown in figure 6–48(b). At the equator, a significant limb brightening is apparent, and at the pole, a transition to limb darkening occurs because of the absence of solar activity. Unlike the K corona, the radio corona appears more elliptical at solar maximum than at minimum. This results because the radio corona is responsive to the electron temperature and the K corona is not.

The calculated variation of $T_b(R)$ at several wavelengths is shown in figure 6–49, which is now used to summarize the general characteristics of solar radio emission. First, as the wavelength increases toward approximately 2 meters, the brightness temperature increases and limb brightening becomes pronounced.

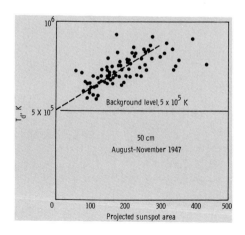

FIGURE 6–46.—Disk temperature as a function of sunspot area. By extrapolating back to zero sunspot area, the quiet-sun background can be determined. It is seen in the above figure that the range of values between 4 to 6×10^5 K is as accurate as the extrapolation can be made. (From Kundu, 1965; copyright 1965, John Wiley & Sons.)

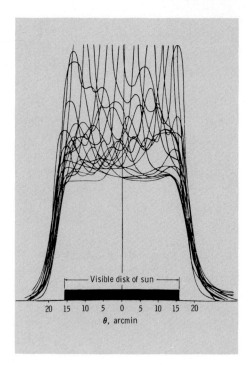

Visible disk of sun

20   15   10   5   0   5   10   15   20
θ, arcmin

FIGURE 6–47.—Brightness temperature scans.
(From Kundu, 1965; copyright 1965, John
Wiley & Sons.)

Because the source is both optically thick and located higher in the atmosphere at longer wavelengths, the increase in brightness temperature and limb brightening are results of the positive temperature gradient. More recent and higher resolution observations of the quiet sun at radio wavelengths less than 75 cm show either no limb brightening or significantly less than that illustrated in figure 6–49 (Simon and Zirin, 1969). This is attributed to the nonhomogeneities of the solar atmosphere whose characteristic dimensions are at least the local atmospheric scale height and which appear at sufficiently high spatial resolution. The atmosphere appears rough and approximately the same from almost all angles, except close to the limb where a "spike" of brightening is still observed.

Second, as the wavelength increases beyond approximately 2 meters, the brightness temperature decreases and a transition from limb brightening to limb darkening occurs. The decrease in brightness temperature results because the optical depth rapidly decreases to values much less than unity. Thus, even though the temperature increases with height in the atmosphere, the net result is a decrease in total emission (eq. (6–50)). The transition to limb darkening is at first surprising since the transition to an optically thin source in the X-ray range (decreasing wavelength) did not cause a shift from limb brightening to limb darkening. The difference here is that the trajectories of the bent rays (fig. 6–42) are such that the optical depth is less along rays at the limb than at sun center, opposite to the X-ray case.

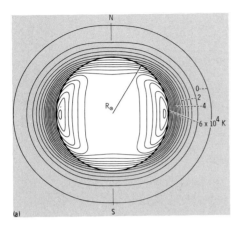
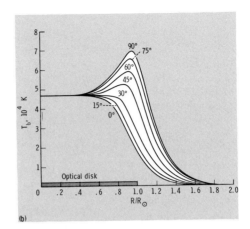

FIGURE 6–48.—Solar radio brightness at 21 cm. (*a*) Brightness temperature isophotes for 21-cm radiation. The central temperature is 4.7×10^4 K. The limb darkening at the poles contrasts with the limb brightening at the equator which is due to solar activity. (*b*) One-dimensional scans of brightness temperature at 21 cm for several angles from the polar direction. (From Kundu, 1965; copyright 1965, John Wiley & Sons.)

Third, as the wavelength increases, the sun becomes larger and less well defined regardless of the optical thickness of the source. The variation of T_d with λ that results from this calculated T_b is shown in figure 6–50.

Radio observations of the corona are not limited to emissions from the sun itself. Occultation of astronomical radio sources by the corona have helped to determine the properties of the outer corona. Because the index of refraction depends upon the electron density (eqs. (6–39) and (6–44)), the density irregularities in the corona randomly refract or scatter the radio waves from distant sources. This refraction, which appears as a change with time of the apparent location of the source, is illustrated in figure 6–51. Scattering by the outer corona has been detected as far out as $119R_\odot$ (Slee, 1961). As expected, the extent of the scattering corona is larger at the equator than at the poles. (See the dashed line in fig. 6–51.)

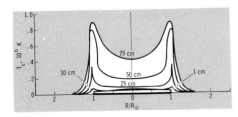
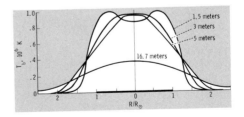

FIGURE 6–49.—Brightness temperature calculated as a function of $R/R_\odot$ at several wavelengths. (From Kundu, 1965; copyright 1965, John Wiley & Sons.)

FIGURE 6–50.—Disk temperature as a function of wavelength corresponding to the calculations of figure 6–49. Data points refer to observations. (From Kundu, 1965; copyright 1965, John Wiley & Sons.)

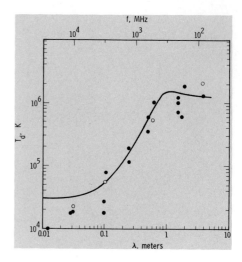

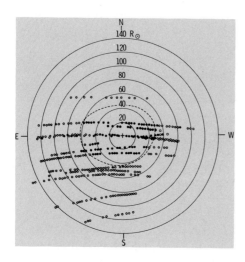

FIGURE 6–51.—Scattering of 13 radio sources. Their position relative to the sun is indicated by the position of the circles. Filled circles indicate that scattering was detected, open circles indicate none was observed. The dotted-line contour shows the average extent of the corona as detected by this scattering. (From Slee, 1961; copyright 1961, Blackwell Scientific Publications.)

6.5 THE SOLAR WIND

In presenting the concept of a static corona, we have implicitly assumed that the gravitational force exerted on the gas particles is sufficient to restrain them from adiabatically expanding into the vacuum of space under the action of the atmospheric pressure gradient. If the loss rate of particles to space is negligible, an average particle's total thermal energy $5/2kT$ must be small with respect to its gravitational potential energy $Mg_\odot R_\odot^2/r$, where $g_\odot$ is the value of solar gravity at $r = R_\odot$. For a fully ionized hydrogen gas (electrons and protons) at $r = R_\odot$ and a temperature of 2×10^6 K, the average thermal energy is 0.8 keV/particle and the gravitational potential energy is 2.0 keV/particle. From this it appears that the existence of a static corona might be possible. However, nonradiative energy is

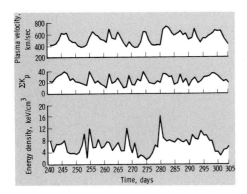

FIGURE 6–52.—Correlation between geomagnetic variations, the solar-wind velocity, and the solar-wind energy density. (Courtesy of Jet Propulsion Laboratory, California Institute of Technology.)

deposited into the corona far above $r = R_\odot$, the thermal conductivity of the gas is very high, and the radiation emission is relatively low. Thus, the thermal energy a few solar radii out remains high and is comparable to the gravitational energy. The result is a continuous outward flow of solar plasma which has been termed the "solar wind." It is important to note that the nonradiative heating provides the energy input for the flow. The details of this heating, which significantly affect the characteristics of the solar wind, are largely unknown. Heating by either the interaction of plasma streams or turbulence, in addition to wave dissipation, could be of importance.

At $215R_\odot$, the location of the earth's orbit, the properties of the solar wind are: $V = 400$ to 700 km/sec, $T = 5 \times 10^4$ to 5×10^5 K, $N_H = 1$ to 10 cm^{-3}, and $B = 10^{-5}$ to 10^{-4} gauss. The observed velocity and energy density of the wind as a function of time is shown in figure 6–52; it is apparent that the velocity is quite variable. Also plotted is ΣK_p, the magnetic activity index, which is approximately proportional to an average over the earth of the log of the deviation from quiet values for the earth's magnetic field. It is seen that there is a good correlation between solar-wind velocity and ΣK_p. In addition to geomagnetic variations, the effects of the solar wind are observable in many other forms such as aurora, ionospheric variations, outward acceleration of comet tails in the sun's vicinity, and perhaps, as is suspected but not demonstrated, an influence on our weather patterns.

Magnetic Forces

In addition to the forces exerted by gravitational and gas pressure gradients, magnetic forces also must be considered. In section 5.3, we saw that the magnetic fields would control plasma motions in the middle chromosphere and above. That is, the plasma-flow streamlines and the magnetic-field lines must coincide in most of the chromosphere and corona. With this constraint on plasma motion, it would appear that the general dipole magnetic field of the sun should contain the solar wind. In reality, as we move outward in the corona, the solar magnetic pressure decreases more rapidly than the plasma pressure, and a point is reached where they are of comparable magnitude. Above this point, the solar wind overpowers the field and transports it outward into interplanetary space. Actually, the concept of an axially symmetric, dipole solar magnetic field is also incorrect because there are numerous strong magnetic-field asymmetries attributed to the active regions of the type shown in figure 6–53. The plasma that makes up the solar wind does not leave the chromosphere uniformly, but rather is issued from preferred locations low in the atmosphere where the field lines are approximately radial and do not close upon themselves. Davis (1966) has described these locations and termed them "magnetic nozzles." These nozzles act as nearly steady plasma sources, each of which has different values of density, temperature, velocity, and orientation to the local vertical. Thus, the solar wind in the inner and intermediate corona is heterogeneous, perhaps more so than in the outer corona where many of the non-uniformities have tended to smooth out.

The overall magnetic-field pattern in the wind, as seen along the axis of solar rotation, is that of an Archimedes spiral (fig. 2–41). The inner sphere, extending out to approximately $3R_\odot$, rotates with the sun because of control by magnetic forces (Newkirk, 1967). Outside this sphere, a magnetic-field line starts to lag behind its source on the surface as it is swept outward by the plasma, which tends to conserve its angular momentum rather than its angular velocity. The solar wind continues outward past the earth to a distance well outside our solar system where its momentum flux is reduced to the same magnitude as that from other stars. In this region, a mixing of these stellar winds, if still distinguishable, occurs.

Basic Equations

The following is a short illustrative discussion of the physical relationships used to describe the dynamics of the solar wind.

It is usually assumed that the flow is steady and that the corona is either spherically symmetric or axially symmetric. In the latter case, only the equatorial plane is investigated. The equation of continuity

$$\nabla \cdot \rho \mathbf{V} = -\frac{\partial \rho}{\partial t} \tag{6–53}$$

becomes

$$\rho u r^2 = \text{constant} \tag{6–54}$$

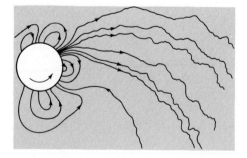

FIGURE 6–53.—A hypothetical model of a coronal magnetic-field configuration. (After L. Davis, Jr.; courtesy of Jet Propulsion Laboratory, California Institute of Technology.)

where u is the radial component of velocity. The general form of the momentum balance is

$$\rho \left(\frac{\partial \mathbf{V}}{\partial t} + \mathbf{V} \cdot \nabla \mathbf{V} \right) = - \nabla p - \rho g_\odot \left(\frac{R_\odot}{r} \right)^2 \mathbf{e}_r + \mathbf{J} \times \mathbf{B} \qquad (6\text{--}55)$$

The radial component of the momentum balance is

$$\frac{dp}{dr} = - \rho \left[g_\odot \left(\frac{R_\odot}{r} \right)^2 + u \frac{du}{dr} - \frac{w^2}{r} \right] + (\mathbf{J} \times \mathbf{B}) \cdot \mathbf{e}_r \qquad (6\text{--}56)$$

where w is the azimuthal component of the velocity. The centrifugal force term w^2/r and the magnetic force term $(\mathbf{J} \times \mathbf{B}) \cdot \mathbf{e}_r$ are both small with respect to the other three terms. The major differences between a static and dynamic coronal pressure gradient is the term $\rho u\, du/dr$. In the dynamic case, the effective value of gravity is $g + u\, du/dr$ and is larger than in the static case. Hence, estimates of the kinetic temperature made from the observed density gradient and assuming hydrostatic equilibrium are lower bounds only. The azimuthal component of the momentum balance is

$$\frac{\rho u}{r} \frac{d(rw)}{dr} = \mathbf{J} \times \mathbf{B} \cdot \mathbf{e}_\phi \qquad (6\text{--}57)$$

and states that only magnetic forces can alter the angular momentum of the outward-flowing plasma. The equation for energy conservation is a complex one because it must include nonradiative energy dissipation, heat conduction, and radiation emission. Because the distribution of the nonradiative energy dissipation (the major source of energy input) is not well defined, a simplified relation between the pressure and density with an adjustable parameter is often assumed.

$$\frac{p}{p_0} = \left(\frac{\rho}{\rho_0} \right)^\gamma \qquad (6\text{--}58)$$

This is called the "ploytropic law" and γ the "ploytropic index." The subscript 0 refers to an arbitrarily chosen reference point. For an adiabatic density change, γ is the ratio of specific heats, 5/3; and for an isothermal change, γ is unity. This law confines all of our ignorance to one parameter, γ, which is actually a function of position but usually is assumed to be a constant. This makes it very difficult to find a solution that matches the correct conditions at both the solar surface and the radius of the earth's orbit. The relations that complete the description are the perfect-gas law

$$p = \rho \frac{kT}{\mu m_H} \qquad (3\text{--}14)$$

and the two of Maxwell's equations which describe the spatial variation of $\mathbf{B}$

$$\nabla \times \mathbf{B}/\mu_0 = \mathbf{J} \qquad (6\text{--}59)$$

and

$$\nabla \cdot \mathbf{B} = 0 \qquad (6\text{--}60)$$

or

$$\frac{d\left(r^2 B_r\right)}{dr} = 0 \tag{6-61}$$

Solar-Wind Solutions

Assuming w and B to be zero and $\gamma = 1$, Parker (1963) has obtained the solution for $u(r)$ shown in figure 6–54. It is seen that most of the acceleration to final solar-wind velocity occurs within the first $20R_\odot$ to $30R_\odot$. The effect of including the azimuthal velocity and magnetic fields into the solution alters $u(r)$ by only a very small amount (Weber and Davis, 1967). The solution for $w(r)$ is shown in figure 6–55, where it was assumed that at the earth's orbit $V = 400$ km/sec, $N_H = 7$ cm^{-3}, $T = 2 \times 10^5$ K, and $B = 5 \times 10^{-5}$ gauss. Because this defines the total mass and energy fluxes, γ must be a calculated rather than a freely specified parameter. It was found to equal 1.221.

Because $w(r)$ is not zero at large r, the solar wind transports angular momentum away from the sun with the net effect that the solar angular momentum is continuously decreased (Parker, 1969). A relation describing this angular momentum loss can be derived from equation (6–57) which, using equation (6–59), is written as

$$\frac{\rho u}{r}\frac{d\left(rw\right)}{dr} = \frac{B_r}{\mu_0 r}\frac{d}{dr}\left(rB_\phi\right) \tag{6-62}$$

Because $\rho u r^2$ and $r^2 B_r$ are both constants, this can be integrated to yield

$$L = rw - \frac{r}{\rho u}\frac{B_r B_\phi}{\mu_0} \tag{6-63}$$

where L is a constant. The first term rw is the angular momentum per unit mass. The second term is the product of the magnetic stress, acting in the azimuthal direction on a surface perpendicular to the radial direction, times r, divided by the rate of mass loss per unit area. The sum of the two terms is a constant and is equal to the total angular momentum taken away from the sun per unit mass loss. These

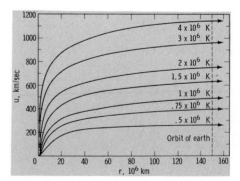

FIGURE 6–54.—Radial velocity as a function of radius as calculated by Parker. (From Parker, 1963; copyright 1963, John Wiley & Sons.)

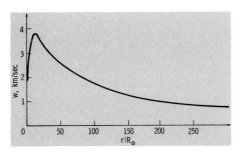

FIGURE 6–55.—Azimuthal velocity as a function of radius as calculated by Weber and Davis. (From Weber and Davis, 1967; copyright 1967, University of Chicago Press.)

two terms are plotted in figure 6–56 for the same parameters used in figure 6–55. It is apparent that the torque exerted by the magnetic field is much more effective in decreasing the sun's angular momentum than is the direct transport away of angular momentum by fluid of the solar wind.

The solution to the solar-wind equations shown in figure 6–55 can be idealized (Modisette, 1967) to a rigid rotation out to some critical radius (established by magnetic forces) and a subsequent decrease of w as $1/r$ (conservation of the fluid's angular momentum). It is instructive to pursue this further by deriving an expression for $w(r)$. Because the fluid streamlines and magnetic-field lines must be parallel, we have

$$\frac{B_\phi}{B_r} = \frac{w - \Omega r}{u} \qquad (6\text{-}64)$$

That is, the fluid streamlines and magnetic-field lines are parallel in the system which rotates with the angular velocity of the sun, Ω. Elimination of B_ϕ from equations (6–63) and (6–64) yields

$$w = r\Omega \, \frac{\dfrac{L M_A^2}{\Omega r^2} - 1}{M_A^2 - 1} \qquad (6\text{-}65)$$

where M_A is the Alfvénic Mach number, the ratio of the radial velocity to the radial Alfvén speed.

$$M_A = \frac{u}{(B_r^2/\mu_0\rho)^{1/2}} \qquad (6\text{-}66)$$

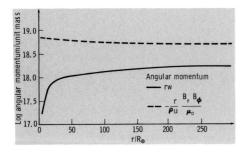

FIGURE 6–56.—The two components of the solar-wind angular momentum as a function of radius. (From Weber and Davis, 1967; copyright 1967, University of Chicago Press.)

Close to the sun, M_A is much less than unity but it increases to approximately 10 at the orbit of earth (1 AU). Thus, there is a critical radius r_A at which M_A is unity and the denominator of equation (6–65) vanishes. Because w is always finite, the numerator must also vanish and

$$L = \Omega r_A^2 \qquad (6\text{–}67)$$

Because Ω is a constant, the total angular momentum carried away by the solar wind per unit mass is fixed by the radius at which M_A is unity. Using the fact that both $\rho u r^2$ and $r^2 B_r$ are constants, our expression for w (eq. (6–65)) can be rewritten in the useful form

$$w = r\Omega \, \frac{1 - u/u_A}{1 - M_A^2} \qquad (6\text{–}68)$$

where u_A is the radial velocity at the Alfvénic critical point. Close to the sun, the fraction is nearly unity and w therefore varies as $r\Omega$, the variation we would expect for rigid rotation. In figure 6–55 the azimuthal velocity matches the sun's velocity at the surface, reaches a maximum at approximately $12R_\odot$, and then slowly decreases. However, at $12R_\odot$ the angular velocity has decreased to approximately one-sixth the value at the solar surface. This together with the calculated value of $24R_\odot$ for r_A implies that much of the angular momentum is carried by the magnetic field. For $r \gg r_A$, both M_A^2 and u/u_A are much greater than 1 and it can be shown from equation (6–68) that $w \sim 1/r$. Lastly, from equation (6–65), the azimuthal velocity at the Alfvénic critical point is

$$w(r_A) = r_A\Omega \left[1 - \left(r_A \, \frac{\partial M_A}{\partial r} \right)^{-1} \right] \qquad (6\text{–}69)$$

By defining the characteristic time for angular momentum decrease as the sun's total angular momentum divided by its loss rate and assuming the sun rotates as a solid body, characteristic times of 7×10^9 years (Weber and Davis, 1967) and 3 to 4×10^9 years (Brandt and Heise, 1970) are calculated. These values are approximately the same as the age of the sun itself, indicating that the solar wind has significantly changed the total solar angular momentum. If most of the momentum has been lost only from the convection zone and above, the solar atmosphere must have rotated many times faster than is currently observed.

We will conclude this discussion by pointing out an interesting contradiction currently existing between the theory summarized above and observations. The calculated azimuthal velocity at the earth's orbit is approximately 1 km/sec (fig. 6–55) to 2 km/sec (Brandt et al., 1969). However, observations of comet tail deflection (Brandt and Heise, 1970) and the nonradial solar-wind direction (Hundhausen et al., 1968) indicate an azimuthal velocity of 9 to 10 km/sec. A magnitude of 10 km/sec implies a very large momentum loss carried by the fluid, which is not related by simple theory to the observed magnetic fields or total solar-wind velocity and density. The answer may lie in the magnetic configuration of the active-sun corona (Schubert and Coleman, 1968) or the anisotropy of pressure observed in the solar wind (Weber, 1970). Resolution of the contradiction will help yield a clearer picture of the evolution of the sun and other rotating stars.

REFERENCES

BILLINGS, D. E.: 1966, A Guide to the Solar Corona. New York: Academic Press.

BLAKE, R. L.; FRIEDMAN, H.; AND UNZICKER, A. E.: 1965, Spectral and Photometric Measurements of Solar X-Ray Emission Below 60 Å. Astrophys. J. *142*, 1–12.

BRANDT, J. C.; AND HEISE, J.: 1970, Interplanetary Gas. XV. Nonradial Plasma Motions From the Orientations of Ionic Comet Tails. Astrophys. J. *159*, 1057–1066.

BRANDT, J. C.; WOLFF, D.; AND CASSINELLI, J. P.: 1969, Interplanetary Gas. XVI. A Calculation of the Angular Momentum of the Solar Wind. Astrophys. J. *156*, 1117–1124.

BURGESS, A.: 1964, Dielectric Recombination and the Temperature of the Solar Corona. Astrophys. J. *139*, 776–780.

DAVIS, L., JR.: 1966, Models of the Interplanetary Fields and Plasma Flow. The Solar Wind, R. Mackin and M. Neugebauer (eds.), Pasadena: Jet Propulsion Lab., Calif. Inst. of Technol.

ELWERT, G.: 1961, Theory of X-Ray Emission of the Sun. J. Geophys. Res. *66*, 391–401.

GOLDBERG, L.: 1969, Ultraviolet Astronomy. Sci. Amer. *220*(6), 92–102.

HINTEREGGER, H. E.; HALL, L. A.; AND SCHWEITZER, W.: 1964, Solar XUV-Spectrum From 310 Å to 55 Å. Astrophys. J. *140*, 319–327.

VAN DE HULST, H. C.: 1953, The Chromosphere and the Corona. The Sun, G. Kuiper (ed.), Chicago: Univ. of Chicago Press, 264.

HUNDHAUSEN, A. J.; GILBERT, H. E.; AND BAME, S. J.: 1968, Ionization State of the Interplanetary Plasma. J. Geophys. Res. *73*, 5485–5493.

KOZLOVSKY, B.-Z.; AND ZIRIN, H.: 1968, The O VI Emission From the Sun. Solar Phys. *5*, 50–54.

KUIPER, E. P., ed.: 1953, The Sun. Chicago: Univ. of Chicago Press.

KUNDU, M. R.: 1965, Solar Radio Astronomy. New York: John Wiley.

MODISETTE, J. L.: 1967, Solar Wind Induced Torque on the Sun. J. Geophys. Res. *72*, 1521–1526.

NEWKIRK, G., JR.: 1967, Structure of the Solar Corona. Ann. Rev. Astron. Astrophys. *5*, 213–266.

NOYES, R. W.; AND KALKOFEN, W.: 1970, The Solar Lyman Continuum and the Structure of the Solar Chromosphere. Solar Phys. *15*, 120.

PAPAS, C. H.: 1965, Theory of Electromagnetic Wave Propagation. New York: McGraw-Hill, 118.

PARKER, E. N.: 1963, Interplanetary Dynamical Processes. New York, Interscience.

PARKER, E. N.: 1969, Theoretical Studies of the Solar Wind Phenomenon. Space Sci. Rev. *9*, 325–360.

PAWSEY, J. L.; AND SMERD, S. F.: 1953, Solar Radio Emission. The Sun, G. Kuiper (ed.), Chicago: Univ. of Chicago Press, 466.

SCHUBERT, G.; AND COLEMAN, P. J., JR.: 1968, Angular Momentum of the Solar Wind. Astrophys. J. *153*, 943–950.

SIMON, M.; AND ZIRIN, H.: 1969, The Coarse Structure of the Solar Atmosphere. Solar Phys. *9*, 317–327.

SLEE, O. B.: 1961, Observations of the Solar Corona Out to 100 Solar Radii. Mon. Notic. Roy. Astron. Soc. *123*, 223–231.

SMITH, A. G.: 1967, Radio Exploration of the Sun. New York: Van Nostrand Reinhold.

WEBER, E. J.: 1970, The Torque on the Interplanetary Plasma Due to Its Anisotropy. Solar Phys. *13*, 240–242.

WEBER, E. J.; AND DAVIS, L., JR.: 1967, The Angular Momentum of the Solar Wind. Astrophys. J. *148*, 217–228.

WITHBROE, G. L.: 1971, Solar Phys. *18*.

ZIRIN, H.: 1966, The Solar Atmosphere. Waltham, Mass.: Blaisdell.

Appendix A

The Strongest Fraunhofer Lines

Table A–I lists the Fraunhofer lines from 2935 to 8770 Å which have a relative width (equivalent width/wavelength) of 2×10^{-4} or greater. The equivalent width

TABLE A–I.—The Strongest Fraunhofer Lines

Wavelength λ, Å	Equivalent width W, Å	Relative width W/λ	Contributing atom or ion
3096.902	0.647	2.09×10^{-4}	Mg I
3168.151	1.077	3.40×10^{-4}	V II
3286.772	.660	2.01×10^{-4}	Fe I
3361.193	.932 (2)	2.65×10^{-4}	Ti II
3380.585	.809	2.39×10^{-4}	Ni I
3440.626	1.243	3.61×10^{-4}	Fe I
3441.019	.634	3.22×10^{-4}	Fe I
3461.667	.758	2.19×10^{-4}	Ni I
3490.594	.830	2.38×10^{-4}	Fe I
3492.975	.826	2.39×10^{-4}	Ni I
3497.843	.726	2.05×10^{-4}	Fe I
3515.066	.718	2.02×10^{-4}	Ni I
3524.536	1.271	3.63×10^{-4}	Ni I
3565.396	.990	2.74×10^{-4}	Fe I
3570.134	1.380	3.87×10^{-4}	Fe I
3581.209	2.144	5.99×10^{-4}	Fe I
3585.339	.839	2.31×10^{-4}	Fe I/Cr II
3608.869	1.046	2.87×10^{-4}	Fe I
3770.63	1.860	6.21×10^{-4}	H I
3797.90	3.463	10.85×10^{-4}	H I
3799.558	.622	3.09×10^{-4}	Fe I
3815.851	1.272	3.30×10^{-4}	Fe I
3820.436	1.712	5.12×10^{-4}	Fe I
3824.452	.519	2.25×10^{-4}	Fe I
3825.891	1.519	4.21×10^{-4}	Fe I
3827.832	.897	2.76×10^{-4}	Fe I
3829.365	.874	3.08×10^{-4}	Mg I
3832.310	1.685	6.00×10^{-4}	Mg I
3834.233	.624	4.97×10^{-4}	Fe I
3835.39	2.362	7.19×10^{-4}	H I

315

TABLE A–I.—The Strongest Fraunhofer Lines—Continued

Wavelength λ, Å	Equivalent width W, Å	Relative width W/λ	Contributing atom or ion
3838.302	1.920	6.41×10^{-4}	Mg I
3840.447	.567	2.57×10^{-4}	Fe I
3859.922	1.554	4.00×10^{-4}	Fe I
3878.027	.555	2.02×10^{-4}	Fe I
3878.580	.724	2.48×10^{-4}	Fe I
3886.294	.920	3.06×10^{-4}	Fe I
3889.05	2.346	7.22×10^{-4}	H I
3618.777	1.410	3.85×10^{-4}	Fe I
3619.400	.568	2.04×10^{-4}	Ni I
3631.475	1.364	3.69×10^{-4}	Fe I/Cr II
3647.851	.970	3.13×10^{-4}	Fe I
3719.947	1.664	5.34×10^{-4}	Fe I
3722.588	.694	2.49×10^{-4}	Ti I/Fe I
3727.634	.632	2.05×10^{-4}	Fe I
3734.37	1.014	3.23×10^{-4}	H I
3734.874	3.027	9.45×10^{-4}	Fe I
3736.917	2.90	2.61×10^{-4}	Ca II
3737.141	1.071	4.28×10^{-4}	Fe I
3745.574	1.202 (2)	4.59×10^{-4}	Fe I
3745.910	.540	3.01×10^{-4}	Fe I
3748.271	.497	2.28×10^{-4}	Fe I
3749.495	1.907	5.78×10^{-4}	Fe I
3750.15	1.388	4.30×10^{-4}	H I
3758.245	1.647	4.97×10^{-4}	Fe I
3763.803	.829	2.55×10^{-4}	Fe I
3905.532	.816	2.19×10^{-4}	Si I
3933.682	20.253	48.74×10^{-4}	Ca II K
3968.492	15.467	34.35×10^{-4}	Ca II H
3970.076	.076	7.76×10^{-4}	H I ϵ
4045.825	1.174	3.16×10^{-4}	Fe I
4063.605	.787	2.19×10^{-4}	Fe I
4101.748	3.133	7.46×10^{-4}	H I δ
4226.740	1.476	3.42×10^{-4}	Ca I
4340.475	2.855	6.59×10^{-4}	H I γ
4383.557	1.008	2.35×10^{-4}	Fe I
4861.342	3.680	7.50×10^{-4}	H I β
5172.698	1.259	2.34×10^{-4}	Mg I
6562.808	4.020	6.49×10^{-4}	H I α
8542.144	3.670	3.98×10^{-4}	Ca II
8662.170	2.600	2.97×10^{-4}	Ca II

W in the second column is defined in section 4.5 (fig. 4–24). The number in parentheses indicates the number of lines blended together to yield the value of W quoted. The relative width given in the third column contains corrections not included in W to account for observational difficulties, and is given for the quoted wavelength only; that is, it is not blended. The last column gives the absorbing atom or ion. Where more than one is identified, the strongest one is underlined. The data have been extracted from Moore et al. (1961).

Features which are evident from this table include

(1) The Ca K and H lines (3934/3968 Å) are the strongest lines.
(2) The hydrogen Balmer series contributes many of the stronger lines (Hα to Hϵ).
(3) Iron is a prolific generator of absorption lines.
(4) The majority of lines are in the 3000- to 4000-Å range.

REFERENCE

Moore, C. E.; Minnaert, M. G. J.; and Houtgart, J.: 1961, The Solar Spectrum 2935 Å to 8770 Å. National Bureau of Standards Monograph 61.

Appendix B

Visible Coronal Lines

Observed lines in the visible range of the spectrum emitted by coronal lines are listed in tables B–I and B–II. The accepted lines are those whose identification has not been disputed and the questionable lines are those whose identity has been questioned, according to Wagner and House (1968). The head of the isoelectronic sequence and the type of transition involved are given in columns 1 and 2. The ion and corresponding wavelength of the lines observed are given in columns 3 and 4. The equivalent width W defined in section 4.5 (fig. 4–24) is given in column 5. The class given in column 6 refers to the degree of confidence that the identification

TABLE B–I.—Accepted Coronal Visible Lines and Identifications

Isoelectronic sequence	Transition	Coronal ion	Wavelength, Å	Equivalent width, Å	Class
Be I	$^3P_2$–$^3P_1$	Ar XV	5926	----------	B
			(5974)		
B I	$^2P_{3/2}$–$^2P_{1/2}$	Si X	14305	----------	-------
O I	$^3P_1$–$^3P_2$	Ca XIII	4086	0.4	A
F I	$^2P_{1/2}$–$^2P_{3/2}$	Ca XII	3327	.7	A
Mg I	$^3P_2$–$^3P_1$	Fe XV	7060	.8	-------
Al I	$^2P_{3/2}$–$^2P_{1/2}$	Ni XVI	3601	1.3	A
		Fe XIV	5303	20.0	A
		Mn XIII	6535	----------	B
Si I	$^1D_2$–$^3P_2$	Fe XIII	3388	10.0	A
		Mn XII	3685	.2	C
		Cr XI	3998	.1	B
	$^3P_2$–$^3P_1$	Ni XV	8024	.3	-------
		Fe XIII	10798	30.0	-------
	$^3P_1$–$^3P_0$	Ni XV	6702	1.2	A
		Fe XIII	10747	50.0	-------
P I	$^2P_{1/2}$–$^2D_{3/2}$	Fe XII	3021	----------	-------
S I	$^1D_2$–$^3P_1$	Fe XI	3987	.7	A
	$^3P_1$–$^3P_2$	Fe XI	6892	6.0	-------
Cl I	$^2P_{1/2}$–$^2P_{3/2}$	Ni XII	4232	1.1	A
	$^2P_{1/2}$–$^2P_{3/2}$	Fe X	6374	5.0	A

TABLE B–II.—Questionable Coronal Visible Lines and Identifications

Isoelectronic sequence	Transition	Coronal ion	Wavelength, Å	Equivalent width, Å	Class
B I	$^2P_{3/2}$–$^2P_{1/2}$	Ar XIV	4412	0.3	A
	$^3P_1$–$^3P_0$	Ca XV	5694	.3	A
	$^3P_2$–$^3P_1$	Ca XV	5446	.2	A
		K XIV	6740	.1	D
			(6777)		
C I		Ar XIII	8467		
O I	$^3P_1$–$^3P_2$	Ar XI	6917		
F I	$^2P_{1/2}$–$^2P_{3/2}$	K XI	4256	.1	D
		Ar X	5536	.3	A
			(5540)		A
Mg I	$^3P_2$–$^3P_1$	Ni XVII	4744		D
		Co XVI	5774		
Al I	$^2P_{3/2}$–$^2P_{1/2}$	Co XV	4351	.1	C
Si I	$^1D_2$–$^3P_1$	Cr XI	3170		
			3180		
		V X	3534	1.0	A
	$^1D_2$–$^3P_2$	V X	4312		C
		Ca VII	5620		C
S I	$^1D_2$–$^3P_1$	Ni XIII	3643	.4	A
		Co XII	3801	.5	A
		Mn X	4220		D
		Cr IX	4566	.5	A
	$^3P_1$–$^3P_2$	Ni XIII	5116	.8	A
		Co XII	6317		
Cl I	$^2P_{1/2}$–$^2P_{3/2}$	Co XI	5188		
Ca I	$^1G_4$–$^1D_2$	Ni IX	7144		

stated is the correct one. An A implies a strong degree of confidence and a D implies that the identification is uncertain, according to Aly et al. (1962). The data are from a summary by Wagner and House (1968).

REFERENCES

ALY, M. K.; EVANS, J. W.; AND ORRALL, F. Q.: 1962, A Spectrographic Atlas of the Solar Corona From λ 3300 to λ 6900. Sacramento Peak Observatory and Helwan Observatory.

WAGNER, W. J.; AND HOUSE, L. L.: 1968, A Survey of Current Coronal Visible Line Identifications. Solar Phys. 5, 55–60.

Appendix C

Coronal UV, XUV, and X-Ray Lines

The stronger emission lines of the coronal spectrum are given in table C–I. They are limited to ions whose ionization energy is greater than 100 eV. The wavelength of the line and ion responsible for the emission are given in columns 1 and 2. The transition involved is given in column 3. The outer configuration of

TABLE C–I.—Coronal UV, XUV, and X-Ray Lines

Wavelength, Å	Ion	Transition	Change in total angular momentum
1058.7	Al VIII	$2p^2\ ^3P_1$ to $2p^2\ ^1S_0$	
1037.6	O VI	Multiplet 1	
1031.9	O VI	Multiplet 1	
780.3	Ne VIII	$2s\ ^2S_{1/2}$ to $2p\ ^2P_{1/2}^0$	
770.4	Ne VIII	$2s\ ^2S_{1/2}$ to $2p\ ^2P_{3/2}^0$	
625.3	Mg X	$2s\ ^2S_{1/2}$ to $2p\ ^2P_{1/2}^0$	
609.8	Mg X	$2s\ ^2S_{1/2}$ to $2p\ ^2P_{3/2}^0$	
558	Ne VI	Multiplet 1	
521.1	Si XII	$2s\ ^2S_{1/2}$ to $2p\ ^2P_{1/2}^0$	
499.4	Si XII	$2s\ ^2S_{1/2}$ to $2p\ ^2P_{3/2}^0$	
465.3	Ne VIII	$2s\ ^1S_0$ to $2p\ ^1P_1^0$	
436.7	Mg VIII	$2s^22p\ ^2P^0$ to $2s2p^2\ ^2D$	$1\frac{1}{2}$ to $1\frac{1}{2}$
430.5	Mg VIII	$2s^22p\ ^2P^0$ to $2s2p^2\ ^2D$	$\frac{1}{2}$ to $1\frac{1}{2}$
368.1	Mg IX	$2s^2\ ^1S$ to $2s2p\ ^1P^0$	0 to 1
360.8	Fe XVI	$3s\ ^2S$ to $3p\ ^2P^0$	$\frac{1}{2}$ to $\frac{1}{2}$
349.9	Si IX	$2s^22p^2\ ^3P$ to $2s2p^3\ ^3D^0$	2 to 3
347.4	Si X	$2s^22p\ ^2P^0$ to $2s2p^2\ ^2D$	$\frac{1}{2}$ to $1\frac{1}{2}$
346	Fe X	$3s^23p^5\ ^2P^0$ to $3s3p^6\ ^2S$	$1\frac{1}{2}$ to $\frac{1}{2}$
345.1	Si IX	$2s^22p^2\ ^2P$ to $2s2p^3\ ^3D^0$	1 to 2
342	Fe XIV	$3s^23p\ ^2P^0$ to $3s3p^2\ ^2D$	$\frac{1}{2}$ to $1\frac{1}{2}$
339.0	Mg VIII	$2s^22p\ ^2P^0$ to $2s2p^2\ ^2S$	$1\frac{1}{2}$ to $1\frac{1}{2}$
335.3	Fe XVI	$3s\ ^2S$ to $3p\ ^2P^0$	$\frac{1}{2}$ to $1\frac{1}{2}$
332.8	Al X	$2s^2\ ^1S$ to $2s2p\ ^1P^0$	0 to 1
319.8	Si VIII	$2s^22p^3\ ^4S^0$ to $2s2p^4\ ^4P$	$1\frac{1}{2}$ to $2\frac{1}{2}$
317.0	Mg VIII	$2s^22p\ ^2P^0$ to $2s2p^2\ ^2P$	$1\frac{1}{2}$ to $1\frac{1}{2}$
316.2	Si VIII	$2s^2p^3\ ^4S^0$ to $2s2p^4\ ^4P$	$1\frac{1}{2}$ to $1\frac{1}{2}$
315.0	Mg VIII	$2s^22p\ ^2P^0$ to $2s2p^2\ ^2P$	$1\frac{1}{2}$ to $1\frac{1}{2}$

TABLE C–I.—Coronal UV, XUV, and X-Ray Lines—Continued

Wavelength, Å	Ion	Transition	Change in total angular momentum
314.3	Si VIII	$2s^2 2p^3\ ^4S^0$ to $2s2p^4\ ^4P$	$1\frac{1}{2}$ to $\frac{1}{2}$
313.3	Mg VIII	$2s^2 2p\ ^2P^0$ to $2s2p^2\ ^2P$	$\frac{1}{2}$ to $\frac{1}{2}$
312.0	Mg VIII	$2s^2 2p\ ^2P^0$ to $2s2p^2\ ^2P$	$\frac{1}{2}$ to $1\frac{1}{2}$
308.3	Si VIII	$2s^2 2p^3\ ^2P^0$ to $2s2p^4\ ^2D$	$1\frac{1}{2}$ to $2\frac{1}{2}$
303.4	Si XI	$2s^2\ ^1S$ to $2s2p\ ^1P^0$	0 to 1
296.2	Si IX	$2s^2 2p^2\ ^3P$ to $2s2p^3\ ^3P$	2 to 1, 2
292.8	Si IX	$2s^2 2p^2\ ^3P$ to $2s2p^3\ ^3P^0$	1 to 0, 1; 1 to 2
290.7	Si IX	$2s^2 2p^2\ ^3P$ to $2s2p^3\ ^3P^0$	0 to 1
284.1	Fe XV	$3s^2\ ^1S^0$ to $3s3p\ ^1P^0$	0 to 1
278.3	Mg VII	$2s^2 2p^2\ ^3P$ to $2s2p^3\ ^3S^0$	2 to 1
	Si VII	$2s^2 2p^4\ ^3P$ to $2s2p^5\ ^3P^0$	1 to 2
277.1	Si VIII	$2s^2 2p^3\ ^2D^0$ to $2s2p^4\ ^2D$	$2\frac{1}{2}$ to $2\frac{1}{2}$
275.3	Si VII	$2s^2 2p^4\ ^3P$ to $2s2p^5\ ^3P^0$	2 to 2; 1 to 1
274.2	Fe XIV	$3s^2 3p\ ^2P^0$ to $3s3p^2\ ^2S$	$\frac{1}{2}$ to $\frac{1}{2}$
272.0	Si X	$2s^2 2p\ ^2P^0$ to $2s2p^2\ ^2S$	$\frac{1}{2}$ to $\frac{1}{2}$
270.4	Fe XIV	$3s^2 3p\ ^2P^0$ to $3s3p^2\ ^2P$	$1\frac{1}{2}$ to $\frac{1}{2}$
264.5	Fe XIV	$3s^2 3p\ ^2P^0$ to $3s3p^2\ ^2P$	$1\frac{1}{2}$ to $1\frac{1}{2}$
264.3	S X	$2s^2 2p^3\ ^4S$ to $2s2p^4\ ^4P$	$1\frac{1}{2}$ to $2\frac{1}{2}$
259.5	S X	$2s^2 2p^3\ ^4S^0$ to $2s2p^4\ ^4P$	$1\frac{1}{2}$ to $1\frac{1}{2}$
258.2	Si X	$2s^2 2p\ ^2P^0$ to $2s2p^3\ ^2P$	$1\frac{1}{2}$ to $1\frac{1}{2}$
257.3	S X	$2s2p^3\ ^4S^0$ to $2s2p^4\ ^4P$	$1\frac{1}{2}$ to $1\frac{1}{2}$
253.8	Si X	$2s^2 2p\ ^2P^0$ to $2s2p^2\ ^2D$	$\frac{1}{2}$ to $1\frac{1}{2}$
251.8	Fe XIV	$3s^2 3p\ ^2P^0$ to $3s3p^2\ ^2P$	$\frac{1}{2}$ to $1\frac{1}{2}$
249.3	Si VI	$2s^2 2p^5\ ^2P^0$ to $2s2p^6\ ^2S$	$\frac{1}{2}$ to $\frac{1}{2}$(?)
248.6	C V	$2p\ ^3P^0$ to $3d\ ^3D$	?
246.1	Si VI	$2s^2 2p^5\ ^3P$ to $2s2p^6\ ^2S$	$1\frac{1}{2}$ to $\frac{1}{2}$
235.4	Si VIII	$2s^2 2p^3\ ^2P^0$ to $2s2p^4\ ^2P$	$1\frac{1}{2}$ to $1\frac{1}{2}$
233.0	Si VIII	$2s^2 2p^3\ ^2P^0$ to $2s2p^4\ ^2P$	$1\frac{1}{2}$ to $\frac{1}{2}$
231.4	Fe XV	$3p\ ^3P^0$ to $3d\ ^3D$	2 to 3(?)
227.1	Si IX	$2s^2 2p^2\ ^3P$ to $2s2p^3\ ^3S^0$	2 to 1
225.1	Si IX	$2s^2 2p^2\ ^3P$ to $2s2p^3\ ^3S^0$	1 to 1
224.7	Si IX	$2s2p^4\ ^3P$ to $2s2p^5\ ^3P^0$	1 to 1; 2 to 2
223.7	Si IX	$2s^2 2p^2\ ^3P$ to $2s2p^3\ ^3S^0$	0 to 1
217.0	Si VIII	$2s^2 2p^3\ ^2D^0$ to $2s2p^4\ ^2P$	$2\frac{1}{2}$ to $1\frac{1}{2}$
214.7	Si VIII	$2s^2 2p^3\ ^2D^0$ to $2s2p^4\ ^2P$	$1\frac{1}{2}$ to $\frac{1}{2}$
211.7	Fe XIV	$3p\ ^2P^0$ to $3d\ ^2D$	$\frac{1}{2}$ to $1\frac{1}{2}$
196.7	Fe XII, XIII		
195.1	Fe XII, XIII		
193.5	Fe XII, XIII		
192.3	Fe XII, XIII		
191.2	Fe		
190.2	Fe XIII		
	S XII		
188.2	Fe XI, XII		
187.0	Fe XIII	$3p^3\ ^2D^0$ to $3p^2(^1D)3d\ ^2F$	$2\frac{1}{2}$ to $3\frac{1}{2}$

TABLE C–I.—Coronal UV, XUV, and X-Ray Lines—Continued

Wavelength, Å	Ion	Transition	Change in total angular momentum
185.5	Fe VIII	$3p^63d\ ^2D$ to $3p^53d^2\ ^2F^0$	$2\frac{1}{2}$ to $3\frac{1}{2}$
184.7	Fe XI, XII		
183.9	O VI	Multiplet 3	
182.2	Fe XI	$3p^4\ ^3P$ to $3p^3(^2P)3d\ ^3D^0$	1 to 2
179.8	Fe XI	$3p^4\ ^1D$ to $3p^3(^2P)3d\ ^1F^0$	2 to 3
177.1	Fe X	$3p^5\ ^2P^0$ to $3p^4(^1D)3d\ ^2P$	$1\frac{1}{2}$ to $1\frac{1}{2}$
175.3	Fe X	$3p^5\ ^2P^0$ to $3p^4(^1D)3d\ ^2D$	$\frac{1}{2}$ to $1\frac{1}{2}$
174.5	Fe X	$3p^5\ ^2P^0$ to $3p^4(^1D)3d\ ^2D$	$1\frac{1}{2}$ to $2\frac{1}{2}$
173.1	O VI	Multiplet 4	
172.9	O VI	Multiplet 4	
171.1	Fe IX	$3p^6\ ^1S$ to $3p^53d\ ^1P^0$	0 to 1
164.1	Ni XIV	$3p^3\ ^2D^0$ to $3p^23d\ ^2F$	$2\frac{1}{2}$ to $3\frac{1}{2}(?)$
160.0	Ni X	$3p^63d\ ^2D$ to $3p^53d^2\ ^2F^0$	$1\frac{1}{2}$ to $2\frac{1}{2}$
158.8	Co X	$3p^6\ ^1S^0$ to $3p^53d\ ^1P_1$	
158.4	Ni X	$3p^63d\ ^2D$ to $3p^53d^2\ ^2F^0$	$2\frac{1}{2}$ to $3\frac{1}{2}$
157.7	Ni XIII	$3p^4\ ^3P$ to $3p^3(^2P)3d\ ^3D^0$	2 to 3
154.1	Ni XII	$3p^5\ ^2P^0$ to $3p^4(^1D)3d\ ^2D$	$1\frac{1}{2}$ to $1\frac{1}{2}$
153.0	Ni XII	$3p^5\ ^2P^0$ to $3p^4(^1D)3d\ ^2D$	$\frac{1}{2}$ to $1\frac{1}{2}$
152.1	Ni XII	$3p^5\ ^2P^0$ to $3p^4(^1D)3d\ ^2D$	$1\frac{1}{2}$ to $1\frac{1}{2}$
150.0	O VI	Multiplet 2	
148.4	Ni XI	$3p^6\ ^1S$ to $3p^53d\ ^1P^0$	0 to 1
145.0	Ni X	$3p^63d\ ^2D$ to $3p^53d^2\ ^2D^0$	$2\frac{1}{2}$ to $2\frac{1}{2}$
144.2	Ni X	$3p^63d\ ^2D$ to $3p^53d^2\ ^2D^0$	$1\frac{1}{2}$ to $1\frac{1}{2}$
129.2	O VI	Multiplet 5	
116.4	O VI	$2p\ ^2P^0$ to $5d\ ^2D$	?
115.8	O VI	$2s\ ^2S$ to $4p\ ^2P^0$	?
111.0	Ca X	$3s\ ^2S$ to $4p\ ^2P^0$	$\frac{1}{2}$ to $1\frac{1}{2}(?)$
106.1	Ne VII	$2s2p\ ^3P^0$ to $2s3d\ ^3D$	1 to 2
105.3	Fe IX	$3p^6\ ^1S$ to $3p^54s\ ^3P^0$	0 to 1
104.8	O VI	$2s\ ^2S$ to $5p\ ^2P^0$	?
103.7	Fe IX	$3p^6\ ^1S$ to $3p^54s\ ^1P^0$	0 to 1
98.1	Ne VIII	$2p\ ^2P^0$ to $3d\ ^2D$	$\frac{1}{2}$ to $1\frac{1}{2}$
96.6	Fe X	$3p^5\ ^2P^0$ to $3p^44s\ ^2P$	$\frac{1}{2}$ to $\frac{1}{2}$
96.1	Fe X	$3p^5\ ^2P^0$ to $3p^44s\ ^2P$	$\frac{1}{2}$ to $1\frac{1}{2}$
95.3	Fe X	$3p^5\ ^2P^0$ to $3p^44s\ ^2P$	$\frac{1}{2}$ to $1\frac{1}{2}$
94.1	Fe X	$3p^5\ ^2P^0$ to $3p^44s\ ^2P$	$1\frac{1}{2}$ to $1\frac{1}{2}$
90.1	Fe XI	$3p^4\ ^3P$ to $3p^34s\ ^3S^0$	1 to 0
89.2	Fe XI	$3p^4\ ^3P$ to $3p^34s\ ^3S^0$	2 to 1
88.1	Fe XI	$3p^4\ ^3P$ to $3p^34s\ ^3D^0$	1 to 2
	Ne VIII	$2s\ ^2S$ to $3p\ ^2P^0$	$\frac{1}{2}$ to $1\frac{1}{2}$
86.8	Fe XI	$3p^4\ ^3P$ to $3p^34s\ ^3D^0$	2 to 3
82.9	Mg VIII	$2p\ ^2P^0$ to $3s\ ^2S$	$1\frac{1}{2}$ to $\frac{1}{2}(?)$
82.6	Mg VIII	$2p\ ^2P^0$ to $3s\ ^2S$	$\frac{1}{2}$ to $\frac{1}{2}(?)$
81.7	Mg VIII	$2p^2\ ^4S$ to $2p3s\ ^4P^0$	
81.6	Si VII	$2p^4\ ^3P$ to $2p3s\ ^3D^0$	2 to 3

TABLE C–I.—Coronal UV, XUV, and X-Ray Lines—Continued

Wavelength, Å	Ion	Transition	Change in total angular momentum
79.5	Fe XII	$3p^3\ ^4S^0$ to $3p^24s\ ^4P$	$1\frac{1}{2}$ to $2\frac{1}{2}$ (?)
77.7	Mg IX	$2p\ ^1P^0$ to $3s\ ^1S$	1 to 0
75.8	Fe XIII	$3p^2\ ^3P$ to $3p4s\ ^3P^0$	1 to 1 (?)
74.8	Mg VIII	$2p\ ^2P^0$ to $3d\ ^2D$	?
74.3	Si VIII	$2p^3\ ^2P^0$ to $2p^23s\ ^2P$	?
72.4	Si VIII	$2p^3\ ^2D^0$ to $2p^23s\ ^2P$	$1\frac{1}{2}$ to $\frac{1}{2}$ (?)
72.3	Mg IX	$2p^2\ ^1D$ to $2p^3d\ ^1D^0$	2 to 2 (?)
69.9	Mg IX	$2p^2\ ^1D$ to $2p3d\ ^1F^0$	2 to 3
	Fe XV	$3s3d\ ^3D$ to $3s4f^3F^0$	?
69.5	Si VIII	$2p^3\ ^4S^0$ to $2p^23s\ ^4p$	?
68.5	Mg VIII	$2p\ ^2P^0$ to $3p\ ^2S$	?
67.2	Ne VIII	$2s\ ^2S$ to $4p\ ^2P^0$	?
	Mg IX	$2s2p\ ^3P^0$ to $2s3d\ ^3D$	?
66.4	Fe XVI	$3d\ ^3D$ to $4f^2F^0$	$2\frac{1}{2}$ to $3\frac{1}{2}$
65.7	Mg X	$2p\ ^2P^0$ to $3s\ ^2S$	$1\frac{1}{2}$ to $\frac{1}{2}$
65.6	Mg IX	$2p\ ^2P^0$ to $3s\ ^2S$	
63.7	Fe XVI	$2p\ ^2P^0$ to $4s\ ^2S$	$1\frac{1}{2}$ to $\frac{1}{2}$
63.3	Mg X	$2p\ ^2P^0$ to $3d\ ^2D$	
	Si VIII	$2p^3\ ^2P^0$ to $2p^23d\ ^2P$	$1\frac{1}{2}$ to $1\frac{1}{2}$
62.8	Si VIII	$2p^3\ ^2P^0$ to $2p^23d\ ^2P$	$\frac{1}{2}$ to $\frac{1}{2}$
	Mg IX	$2s^2\ ^1S$ to $2s3p\ ^1P^0$	0 to 1
62.7	Mg IX	$2s^2\ ^1S$ to $2s3p\ ^1P^0$	
61.9	Si IX	$2p^2\ ^3P$ to $2p3s\ ^2P^0$	2 to 1
61.6	Si IX	$2p^2\ ^3P$ to $2p3s\ ^3P^0$	1 to 2
61.1	Si VIII	$2p^3\ ^4S^0$ to $2p^23d\ ^4P$	$1\frac{1}{2}$ to $\frac{1}{2}$, $1\frac{1}{2}$, $2\frac{1}{2}$
60.7	Ne VIII	$2s\ ^2S$ to $5p\ ^2P^0$	$\frac{1}{2}$ to $\frac{1}{2}$, $1\frac{1}{2}$ (?)
59.3	Fe XIV	$3p\ ^2P^0$ to $4d\ ^2D$	$1\frac{1}{2}$ to $2\frac{1}{2}$
58.8	Fe XIV	$3p\ ^2P^0$ to $4d\ ^2D$	$\frac{1}{2}$ to $1\frac{1}{2}$
57.6	Mg X	$2s\ ^2S$ to $3p\ ^2P^0$	$\frac{1}{2}$ to $\frac{1}{2}$, $1\frac{1}{2}$
56.8	Si X	$2s2p^2\ ^2P$ to $2s2p3d\ ^2D^0$	$1\frac{1}{2}$ to $2\frac{1}{2}$ (?)
56.6	Si X	$2s2p^2\ ^2P$ to $2s2p3d\ ^2D^0$	$1\frac{1}{2}$ to $2\frac{1}{2}$ (?)
56.0	Si IX	$2p^2\ ^1D$ to $2p3d\ ^1F^0$	2 to 3 (?)
55.3	Si IX	$2p^2\ ^3P$ to $2p3d\ ^3D^0$	
55.1	Si IX	$2p^2\ ^3P$ to $2p3d\ ^3P^0$	
54.8	Fe XVI	$3p\ ^2P^0$ to $4d\ ^2D$	?
54.6	Si X	$2p\ ^4P^0$ to $3s\ ^4P$	?
54.2	Fe XVI	$3s\ ^2P^0$ to $4p\ ^2D$	$\frac{1}{2}$ to $1\frac{1}{2}$ (?)
	S IX	$2p^4\ ^3P$ to $2p^33s\ ^3D^0$	2 to 3 (?)
52.8	Si IX		
52.5	Si X	$2s2p^2\ ^2D$ to $2s2p3d\ ^2F$	$2\frac{1}{2}$ to $1\frac{1}{2}$ (?)
52.3	Si XI	$2s2p\ ^1P^0$ to $2s3s\ ^1S$	1 to 0 (?)
52.1	Si X	$2s2p^2\ ^2P^0$ to $2s2p3d\ ^2D$	
50.7	Si X	$2p\ ^2P^0$ to $3d\ ^2D$	$1\frac{1}{2}$ to $2\frac{1}{2}$
50.5	Si X	$2p^2P^0$ to $3d\ ^2D$	$\frac{1}{2}$ to $1\frac{1}{2}$
50.3	Fe XVI	$3s\ ^2S$ to $4p\ ^2P^0$	$\frac{1}{2}$ to $1\frac{1}{2}$ (?)

TABLE C–I.—Coronal UV, XUV, and X-Ray Lines—Concluded

Wavelength, Å	Ion	Transition	Change in total angular momentum
49.7	Si X	$2s2p\ ^2D$–$2s2p3d\ ^2F^0$	?
49.2	Si XI	$2s2p\ ^1P^0$ to $2s3d\ ^1D$	1 to 2
47.6	Si XI	$2s2p\ ^3P^0$ to $2s3d\ ^3D$	?
	S X	$2p^3\ ^4S^0$ to $2p^23s\ ^4P$	
46.3	Si XI	$2s2p\ ^3P^0$ to $2s3d\ ^3D$	
45.7	Si XII	$2p\ ^2P^0$ to $3s\ ^2S$	$1\frac{1}{2}$ to $\frac{1}{2}$
44.2	Si IX	$2p^2\ ^3P$ to $2p4d\ ^3D^0$	
	Si XII	$2p\ ^2P^0$ to $3d\ ^2D$	
	Mg X	$2s\ ^2S$ to $4p\ ^2P^0$	
43.8	Si XI	$2s^2\ ^1S$ to $2s3p\ ^1P^0$	0 to 1
42.5	S X	$2p^3\ ^4S^0$ to $2p^23d\ ^4P$	$1\frac{1}{2}$ to $\frac{1}{2}$; $1\frac{1}{2}$ to $1\frac{1}{2}, 2\frac{1}{2}$
40.9	Si XII	$2s\ ^2S$ to $3p\ ^2P^0$	$\frac{1}{2}$ to $\frac{1}{2}, 1\frac{1}{2}$
33.8	C VI	$1s\ ^2S$ to $2p\ ^2P^0$	$\frac{1}{2}$ to $\frac{1}{2}, 1\frac{1}{2}$
24.8	N VII	$1s\ ^2S$ to $2p\ ^2P^0$	$\frac{1}{2}$ to $\frac{1}{2}, 1\frac{1}{2}$
23.2	N VI	$1s^2\ ^1S$ to $1s4p\ ^1P^0$	0 to 1(?)
21.7	O VII	$1s^2\ ^1S$ to $1s2p\ ^3P^0$	0 to 1
21.6	O VII	$1s^2\ ^1S$ to $1s2p\ ^1P^0$	0 to 1
20.8	N VII	$1s\ ^2S$ to $3p\ ^2P^0$	$\frac{1}{2}$ to $\frac{1}{2}, 1\frac{1}{2}$
18.8	O VIII	$1s\ ^2S$ to $2p\ ^2P^0$	$\frac{1}{2}$ to $\frac{1}{2}, 1\frac{1}{2}$
18.6	O VII	$1s^2\ ^1S$ to $1s3p\ ^1P^0$	0 to 1
17.7	O VII	$1s^2\ ^1S$ to $1s4p\ ^1P^0$	0 to 1
16.3	Fe XVII	$2p^6\ ^1S$ to $2p^53s\ ^1P^0$	0 to 1
16.0	O VIII	$1s\ ^2S$ to $3p\ ^2P^0$	$\frac{1}{2}$ to $\frac{1}{2}, 1\frac{1}{2}$
15.3	Fe XVII	$2p^6\ ^1S$ to $2p^53d\ ^2P^0$	0 to 1
15.0	Fe XVII	$2p^6\ ^1S$ to $2p^53d\ ^3P^0$	
13.7	Fe XVII	$2s^22p^6\ ^1S$ to $2s2p^63p\ ^1P^0$	0 to 1

the electrons is given before the term symbol (sec. 6.3). The change in total angular momentum made by the transition is given in column 4. A study of this table reveals that most of the lines arise from ions with relatively few electrons in the outer shell and many similar transitions. The data are from Tandberg-Hanssen (1967).

REFERENCE

TANDBERG-HANSSEN, E. E.: 1967, Solar Activity. Waltham, Mass.: Blaisdell.

Index

☆ U.S. GOVERNMENT PRINTING OFFICE: 1973 O—469-199